GAS TURBINES FOR AIRCRAFT

WESTINGHOUSE—McGRAW-HILL ENGINEERING BOOKS FOR INDUSTRY

GIBBS—*Transformer Principles and Practice (2d ed.)*
GODSEY and YOUNG—*Gas Turbines for Aircraft*
MARBURY—*Power Capacitors*

PREVIOUSLY PUBLISHED McGRAW-HILL BOOKS BY WESTINGHOUSE AUTHORS

HALL—*Industrial Applications of Infrared*
JAMES and MARKLE—*Controllers for Electric Motors*
VEINOTT—*Fractional Horsepower Electric Motors (2d ed.)*
WAGNER and EVANS—*Symmetrical Components*

The Westinghouse 24 C (J-34) turbojet engine.

GAS TURBINES FOR AIRCRAFT

BY

F. W. GODSEY, JR.

Manager, New Products Division
Westinghouse Electric Corporation

AND

LLOYD A. YOUNG

Rand Corporation
Formerly of New Products Division
Westinghouse Electric Corporation

First Edition

McGRAW-HILL BOOK COMPANY, INC.

NEW YORK   TORONTO   LONDON

1949

GAS TURBINES FOR AIRCRAFT

PRINTED BY MAPLE PRESS COMPANY, YORK, PA.

PREFACE

This book on aircraft gas turbines was written in the hope that it would make available in one place a useful store of information on a new type of aircraft prime mover. Such information should be useful to the student of aeronautical engineering, to engineers in the aviation industry, and to all those seriously interested in the future of aviation. Some of the basic material will be of interest and useful to those interested in the use of the gas turbine as a prime mover in stationary and marine applications.

The gas-turbine idea is not new, but its practical realization as an aircraft turbojet or turboprop power plant has come within the last five years. This newness, coupled with the fact that many developments are still held under military security regulations, has made the task of presentation a difficult one.

Basically, the gas-turbine cycle is simple. However, the mathematical description of such cycles becomes algebraically complex. This is due to the fractional powers of compression and expansion ratios that are involved in the near-adiabatic changes of state involved in the cycle, as well as to the nonuniform thermodynamic properties of air and the combustion products. In the aircraft gas turbine, too, we are generally dealing with flow velocities so high that compressibility and shock phenomena play an important role in determining performance and performance limits.

The first three chapters are introductory. Here is presented most of the basic information that will be needed in the succeeding five chapters on gas-turbine components and cycles. The book is concluded by chapters on controls and accessories, hybrid types of power plants and other power plants that are related to the gas turbine, and performance of aircraft powered by gas turbines. The reader who is interested primarily in the characteristics of gas turbines and their components will find it possible to start reading at Chap. 4 without serious loss of continuity.

Some of the subject matter is strictly limited to the state of the art as it existed at the time of writing. This material may be short-lived in its validity and applicability. In spite of this, we felt that its inclusion was necessary to give a rounded picture of the development of the aircraft gas turbine.

Acknowledgments are due, with sincere appreciation, to all the aircraft companies and gas-turbine manufacturers who have supplied information and illustrations. Special thanks are due the General Electric Company and the Westinghouse Electric Corporation. We are deeply appreciative for the careful constructive review of the manuscript by O. E. Rodgers, A. N. Tifford, C. A. Meyer, L. R. Woodworth, E. P. Walsh, and A. H. Redding of the Westinghouse Aviation Gas Turbine Division.

F. W. GODSEY, JR.

LLOYD A. YOUNG

PITTSBURGH, PA.

SANTA MONICA, CALIF.

May, 1949

CONTENTS

Chapter 7. The Jet Nozzle

Chapter 8. Gas-turbine Cycles

Chapter 9. Variants of Simple Gas-turbine Cycles

Chapter 10. Aircraft-gas-turbine Accessories and Controls

Chapter 11. Present Development Status of Gas Turbines for Aircraft

SYMBOLS AND NOTATION

a	Profile drug coefficient; velocity of sound, fps; subscript
b	Span of wing or airfoil, ft; subscript
A	Area, sq ft
$\cancel{R}$	Aspect ratio
c	Chord, ft; subscript
c_p	Specific heat at constant pressure, Btu/(lb)(°F)
c_v	Specific heat at constant volume, Btu/(lb)(°F)
C_L	Coefficient of lift
C_D	Coefficient of drag
C_M	Coefficient of moment
C_p	Coefficient of parasitic drag
C_P	Pressure coefficient, compressor
D	Drag, lb; diameter, ft
e	Ratio of eye diameter to tip diameter, centrifugal compressor; airfoil efficiency factor
E	Energy, Btu
f	Fineness ratio; friction factor
F	Force, lb
F_g, F_n	Gross and net thrusts, lb
g	Acceleration of gravity, 32.172 ft/sec^2
h	Altitude, ft; enthalpy relative to standard state, Btu/lb; hub diameter/tip diameter ratio, compressor
h_f	Enthalpy of liquid fuel
H	Lower heating value of fuel, Btu/lb; enthalpy relative to absolute zero, Btu/lb
hp	Horsepower
J	Mechanical equivalent of heat, 778.26 ft-lb/Btu; advance ratio of propeller
k	Ratio of specific heats, c_p/c_v
K	Flow restriction factor
L	Length, ft; lift, lb
M	Moment, lb-ft; Mach number $= V/a$
n	Rotational speed, rps
N	Rotational speed, rpm
p	Static pressure, psi or psf
P	Total pressure, psi or psf; power, ft-lb/sec
q	Dynamic pressure, $\rho V^2/2$
Q	Volume flow, cfs
r	Radius, ft
R	Gas constant [for air, 0.0335 Btu/(lb)(°F) or 53.33 ft-lb/(lb)(°F)]
RN	Reynolds number
s	Pitch, ft
S	Wing or airfoil area, sq ft; entropy relative to a standard state, Btu/(lb)(°F)
t	Static absolute or Rankine temperature, °R; thickness, ft
T	Total absolute or Rankine temperature, °R

U	Speed, compressor, turbine blades, fps
V	Flight speed, fps
V_0	Free-stream velocity, fps
V_a	Axial velocity, fps
V_u	Tangential velocity, fps
W_a	Air flow, lb/sec
W_f	Fuel flow, lb/sec
y	Camber, ft
α	Atmospheric temperature lapse rate; angle of attack; angle
ϵ	Gliding angle
β	Angle
γ	Angle
η	Efficiency
ρ	Density, slugs/cu ft (1 slug = 32.172 lb)
ψ	Ratio of pressures, expansion or compression ratio
μ	Coefficient of viscosity, lb-sec/sq ft
θ	Angle
λ	Subscript
π	Ratio of circumference to diameter of circle = 3.1416
ω	Angular velocity, radians/sec
Ω	Vorticity, sec^{-1}

CHAPTER 1

BASIC AERODYNAMICS OF AIRCRAFT

1. The Atmosphere. It is appropriate, for two reasons, that a book on the application of gas turbines to aircraft should begin with a discussion of the atmosphere. First, air, which makes up the atmosphere, is the working medium for the aerodynamic-thermodynamic cycle of the aviation gas turbine. Second, an airplane is supported by aerodynamic lift forces and impeded in its forward motion by drag forces resulting from the reaction of the atmosphere upon the moving craft.

Except for special situations, to which attention will be called, we shall be working with ranges of pressures and temperatures in which air can be treated as a perfect gas obeying the equation of state

$$p = 11.913\rho t \tag{1}$$

where p = pressure, psi

ρ = density, slugs/cu ft

t = absolute Fahrenheit, or Rankine, temperature, which is 459.7° greater than common Fahrenheit temperature

In Fig. 1, the pressure-density relationship of Eq. (1) is depicted graphically for a number of different temperatures.

Although it might seem desirable to use a completely consistent, unambiguous, set of symbols throughout, it is often convenient not to do so. For example, the equation of state frequently will be used in the form

$$p = \rho R t \tag{2}$$

where p = pressure, psf

ρ = specific weight, lb/cu ft (loosely called density)

R = gas constant, ft/deg = 53.33 for air

It is also convenient at times, since pressure divided by specific weight has the dimensions of energy per unit weight, to express the gas constant in thermal energy units. For air, $R = 0.0685$ Btu/(lb)(deg). The context will make clear which set of units is being used.

Normal sea-level atmospheric pressure will be taken as 14.70 psi throughout this work. At 60°F or approximately 520°R and normal sea-level pressure, the density of the atmosphere is 0.00238 slug/cu ft, and the specific weight is 0.0766 lb/cu ft.

For convenient description the atmosphere is divided into two regions

1

or layers—the troposphere or lower region, and the stratosphere or upper atmosphere. The dividing surface, called the tropopause, varies in altitude with meteorological conditions. This results in a marked variation with latitude. The average height of the tropopause at the equator is approximately 60,000 ft; at the poles it is about 30,000 ft. Within the

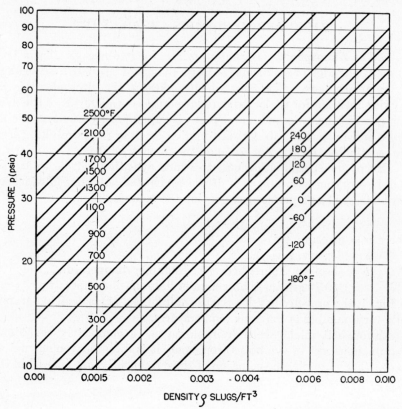

Fig. 1. Equation of state for dry air. Pressure vs. density for temperatures from −180 to 2500°F.

troposphere the temperature normally drops with increasing altitude at a more or less constant lapse rate. The tropopause temperature is relatively more constant than the temperature at the earth's surface. In consequence, the tropospheric lapse rate is greater on hot days than on cold and varies from 0.0045 to 0.0020°F/ft. Although the stratosphere is sometimes considered an isothermal layer, a small daytime temperature rise with increasing altitude is frequently found. In Fig. 2 a number of temperature-altitude curves are presented. These were obtained as averages of U.S. Weather Bureau data taken at representative observation points in the United States. Curve *A* combines observations for coastal and inland stations for typical hot summer days. Curve *B* presents similar data for cold winter days. Curves *C* and *D* are, respectively, July and January average night temperatures. Curve

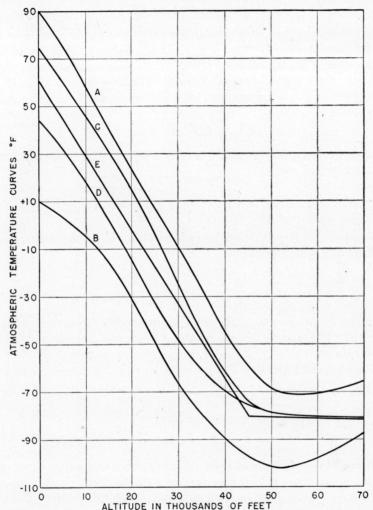

FIG. 2. Average-atmospheric-temperature curves vs. altitude for United States observation points.

E is a rough average representing a constant-lapse-rate troposphere and a constant-temperature stratosphere. This varies slightly from the familiar NACA standard atmosphere, which is much used for qualitative purposes.[1]

[1] *NACA Report* 147, 1922.

Change of atmospheric pressure with altitude is determined by Eq. (1) and the barometric law that the change in pressure Δp is going from an altitude h to $h + \Delta h$ is given by

$$\Delta p = -\tfrac{1}{144}\bar{\rho}g\,\Delta h \tag{3}$$

where $\bar{\rho}$ is the average air density in the range of altitude considered and g is the acceleration of gravity ($g = 32.172$ ft/sec^2). The problem is easily soluble if the temperature is known as a function of altitude. Two particular cases are of especial interest. The first is for a layer of the atmosphere in which the temperature varies uniformly with altitude at a lapse rate α

$$t(h) = t_0 - \alpha(h - h_0)$$

The entire troposphere normally is such a layer. The pressure-altitude relationship that results is

$$\frac{p}{p_0} = \left[1 - \frac{\alpha}{t_0}(h - h_0)\right]^{\frac{0.01875}{\alpha}} \tag{4}$$

The second is for an isothermal layer ($\alpha = 0$) in which the pressure varies exponentially with altitude

$$\log_e \frac{p}{p_0} = -0.01875\,\frac{h - h_0}{t_0} \tag{5}$$

In Fig. 3 a pressure-altitude curve, corresponding to curve E of Fig. 2, is drawn. The relative density for the same temperature-altitude variation is also plotted.

The composition of dry air by weight is

$$O_2 = 0.232$$
$$N_2 = 0.755$$
$$A = 0.012$$
$$CO_2 = 0.001$$

There are, of course, small amounts of other permanent gases—hydrogen, helium, neon, etc. If the atmosphere were in static equilibrium the composition would change with altitude rather markedly. There is evidence, however, that up to altitudes of 100,000 ft the composition is practically constant. The continual and rapid mixing brought about by winds and vertical air currents effectively prevents the equilibrium distribution from establishing itself.

Moisture content of the atmosphere varies greatly from day to day, and the range is different for different locations. At sea level the relative humidity ranges from about 30 to 100 percent. At altitude the variation is less; for example, at 25,000 ft the relative humidity usually ranges from 30 to 50 percent. Average absolute moisture content, expressed as pounds of water per pound of air, varies from 0.01 at sea level to about 0.00001 at the tropopause.

Thus the atmosphere can be considered, for all practical purposes, to be made up of five gases: oxygen, nitrogen, argon, and carbon dioxide

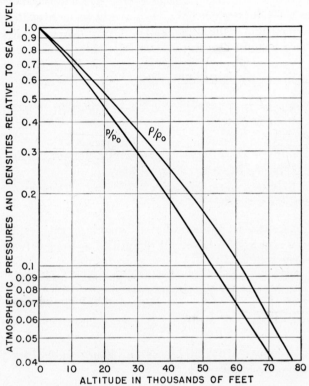

Fig. 3. Relative atmospheric pressure and density vs. altitude.

present in fixed proportions, and water vapor in varying quantities depending on temperature and relative humidity.

Since dry air obeys the perfect-gas law [Eq. (1)] through fairly wide temperature ranges, specification of any two of the quantities pressure, density, and temperature determines the third. To complete the description of air as a thermodynamic working substance, however, it is necessary to give some data connected with the internal energy or energy changes of the gas. This information may be given most conveniently in terms of the specific heats. The specific heat at constant pressure, c_p, is the amount of heat necessary to raise the temperature of one pound of air one degree Fahrenheit letting the gas expand, as it must, to maintain the pressure invariable. The specific heat at constant volume, c_v, is the amount of heat necessary to raise the temperature of one pound of air one degree Fahrenheit without change of volume. The British thermal unit (Btu) will be used as the measure of heat energy. Specific heat, then, will be measured in Btu per pound per degree Fahrenheit.

If it is granted that the internal energy of the molecules of the gas depends on the temperature only, then c_p will be greater than c_v by the work of expansion against the external pressure and intermolecular forces. For a gas obeying Eq. (1), strictly, these latter forces are zero. For air at the pressures and temperatures considered, they are inappreciable. In consequence, the difference $c_p - c_v$ is essentially constant.

$$c_p - c_v = R = \frac{11.913 \times 144}{32.172 \times 778.26} = 0.0685 \text{ Btu/(lb)(°F)}$$

since 778.26 ft-lb = 1 Btu.

The enthalpy h and internal energy u of a perfect gas are defined in terms of the specific heats by the relations

$$h = \int_{t_0}^{t} c_p \, dt \qquad u = \int_{t_0}^{t} c_v \, dt \qquad (6)$$

It is seen, therefore, that these thermodynamic quantities are measures of the energy required to raise unit quantities of the gas from any arbitrary reference temperature t_0 to the temperature t.

The entropy S of unit quantity of a gas may be defined within an additive constant by the differential law

$$dS = c_p \frac{dt}{t} - R \frac{dp}{p} \qquad (7)$$

The entropy of any state relative to an arbitrary state of temperature t_0 and pressure p_0 becomes

$$S = \int_{t_0}^{t} c_p \frac{dt}{t} - R \log \frac{p}{p_0} \qquad (8)$$

Entropy is measured in units of Btu per pound per degree Fahrenheit.

Table 1 covers most of the temperature range of interest for gas-turbine calculations. Values of c_p, h, and p_r are tabulated (an extended chart of p_r and h for a wider range of temperatures is reproduced in the Appendix). The quantity, p_r, is the relative pressure change resulting from an isentropic or adiabatic process in which air is taken from the standard conditions of the table ($t = 520°R$) to the given temperature. Methods of correcting for moisture, fuel, or combustion products are discussed in appropriate sections of the following chapters. It should

TABLE 1. THERMODYNAMIC PROPERTIES OF AIR*

t, °F	c_p	h	p_r	t, °R†
0	0.2400	−14.40	0.6509	460
20	0.2400	− 9.60	0.7556	480
40	0.2400	− 4.80	0.8717	500
60	0.2401	0	1.0000	520
80	0.2402	4.81	1.141	540
100	0.2403	9.61	1.296	560
120	0.2405	14.42	1.466	580
140	0.2406	19.23	1.652	600
160	0.2408	24.04	1.853	620
180	0.2411	28.86	2.071	640
200	0.2413	33.68	2.309	660
220	0.2416	38.51	2.565	680
240	0.2418	43.34	2.841	700
260	0.2421	48.18	3.138	720
280	0.2425	53.02	3.457	740
300	0.2429	57.88	3.799	760
340	0.2436	67.60	4.557	800
380	0.2446	77.36	5.422	840
420	0.2455	87.16	6.403	880
460	0.2466	97.00	7.510	920
500	0.2477	106.89	8.755	960
540	0.2488	116.82	10.15	1000
580	0.2500	126.80	11.71	1040
620	0.2512	136.82	13.44	1080
660	0.2524	146.89	15.36	1120
700	0.2537	157.01	17.49	1160
740	0.2549	167.18	19.82	1200
780	0.2562	177.40	22.41	1240
820	0.2574	187.67	25.24	1280
860	0.2587	198.00	28.34	1320
900	0.2601	208.38	31.73	1360
1000	0.2632	234.54	41.59	1460
1100	0.2661	261.01	53.71	1560
1200	0.2690	287.77	68.46	1660
1300	0.2717	314.79	86.23	1760
1400	0.2742	342.09	107.5	1860
1500	0.2766	369.64	132.6	1960
1600	0.2788	397.41	162.3	2060

* Adapted from "Thermodynamic Properties of Air" by J. H. Keenan and J. Kaye, John Wiley & Sons, Inc., New York, 1945.

† The 0.3° difference in t(°R) $= t$(°F) $+ 459.7°$ is ignored as inconsequential as long as a consistent temperature scale is used in this text.

be pointed out that these corrections are generally small.   For example, the gases resulting from the combustion of gasoline at an air/fuel ratio of 15:1 have a specific heat only about 10 percent greater than the value for air at the same temperature.

As an example of the use of this table, consider a compressor inducting 50 lb of air per second at 0°F and atmospheric pressure and compressing it to a pressure of 4 atm with 85 percent efficiency.   (Compressor efficiency is defined as the ratio of the actual work of compression to the work of compression for an adiabatic process.)   To calculate the power required to drive this compressor, we note from the table that for 0°F the relative pressure $p_{r1} = 0.6509$.   For a compression ratio 4 then, $p_{r2} = 4 \times 0.6509 = 2.604$ which, by interpolation, corresponds to an enthalpy $h_2 = 39.19$ or an enthalpy increase of

$$h_2 - h_1 = 39.19 - (-14.40) = 53.59 \text{ Btu/lb of air}$$

This would be the required work of compression per pound of air for 100 percent efficiency.   The actual work of compression is

$$\frac{53.59}{0.85} = 63.1 \text{ Btu/lb}$$

Therefore the power required to drive the compressor is

$$\text{hp} = \frac{63.1 \times 50 \times 778.26}{550} = 4,450$$

The final temperature at the compressor exit is determined from the table for the final enthalpy, $63.1 - 14.4 = 48.7$, corresponding to 262°F.

To continue this illustrative example, suppose the compressed air is heated to 1600°F in a 90 percent efficient isobaric process and that the useful work is extracted from the hot gases by expansion to atmospheric pressure through an 85 percent efficient turbine or nozzle.   The specific enthalpy of air at 1600°F is, from the table, 397.4 Btu, and the heat energy required per pound of working medium will be

$$\frac{397.4 - 48.7}{0.90} = 387 \text{ Btu}$$

From the table $h = 397.4$ corresponds to a $p_r = 162.3$, and $p_r/4 = 40.56$, which corresponds to an enthalpy $h = 231.8$.   The useful work recovered is then

$$0.85(397.4 - 231.8) = 141 \text{ Btu}$$

The enthalpy of the escaping gas is

$$397 - 141 = 256 \text{ Btu}$$

corresponding to a temperature of 1080°F. If we subtract from the useful work the energy required to drive the compressor and divide by the heat input, we get the over-all efficiency

$$\eta = \frac{141 - 63}{387} = 0.20$$

. Another property of air, of prime importance in determining both the aerodynamic properties of an airplane and the efficiencies of gas turbines, is the viscosity or internal friction, which is responsible for shearing stresses being transmitted across streamline tube boundaries in a varying velocity field. This property is responsible for the profile drag of an airplane, for a part of a propeller's inefficiency, for duct losses, and for a portion of the losses in the compressor and turbine of a gas-turbine power plant. The coefficient of viscosity μ (defined as stress per unit velocity gradient) of air is independent of pressure over a wide range but depends on temperature to a marked degree. In contrast to liquids whose viscosity decreases with increasing temperature, the coefficient for air increases with increasing temperature. Its value in pound-seconds per square foot is given in Table 2.

In fluid flow equations the combination μ/ρ occurs frequently. This ratio has been given the name kinematic viscosity. It has the dimensions of velocity times length. For a series of incompressible flows of velocities V about similar objects of linear dimensions L, it can be shown that, if $VL\rho/\mu$ is constant, the flows will be similar. This fact is the basis for most model (wind-tunnel) investigations. The above ratio is dimensionless and is called the Reynolds number, symbol RN. This dimensionless number is, essentially, the ratio of inertial forces to the viscous forces. High Reynolds number indicates predominance of inertial forces, low Reynolds number that viscous forces play the determining role in the flow. The range of Reynolds numbers of practical aerodynamic interest varies from 10^5 to 10^8.

At flight speeds approaching the velocity of sound, compressibility effects accompanied by shock phenomena and a large increase of drag are encountered. Similar effects may occur when propeller tips or the blade tips in compressor or turbine approach this critical velocity. At 60°F the velocity of sound in dry air has the value 1,116 fps or 760 mph. For small changes in temperature from this value, the velocity of sound increases by 1 fps for each Fahrenheit degree rise in temperature. Over a wide range of temperatures the speed of sound in fps is accurately given by

$$a = 41.45 \sqrt{kt} \tag{9}$$

where $k = c_p/c_v$. The speed of sound in dry air is given as a function of temperature in Table 2 along with the viscosity coefficient.

TABLE 2. VELOCITY OF SOUND AND VISCOSITY COEFFICIENT FOR DRY AIR

t, °F	a, fps	$\mu \times 10^3$, lb-sec/sq ft
−100	930	27
0	1,051	33
60	1,116	37
100	1,160	40
200	1,258	45
400	1,431	54
600	1,582	63
800	1,618	70
1000	1,840	77
1200	1,956	84
1400	2,063	90
1600	2,165	96
1800	2,263	101
2000	2,366	106

At $-100°F$, $a = 930$ fps or 633 mph. Since temperatures as low as $-100°F$ are not uncommon in the stratosphere and maximum speeds of the order of 650 mph have been exceeded in modern gas-turbine-propelled airplanes, it is apparent that the velocity of sound is an atmospheric constant of considerable practical significance in aircraft design. Similarly, in designing aircraft gas turbines, to achieve maximum output for a given size or weight, relative flow velocities may be pushed toward the local velocity of sound.

2. The Airfoil—Lift and Drag. An airplane in flight is acted upon by aerodynamic forces; it is supported by aerodynamic lift and impeded in its forward motion by aerodynamic drag. To understand these forces it is necessary to build up a considerable body of empirical facts correlated by aerodynamic theory wherever available. The airplane wing is the component mainly responsible for lift. In fact, the main objective in wing design is to secure the maximum lift and the minimum drag consistent with structural and stability requirements.

An actual wing may be complicated by such things as taper, sweepback, twist, change of profile, not to mention control surfaces and protuberant engine nacelles. For this reason, the basic data of lifting structures (wing, propeller blades, turbine and compressor blades) are usually developed in terms of a simpler structure known as an airfoil.

An airfoil is an especially simple type of wing of constant profile. In Fig. 4 an airfoil of span b, chord c, and area $S = bc$ is sketched. This airfoil has an aspect ratio $R = b/c = b^2/S = S/c^2$. The profile of an airfoil section with the thickness exaggerated for purposes of illustration is shown in Fig. 5. This shows the straight chord line of length c connecting the two points of the profile farthest apart and the curved mean camber line, the locus of the centers of all segments of perpendiculars to the chord line enclosed within the profile. The thickness t of the profile is the length of the maximum perpendicular segment. The camber at any point is the distance from the mean camber line to the chord line measured along the perpendiculars to the chord.

Fig. 4.   Airfoil of span b and chord c.

In Fig. 6 an airfoil is drawn with vectors representing the relative wind V and the resulting lift and drag forces L and D. The angle α between the relative wind and the chord line is called the angle of attack of the airfoil.

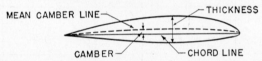

Fig. 5.   Sketch of airfoil profile illustrating chord, camber, and thickness.

In addition to the magnitudes of the forces L and D, it is necessary to know the effective point of their application. Instead of giving this information directly, it is customary to give instead the moment M of these forces about an arbitrary reference point, usually taken as a point on the chord line one-fourth of the chord length back from the leading

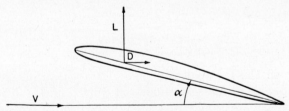

Fig. 6.   An airfoil at angle of attack α, showing lift and drag forces. The relative wind is of velocity V.

edge. This moment is counted positive if it is of such a sense that it tends to increase the angle of attack.

The basic facts concerning lift, drag, and moment can be best expressed in terms of the well-founded theoretical formulas

$$L = \tfrac{1}{2}\rho V^2 S C_L$$
$$D = \tfrac{1}{2}\rho V^2 S C_D \left.\vphantom{\begin{matrix}1\\1\\1\end{matrix}}\right\}$$
$$M = \tfrac{1}{2}\rho V^2 S c C_M$$
$$(10)$$

where the symbols have their usual significance and C_L, C_D, and C_M are coefficients that depend on the angle of attack, aspect ratio, profile form,

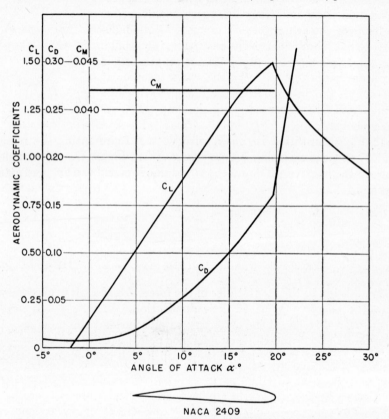

NACA 2409

FIG. 7. Aerodynamic coefficients of NACA 2409 airfoil vs. angle of attack.

and slightly on the Reynolds number. Data on airfoils are obtained from reduced-scale or full-scale models in wind tunnels. The results of these experiments are usually presented in the form of plots of the basic coefficients vs. angle of attack, known as the characteristic curves of the airfoil. Figure 7 presents characteristic curves for the NACA 2409 section for $R = 6$.

These curves illustrate well the salient facts of airfoil performance. First of all there is a range of angles of attack within which C_L varies approximately linearly with angle of attack. That is, if α' is an angle measured from the angle of attack for zero lift

$$C_L = K\alpha'$$

For the NACA 2409 with $R = 6$, $K = 0.0715$ if α' is measured in degrees, and $K = 1.25$ if α' is measured in radians. At $\alpha' = 19°$, the lift-coefficient curve breaks abruptly, signalizing the beginning of an entirely new type of flow over the wing (initiation of stall).

Over the linear range of C_L it will be noticed that C_D varies parabolically with α or α'. As a matter of fact, a semiempirical, semitheoretical relation, based on the work of Prandtl and others, predicts that

$$C_D = a + \frac{C_L^2}{b} \tag{11}$$

The two terms of this equation have been designated, appropriately, the profile drag coefficient and the coefficient of induced drag. As its name implies, the first term depends on the shape of the profile. The induced drag coefficient depends on the lift in the manner indicated. The parameter b is primarily a function of aspect ratio. Under certain reasonable simplifying assumptions, the theoretical value

$$b = \pi R$$

may be derived. To bring observed values of induced drag into agreement with this formula, it is necessary to introduce an efficiency factor e into the expression for b

$$b = \pi e R$$

Empirical data for normal profiles are well represented with values of e of the order of 1.0. For an airplane wing with normal protuberances (nacelles, etc.) and deviations from a simple airfoil, the efficiency factor may vary from 0.85 to 0.90.

As would be expected, the profile drag coefficient depends on the airfoil thickness and maximum camber. Expressing these as fractions of the chord by t/c and y/c, a formula capable of giving the order of magnitude of a for modern, thin, slightly cambered profiles is

$$a = 0.005 + 0.025 \frac{y}{c} + 0.01 \frac{t}{c} + 0.1 \left(\frac{t}{c}\right)^2 \tag{12}$$

The slope of the C_L vs. α curves depends principally upon the aspect ratio and obeys the empirical relation

$$K = \frac{0.1}{1 + 2/R}$$

(for α measured in degrees) with reasonable accuracy. Stall occurs at values of C_L that vary with Reynolds number, airfoil thickness, and maximum camber. Figure 8 depicts the qualitative variation of $C_{L,\max}$ with Reynolds number, t/c, and y/c. For optimum thickness ratio and for values of Reynolds number between 10^6 and 10^7, $C_{L,\max}$ generally lies between 1.4 and 1.8. It will be seen that increase of camber can be used to raise the maximum lift coefficient. This cannot be carried very far, however, because of the large dependence of profile drag on camber [see Eq. (12)].

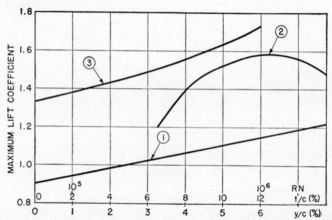

FIG. 8. Variation of maximum lift coefficient with (1) RN for zero camber, 12 percent section (2) t/c for 3 percent camber section, (3) y/c for 10 percent section.

Since the beginning of flight, the question of variable wings has occupied the attention of aerodynamicists and airplane designers (birds can vary the size, shape, camber, and twist of their wings). The whole idea back of this preoccupation is to produce large lift coefficients when needed (landing, take-off, etc.) without paying for this by a big increase in drag during other flight conditions.

This interest has resulted in the development of the various types of slots and flaps sketched in Fig. 9. Several other ingenious methods of control of the flow over the airfoil have been proposed but have not yet been reduced to successful practice.

A 20 percent split flap deflected 60 deg raises the maximum C_L by about 50 percent, but the profile drag is increased five- to tenfold. The increased drag makes this type of flap useful in reducing the landing speed but limits its usefulness during take-off. The simple hinged flap increases the maximum lift coefficient by about 25 percent with only a moderate increase in profile drag. A 35 percent Fowler flap, deflected 40 deg, is capable of producing a maximum lift coefficient of about 3.0

referred to the original wing area. This is accompanied by about 50 percent increase in profile drag.

The Handley-Page slot has proved itself a very successful high-lift device. This is particularly true since the slot can be arranged to open

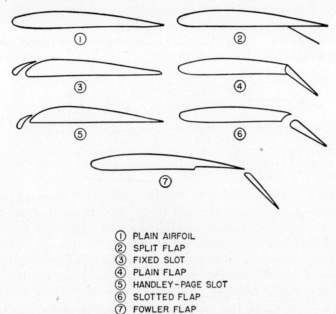

① PLAIN AIRFOIL
② SPLIT FLAP
③ FIXED SLOT
④ PLAIN FLAP
⑤ HANDLEY-PAGE SLOT
⑥ SLOTTED FLAP
⑦ FOWLER FLAP

Fig. 9. Common types of slots and flaps.

automatically at high attack angles when the augmented lift coefficient is needed. Increases of 20 percent in $C_{L,\max}$ can be obtained with this simple device.

Brakes and *spoilers* are aerodynamic devices for increasing the drag and are not intended to increase the lift. Both achieve the desired effect on the drag by spoiling the smooth flow over the airfoil (see Fig. 10).

Delay of separation and stall by means of suction slits that scavenge boundary-layer air and prevent the initiation of turbulent flow has been proposed. This idea has especially intriguing possibilities in conjunc-

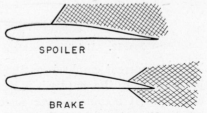

SPOILER

BRAKE

Fig. 10. Brakes and spoilers. Note region of disturbed and turbulent flow.

tion with gas-turbine power plants, for the scavenged air may be used to supply the large volume of working medium required to these engines. This would make possible, in theory, a no-drag engine installation.

Figure 11 shows the use of suction slits and indicates the large improvement in smoothness of flow that may be expected in a properly designed installation.   Experimental results indicate that maximum lift coefficients from 5 to 10 may be obtained in this way.   Design of airfoils specifically for suction removal of the boundary layer is at this time in the experimental stage.[1]

It should be pointed out that the airfoils used on the early airplanes were thin sections of relatively high camber (3 to 5 percent relative thick-

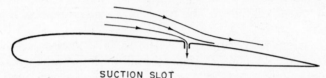

SUCTION SLOT

FIG. 11.   The suction slot.   Air inside the wing is maintained at a reduced pressure by pumping.   Note the stabilizing effect on the boundary layer as shown by the altered streamlines.

ness, 4 to 6 percent maximum relative camber).   These airfoils had minimum drag coefficients of about 0.04.   Developments from 1915 to 1930 were concentrated on thicker airfoils with attendant increases in structural strength.   This trend culminated in the true cantilever wing. At the same time a great deal was learned as to how to reduce the drag by the use of smooth, rounded leading edges, a smaller camber, and in some cases a slight reflexing of the trailing edge.   These refinements brought a lowering of the minimum drag coefficient to 0.01 to 0.02.

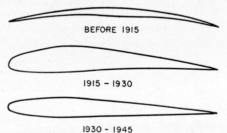

BEFORE 1915

1915 – 1930

1930 - 1945

FIG. 12.   Airfoils representing different periods of development.

With the current emphasis on the higher flight speeds made possible by jet propulsion, the emphasis is again on thinner airfoils of still smaller cambers.   If boundary-layer removal by suction proves successful in practice, this trend toward thinner airfoils may be reversed.

In Fig. 12 airfoils representative of the three periods discussed above are sketched.   Recent work on supersonic airfoils, swept-back wings, etc.,

---

[1] This subject is discussed in an article by S. Goldstein, Low Drag and Suction Airfoils, *J. Aeronaut. Sci.*, vol. 15, p. 189, 1948.

will not be discussed in any detail in this book. Much useful information has been accumulated, but it is still too early to make a worth-while condensation of the results.

3. Nonlift Structures and Components. Unlike the drag of an airplane's wing, which is intrinsically tied up with lift, the drag resulting from fuselage, engine nacelles, control surfaces, landing gear, external radio and radar antennas, etc., is due to the presence of protuberances that do not contribute to normal wing lift. For this reason the drag forces on all nonlift structures and components are referred to as parasitic drag.

In studying parasitic drag, it is useful to have, as standards for comparison, drag data on solids of different shapes. For these we shall choose the flat plate parallel to and normal to the relative wind, the sphere, ellipsoids of revolution of different ratios of length to diameter, and streamlined fuselage models. This data will be presented usually as a function of Reynolds number defined in terms of $\sqrt{A}$, where A is the maximum frontal area of the moving solid.

On this list, the flat plate parallel to the relative wind occupies a special place, because this body possesses a minimum of eddy-making drag. Even here, however, at sufficiently high Reynolds numbers, turbulent flow sets in near the trailing edge of the plate and moves forward toward the leading edge for higher speeds (or Reynolds numbers).

Figure 13 shows the coefficient of parasitic drag C_p on one side of such a flat plate in terms of $A = bc$, the "wetted" area, vs. RN (based on c). Included are plots of the Blasius and von Kármán equations for laminar- and turbulent-flow coefficients.

$$C_p = \frac{1.33}{\sqrt{RN}} \qquad \text{Blasius—laminar flow} \qquad (13)$$

$$0.24 \sqrt{C_p} = \log_{10} (C_p \times RN) \qquad \text{von Kármán—turbulent flow} \qquad (13a)$$

Transition from one type of flow to the other occurs in the region of Reynolds numbers from 0.5×10^6 to 5×10^6. Experimental data are in good agreement with these limiting values and usually show a transition of the type sketched in Fig. 13.

It is of great interest to compare the values of Eqs. (13) and (13a) (doubled) with the airfoil drag coefficient of Eq. (12). It is then readily apparent that any design or device that preserves laminar flow to higher Reynolds numbers can pay real dividends in drag reduction.

The flat plate normal to the relative wind is notable for its high drag. The average excess pressure on the front side of the plate is only slightly less than $q = \frac{1}{2}\rho V^2$, the dynamic pressure, while an underpressure of approximately $q/3$ exists in the turbulent region behind the plate.   As a result the parasitic-drag coefficient is somewhat greater than unity. For square or round plates $C_p = 1.15$ for moderate Reynolds numbers. The scale effect is small.

A comparison of the drag for spheres and ellipsoids of revolution of the same frontal area gives some idea of what may be accomplished by streamlining.   In Fig. 14, curves of the variation of drag with Reynolds number are given for ellipsoids and the sphere.

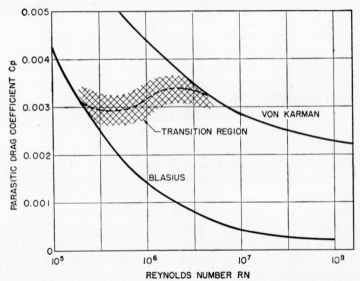

Fig. 13.   Coefficient of parasitic drag vs. Reynolds number for flat plate parallel to flow.

The object of streamlining is to produce a body such that the flow past it is as nearly free as possible of regions of turbulence.   Engine nacelles and fuselage are examples of streamlined solids of revolution with the axis of symmetry parallel to the relative wind.   Drag coefficients as low as 0.05 can be obtained by careful design.

Fuselages and engine nacelles are excellent examples of the practical application of streamline design.   Figure 15 exhibits currently popular forms.   These differ from one another primarily in the ratio of over-all length to maximum diameter (technically known as fineness ratio). The reason one has a fineness ratio of about six while the other has a fineness ratio of approximately two may be found in the design problem. The problem of nacelle design is to produce a minimum-drag housing for the engine.   The fineness ratio is therefore chosen to minimize C_p.   In contrast the fuselage (for commercial planes) must be designed to give minimum drag for given usable enclosed volume.   This is roughly equivalent to minimizing $C_p f^{-\frac{3}{4}}$ where f is the fineness ratio. In Fig. 16, curves of C_p and $C_p f^{-\frac{3}{4}}$ are drawn as a function of f. These are drawn for a streamlined form that has been used in lighter-than-air craft. The positions of the minima for these curves explain why the nacelle and fuselage have the approximate fineness ratios mentioned above.

In practice, it has not yet been possible to realize these low drag coefficients. This is due to the fact that real components are never

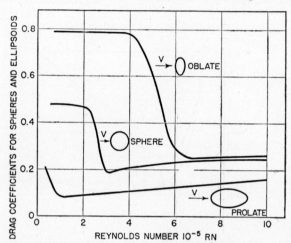

FIG. 14. Drag coefficients of spheres and 2:1 ellipsoids of revolution. Oblate-spheroid-disc surface normal to relative wind; prolate ellipsoid with major axis (revolution) parallel to relative wind.

FIG. 15. Examples of streamlining as applied to the fuselage and engine nacelle.

completely "clean." There are always protuberances and deviations from the ideal streamline form. Then, too, these components must be structurally joined to the rest of the plane. No matter how carefully a fuselage is "faired into" a wing, the resulting drag is greater than the sum of the drags of the isolated fuselage and wing. In measuring the drag of spheres, coefficients differing by a factor of 2 have been obtained as a result of different methods of suspending the sphere in the wind tunnel.

The practical range of values for drag coefficients of fuselage and nacelles is currently

Fuselage (clean)... 0.06–0.10
Nacelles (leading edge)................................. 0.08–0.12

The drag coefficient for tail surfaces, expressed in terms of total tail-surface area rather than frontal area, usually is between 0.005 and 0.010. If the tail surfaces lie in the propeller slip stream or jet, these values have to be revised upward or the actual relative wind speed used in computing the contribution of the tail to the total drag.

4. Compressibility and High-speed Flight. The usual aerodynamic theory derives forces by considering the flows around airfoils or other bodies as motions of an incompressible fluid. Aside from viscous forces, these are obtained by integrating the pressure forces over the body. A

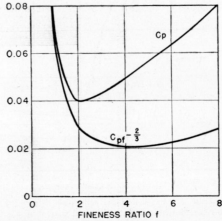

FIG. 16. Specific drag vs. fineness ratio for a family of streamlined bodies. C_p is a measure of the drag per unit frontal area, while $C_p f^{-2/3}$ is a measure of the drag per unit enclosed volume.

resultant force different from zero can exist then only when pressure differences are present. These pressure differences are dynamic, *i.e.*, they exist because of the motion of the fluid.

Air is not strictly incompressible. Density changes accompany pressure changes according to Eq. (1), the perfect-gas law. A reasonable criterion for the neglect of compressibility is that the dynamic pressures encountered be small compared to the static pressure.

$$\frac{\rho V^2}{2} \ll p$$

$$V \ll \sqrt{\frac{2p}{\rho}}$$

The right-hand side of the inequality is, aside from a factor $\sqrt{k/2}$, equal to a, the velocity of sound as given by Eq. (9). We may write our criterion, therefore,

$$M = \frac{V}{a} \ll 1 \tag{14}$$

The dimensionless ratio M, defined by this equation, is the Mach number characterizing the relative motion. It is the ratio of the relative velocity to the velocity of sound in the air or working fluid. The velocity of propagation of sound in a gas is proportional to the mean velocity of thermal motion of the gas molecules, so we may look on the Mach number as a measure of the ratio of the directed flow velocity or energy of the flowing gas to the mean random velocity corresponding to the heat energy of the molecules.

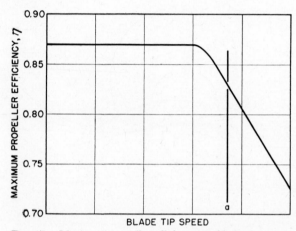

FIG. 17.   Maximum propeller efficiency vs. blade tip speed.

Compressibility effects first became of practical importance in connection with propellers. In order that propellers may absorb the amounts of power demanded on modern commercial and military planes without becoming unreasonably large, the propeller rpm is increased to the point where the blade tips are traveling at or near the speed of sound. Attempts to increase the tip speed further have resulted in inadmissably high power losses, vibration, and noise (see Fig. 17). Even before the onset of these effects, which we know are connected with the formation of shock waves near the ends of the blades, compressibility makes itself felt through gradual changes in the power and thrust coefficients (analogous to drag and lift coefficients for airfoils).

Similar effects are encountered on airfoils themselves. Inasmuch as the velocity of sound under standard sea-level conditions is 1,116 fps or 760 mph, it might be argued that these effects should remain of academic interest except when flight speeds of this order of magnitude are encountered. This is not so. It is not the free-stream Mach number that should be used as a compressibility criterion but the local Mach number for points within the flow pattern.   Local Mach numbers equal to unity may be reached at flight speeds as low as one-half the speed of sound. This is the case for flows over thick wings, especially at high angles of attack, or around nacelles and fuselages.   Figure 18 shows the velocity contours around a thick airfoil at a fairly high angle of attack.   It will be noted that local velocities as high as twice the free-stream speed are found well forward on the upper airfoil surface.   It is fortunate, in level flight, that decreasing angles of attack go along with increasing speed. On the other hand, shock phenomena may be expected quite generally

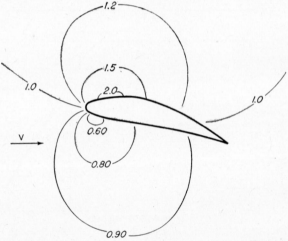

FIG. 18.   Equal velocity contours around an airfoil at high lift.   The numbers represent the ratio of the local velocities to the free-stream velocity V.

during such maneuvers as pulling out of a dive where high speed and high lift occur simultaneously.

Thus, in designing planes to fly at speeds of over 400 mph, close attention should be given to compressibility phenomena in connection with propellers, wings, fuselages, engine nacelles, and control surfaces.

The gas-turbine and jet-propulsion engines bring additional reasons for being concerned with compressibility effects and shock phenomena. Compressor-blade tip speeds must be limited in exactly the same manner as propeller tip speeds, except when designs are made to utilize shock phenomena.   Then, too, the exit velocity of the hot gases may be super-sonic.   This leads to the possibility of shock limitations in the exit section of gas-turbine power plants, particularly jet-propulsion engines.

Certain general results concerning compressible subsonic flows over thin airfoils have wide application.   Consider a flow with free-stream

Mach number M_0 over a thin airfoil of thickness t at an angle of attack α. The drag and lift are affected by compressibility as if the flow were an incompressible one for a similar airfoil having thickness, not t, but $t/\sqrt{1 - M_0^2}$; having the angle of attack, not α, but $\alpha/\sqrt{1 - M_0^2}$; and

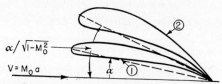

Fig. 19. Airfoil (1) at Mach number M will behave like airfoil (2) in an incompressible medium. Angle of attack, thickness, and camber of (2) are $1/\sqrt{1 - M^2}$ times the corresponding values for (1).

having its camber increased in the ratio $1/\sqrt{1 - M_0^2}$. Figure 19 shows the relationship between the actual and effective airfoil for a free-stream Mach number M_0.[1]

Figure 20 shows the qualitative effects of compressibility on lift and drag coefficients for one particular airfoil. It will be noted that the effect

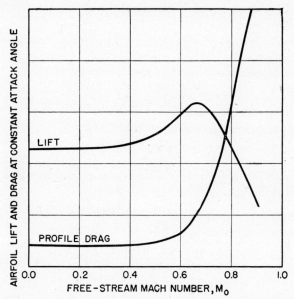

Fig. 20. Variation of lift and drag with Mach number for constant angle of attack.

of compressibility on lift is to increase the lift for a given angle of attack up to a certain point and then to produce what may be called a "com-

[1] These results were first derived by Glauert. See von Mises, "Theory of Flight," McGraw-Hill Book Company, Inc., New York, 1945, p. 279.

pressibility stall." Note the sudden increase in drag associated with the first appearance of shock waves on the airfoil.

The characteristic break in the drag curve for subsonic airfoils seen in Fig. 20 usually occurs at values of the free-stream Mach number ranging from 0.7 to 1.0. One of the most important aerodynamic problems of the day is the design of planes for which the incidence of shock phenomena is further delayed. Only in this way can we take advantage of the high-speed possibilities of jet-propulsion and geared gas-turbine power plants. As striking evidence of the needed improvement in high-speed performance, the L/D ratio of lift to drag at the speed of sound may be as low as three to five, while the corresponding figure at the lower speed for which this ratio is a maximum may be as large as 25 to 30.

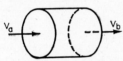

FIG. 21. Element of parallel streamline supersonic flow; $V_b < V_a$ is evidence of a shock wave within the element.

Up to now we have not given any discussion of the nature of shock phenomena and shock waves. Although our knowledge of this field of aerodynamics is far from complete, the basic physics is not too difficult. The first question for which we shall seek an answer concerns the properties of shock waves and when they can occur.

Consider an element of a perfect gas in parallel streamline flow (see Fig. 21) entering cross section a and leaving through cross section b. Conservation of mass requires that the entering and leaving amounts of fluid be equal

$$\rho_a V_a = \rho_b V_b \tag{15}$$

Conservation of momentum requires that

$$p_a + \rho_a V_a^2 = p_b + \rho_b V_b^2 \tag{16}$$

while the condition for conservation of energy requires that the static enthalpy plus kinetic energy remain constant.

$$h_a + \frac{V_a^2}{2} = h_b + \frac{V_b^2}{2} \tag{17}$$

Further, the requirement that the fluid be a perfect gas permits us to write

$$p = \rho R t$$

$$h_a - h_b = \frac{k}{k-1}\left(\frac{p_a}{\rho_a} - \frac{p_b}{\rho_b}\right) \tag{18}$$

One obvious solution of these equations is $V_b = V_a$, that is, the gas flows through the section with no change in properties whatsoever. However if we eliminate from this set of simultaneous equations all properties with a subscript b except V_b, we arrive at a quadratic equation for V_b

$$V_b^2 - \frac{2k}{k+1}\left(\frac{p_a}{\rho_a V_a^2} + 1\right) V_a V_b + \left(\frac{2k}{k+1}\frac{p_a}{\rho_a V_a^2} + \frac{k-1}{k+1}\right) V_a^2 = 0 \quad (19)$$

Mathematically this equation has a real solution in addition to the physically obvious one $V_b = V_a$. It is

$$V_b = \left[\frac{2k}{k+1}\frac{p_a}{\rho_a V_a^2} + \frac{k-1}{k+1}\right] V_a \quad (20)$$

Now $k p_a/\rho_a = a_a^2$, so that Eq. (20) may be rewritten in terms of the Mach number M_a

$$V_b = \left[\frac{2}{(k+1)M_a^2} + \frac{k-1}{k+1}\right] M_a a_a \quad (21)$$

No restriction was placed on the length of the streamline tube from a to b, so we may take it as short as we please. The above solution then implies that a discontinuity exists in the flow; *i.e.*, at some point between a and b the motion can change character abruptly. Velocity, pressure, density, and enthalpy suddenly take on new values in such a way that the necessary conservation conditions are still obeyed. For values of $M_a < 1$, the predicted discontinuity is in the nature of a sudden expansion—air leaves the tube with higher velocity than it had when it entered. The entropy change across such a discontinuity would be negative. Therefore such a solution for M_a less than unity is inadmissible. For $M_a > 1$, the discontinuity is a sudden compression with slowing down of the flow and an increase in entropy. The process can occur. The fact that the solution is a stationary one means that the compression disturbance is traveling with a velocity $V_a > a_a$. This is a shock wave. The relative pressure change across the wave is

$$\frac{p_b - p_a}{p_a} = \frac{2k}{k+1}(M_a^2 - 1) \quad (22)$$

while the relative density change obeys the relation

$$\frac{\rho_b - \rho_a}{\rho_a} = \frac{M_a^2 - 1}{1 + [(k-1)/2]M_a^2} \quad (23)$$

Physical shock waves are, of course, not infinitely thin. Neglect of the effects of viscosity and thermal conductivity has resulted in this unphysical result. However, we need not be too concerned with this, for more detailed study has shown that even for velocity differences as small as a few feet per second the thickness is a very small fraction of an inch. It is inversely proportional to the velocity difference across the discontinuity, and increases in either viscosity or thermal conductivity increase the thickness of the shock.   For air with normal values of k, ρ, μ, and thermal conductivity, the thickness of the shock wave within which 90 percent of the velocity change takes place is approximately 0.013 in. divided by the total velocity difference in fps.

This elementary treatment, being essentially one-dimensional, has also failed to show up the important possibility of oblique shock waves, *i.e.*, shock waves in which the discontinuity is inclined at an angle to the direction of the oncoming fluid.   Both normal and inclined shocks will be discussed in greater detail in Chap. 3.

The study of the flow patterns over airfoils throws considerable light on the phenomena associated with shock formation.   For free-stream

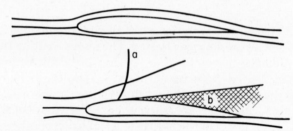

Fig. 22.   Comparison of streamline flow and flow with shock wave (*a*).   Note separation at point of contact and the resulting turbulent region (*b*).

velocities so low that the velocity of sound is not locally reached anywhere on the airfoil, disturbances originating at or near the trailing edge travel forward and affect the entire flow pattern.   With increasing velocity, the local flow Mach number takes on the value unity at some point of the airfoil.   A shock wave then starts to grow out from this point.   Downstream disturbances now are unable to travel through this shock, so that the motion ahead of the front is independent of what happens behind it. The shock has a profound affect, however, on the flow over the after portion of the airfoil.   The sharp pressure change at the wave front affects the motion in the boundary layer, thickening it and promoting separation.   This finally results in a large region of intense turbulence behind the wing, which is the main source of the increased drag accompanying the incidence of shock waves.

The total entropy increase across the shock wave is associated with an energy transfer that can come only from the motion of the airfoil through the air; this energy loss then appears ultimately as increased drag.

Control surfaces of a conventional-type plane are operated in regions of flow that become turbulent at speeds above the critical, so that their influence cannot be felt ahead of the shock zone.   This may result in loss of control. Future designs of high-speed aircraft must necessarily introduce different methods of control or basically new types of airfoils to surmount these difficulties.

Figure 22 contrasts the types of flow over a wing at speeds below and above the critical speed for shock formation. Note the extreme width of the turbulent region in the latter case.

CHAPTER 2

AIRCRAFT PROPULSION

5. Fundamentals of Aircraft Propulsion. All aircraft are propelled by jets. The reciprocating-engine–propeller combination drives a plane through the air by giving rearward momentum to the airstream intercepted by the rotating propeller. The turbojet engine produces thrust by accelerating the gases flowing through it. Rockets are propelled by the reaction of the jet of hot gases produced by the combustion of the propellant.

In each of these cases, the propulsion mechanism accelerates a jet of air (or other gases), imparting energy to it. The useful result is a thrust force F. If V is the forward velocity, the thrust power is equal to the product FV. The mechanical power P expended in producing this thrust power divided into the thrust power gives a ratio η_F called the propulsive efficiency.

$$\eta_F = \frac{FV}{P} \tag{24}$$

Kinetic energy left behind is energy wasted. On the basis of this simple concept, an ideal propulsive efficiency can be derived. This ideal efficiency, which we shall denote by η_i neglects all frictional losses and is, therefore, larger than η_F. It is a useful quantity because its meaning is conceptually clear and because the complex corrections that must be made to allow for friction, etc., are frequently small.

To arrive at the simplest expression for η_i, the jet efficiency, consider the case where the propulsive device imparts only a straight rearward momentum to the gas stream without swirling motion or angular divergence. The flight velocity is V, and the leaving jet has a velocity relative to the plane V_j. Then the thrust

$$F = \frac{W_a}{g} (V_j - V) \tag{25}$$

where W_a is the number of pounds of air per second to which the jet velocity V_j is given. The kinetic energy per second lost in the jet is

$$P_L = \frac{W_a}{2g} (V_j - V)^2 \tag{26}$$

28

and

$$\eta_i = \frac{FV}{P_L + FV} = \frac{2(V_i - V)V}{(V_i - V)^2 + 2(V_i - V)V} = \frac{2V}{V + V_i} \qquad (27)$$

It will be noticed from Eq. (27) that the wake or jet efficiency depends only on the velocity ratio V_i/V, which, from Eq. (25), may be written

$$\frac{V_i}{V} = 1 + \frac{gF}{W_a V} \qquad (28)$$

In Fig. 23 contours of equal jet efficiency are plotted with flight speed V and specific thrust F/W_a as abscissa and ordinate, respectively. From

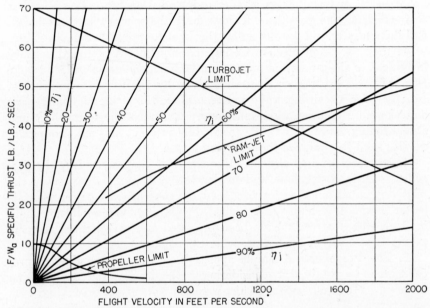

Fig. 23. Contours of equal jet efficiency plotted as a function of flight speed and specific thrust. Approximate specific thrust limits are shown for propeller, turbojet, and ramjet as a function of flight speed.

this figure it can be seen that, at any given flight speed, wake efficiency falls off with increasing specific thrust. However, the higher the flight speed the higher the specific thrust for a given efficiency. For example, at $V = 400$ fps, F/W_a can be no larger than 6 lb of thrust per pound of air handled per second without having the jet efficiency fall below 80 percent. At 2,000 fps, in contrast, the propulsive device can deliver 30 lb of thrust per pound of air handled per second with 80 percent jet efficiency.

On this same figure there is sketched a limiting curve showing approximate maximum specific thrusts that are obtained with present turbojet power plants. This is determined by design limits such as top turbine temperatures, etc. For flight at 600 mph (880 fps) present-day simple-cycle turbojets will have wake efficiencies between 50 and 70 percent and specific thrusts from 25 to 55 lb/(lb)(sec). Specific thrusts produced by propellers will generally be less than 10, and at 400 mph (590 fps) the wake efficiency may be well above 90 percent. To improve the wake efficiency of the turbojet power plant at low flight speeds, it is necessary to impart kinetic energy to a larger mass of air than that which goes through the engine. This results in a lower specific thrust and a higher wake efficiency. One way in which this can be done is to design a turbine to extract enough energy from the hot gases to drive either an open or a ducted propeller. This improves wake efficiency in two ways. It slows down the primary jet at discharge, and it increases the total mass flow through the propulsive device.

If the propulsion mechanism imparts not only a rearward velocity increment to the air stream but tangential components as well, the wake efficiency will be smaller than that given by the simple expression of Eq. (27), for a swirling wake represents additional kinetic energy lost and therefore a lower wake efficiency. Contrarotating propellers and straightening vanes at the turbine exit of a turbojet unit are examples of devices used to minimize these leaving losses.

In general, we may say that the extended jet produced by the propeller is suitable for low- and moderate-speed applications, while the relatively much smaller jet produced by the turbojet power plant is better adapted to high-speed flight. Propulsive systems intermediate between these extremes have been proposed and investigated to some extent (*e.g.*, open- or ducted-propeller thrust augmenters).

6. The Propeller. A simple approach to an understanding of propellers may be obtained by considering the blades as aerodynamic lifting surfaces. Modern propeller blades resemble strongly twisted wings with some taper. The problem is complicated because (*a*) the relative velocity of the blade elements depends on forward speed, rotational speed, and distance from the propeller axis to the element, and (*b*) the blade profile, for structural reasons, varies with this distance. In spite of these difficulties, the type of arguments used in connection with airfoils forms the basis for a theory of propellers.

Consider an element of a propeller blade as sketched in Fig. 24. The propeller is moving forward with a velocity V and rotating at a speed of n rps. The element's velocity V_r then has components V and ωr, where $\omega = 2\pi n$ is the angular velocity of the propeller and r is the radial distance from the axis of rotation to the element. The angle β is the angle of advance of the blade element, and $\alpha - \beta$ is the angle of attack or incidence.   The element is subject to an aerodynamic force per unit area having lift and drag components l and d.   The angle γ is defined by the relation

$$\frac{l}{d} = \cot \gamma \tag{29}$$

The thrust f per unit area and the torque q per unit area may be written

$$\left. \begin{aligned} f &= l \cos \beta - d \sin \beta \\ q &= r(d \cos \beta + l \sin \beta) \end{aligned} \right\} \tag{30}$$

whence the efficiency of the element is

$$\eta_{F,\text{el}} = \frac{fv}{2\pi nq} = \tan \beta \left(\frac{l \cos \beta - d \sin \beta}{d \cos \beta + l \sin \beta} \right) = \frac{\tan \beta}{\tan (\beta + \gamma)} \tag{31}$$

Figure 25 shows the dependence of $\eta_{F,\text{el}}$ on β for several values of l/d. Note that $\eta_{F,\text{el}}$ has a maximum at $\beta = (\pi/4) - (\gamma/2)$ and that the value at this maximum is, for large l/d, approximately equal to $1 - 2d/l$.

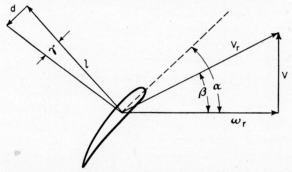

FIG. 24.   Propeller-blade elements, showing angles, forces, and relative velocities.

Individual elements of propellers will generally have l/d no greater than 50 or maximum efficiencies of the order of 96 percent.   Maximum efficiency of modern propellers on test may run as high as 88 to 92 percent, which is an indication of how well the propeller designer has done in solving the intricate design problems.

The thrust produced by the entire propeller and the power required to drive it can be calculated as a summation of the elemental thrust f and power $2\pi nq$.   Expressing l and d in terms of the usual coefficients of lift and drag, C_L and C_D, by

$$l = \tfrac{1}{2}\rho V_r^2 C_L$$
$$d = \tfrac{1}{2}\rho V_r^2 C_D$$

Then

$$F = \tfrac{1}{2}m\rho \int_0^R V_r^2 C_L \ (\cos \beta - \tan \gamma \sin \beta)c \ dr \\ P = \tfrac{1}{2}m\rho\omega \int_0^R V_r^2 C_L \ (\tan \gamma \cos \beta + \sin \beta)c \ dr \Bigg\}$$ (32)

where m = number of propeller blades
R = blade length
c = blade chord at radius r

After certain transformations these expressions can be rewritten

$$F = \tfrac{1}{2}\rho V^2 m \int_0^R \left[1 + \left(\frac{\omega r}{V}\right)^2\right]^{\frac{1}{2}} \left(C_L \frac{\omega r}{V} - C_D\right) c \ dr$$ (33a)

$$P = \tfrac{1}{2}\rho V^2 m V \int_0^R \frac{\omega r}{V}\left[1 + \left(\frac{\omega r}{V}\right)^2\right]^{\frac{1}{2}} \left(C_D \frac{\omega r}{V} + C_L\right) c \ dr$$ (33b)

These equations are general. In deriving them, we have assumed that the elements of each blade are independent of one another and that there

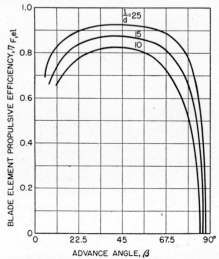

Fig. 25. Blade-element efficiency as a function of advance angle for several values of lift/drag ratio l/d.

is no interaction from one blade to another. These assumptions are not strictly true, but they are good enough to make Eqs. (33) useful in predicting propeller performance.

For example, the static thrust and power performance can be estimated from Eqs. (33) by letting $V \to 0$ and making simplifying assumptions that permit the remaining integrals to be evaluated approximately. In this way, it can be shown that the static thrust per square foot of propeller disc area is roughly

$$\frac{F_s}{\pi R^2} = \tfrac{1}{6}\rho V_t^2 C_L s \tag{34}$$

where F_s = static thrust
  V_t = propeller tip speed
  C_L = effective or average lift coefficient
  s = the solidity, or fraction of disc area occupied by the blades
Substituting for ρ the standard sea-level value and letting V_t equal the velocity of sound (see Fig. 17), we find for the static sea-level thrust

$$\frac{F_s}{\pi R^2} = 500sC_L \tag{35}$$

In terms of total blade area, this corresponds to a blade thrust loading of approximately $500C_L$ pounds per square foot. Similarly we can calculate the power absorption per unit area

$$\frac{\text{hp}}{\pi R^2} = \frac{P_s}{550\pi R^2} = \tfrac{3}{4}\frac{C_D V_t F_s}{550 C_L \pi R^2} \tag{36}$$

An approximate expression for the static thrust per shaft horsepower when the blade tips are moving with a relative velocity equal to the speed of sound is then

$$\frac{F_s}{\text{hp}} = \tfrac{2}{3}\frac{C_L}{C_D} \tag{37}$$

In using these equations it should be remembered that the coefficients C_L and C_D are average values for the entire propeller and that the designing of a propeller involves a number of compromises. As we shall see later, the efficiency of a propeller at the speed for which it is designed may correspond to a value of C_L/C_D in the neighborhood of 15 to 25. The pitch distribution is largely determined by this requirement, and it may not be the best pitch distribution for producing the highest static thrust. For adjustable-pitch propellers, F_s/hp usually has a maximum value at take-off of 2 to 4, corresponding to an effective C_L/C_D ranging from 3 to 6.

The value of the propulsive efficiency η_F may be calculated from Eqs. (33) using the defining relation

$$\eta_F = \frac{FV}{P}$$

The integrals involved can be evaluated, by numerical methods if necessary, for any given propeller. This would involve substituting, under the integral sign, appropriate values for c and for C_L and C_D as functions of r as determined from the blade profile and the pitch distribution. An approximation solution will, however, indicate the capabilities and the limitations of propellers as propulsive devices.   This is done by assuming that C_L and C_D are constant throughout the integration and that the chord distribution is a reasonable one such that the integrals can be carried out in closed form.   We shall choose for such a chord distribution

$$mc = 8s \sqrt{r(R - r)} \tag{38}$$

which leads to a symmetrical blade plan form, a compromise between the blunt-ended and the highly tapered plan forms in common use.

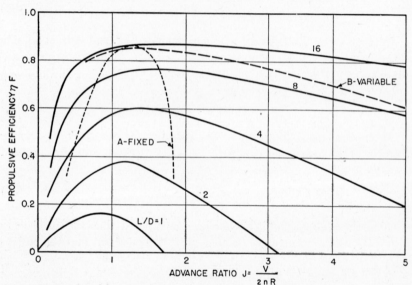

FIG. 26.   Efficiency vs. advance ratio for (*A*) fixed- and (*B*) variable-pitch propeller. Theoretical contour curves are for constant L/D.

The efficiency turns out to be a function of C_L/C_D and $J = V/2nR$, the advance ratio.

In Fig. 26, η_F is plotted against J for several values of C_L/C_D or L/D. On the same figure experimental efficiency curves *A* for a fixed-pitch propeller and *B* for an adjustable-pitch propeller have been drawn.   It is interesting to note that, for both these cases, at the design point L/D values of the order of 16 are realized.   Note that for both higher and lower J values the effective L/D is less.   This is especially true of the fixed-pitch propeller.   Returning to Eqs. (33) and noting that

$$P = FV + P_L + P_f \tag{39}$$

where P_L represents power lost as kinetic energy in the wake and P_f power dissipated in overcoming friction, we may write

$$P_L + P_f = \tfrac{1}{2}\rho V^3 m \int_0^R C_D \left[1 + \left(\frac{\omega r}{V}\right)^2 \right]^{\frac{3}{2}} c \, dr \qquad (40)$$

The right-hand side of this equation, as it stands, is not split into separate terms representing wake and frictional power losses, but if we remember the result from airfoil theory that

$$C_D = a + \frac{C_L^2}{\pi e R}$$

it is reasonable to assume that the frictional loss may be roughly correlated with the profile drag coefficient a and the wake loss with the induced drag term $C_L^2/\pi e R$.

The foregoing blade-element theory of the propeller has been presented with two purposes in mind: (a) to show the close relationship between the action of propellers and airfoils or other lifting surfaces and (b) to provide a basis for understanding the performance limits and limitations of this type of propulsive device.

We have pointed out that the tip speed of propeller blades is limited to the neighborhood of the speed of sound. At these speeds compressibility begins to play a role, resulting in decreased lift and increased drag. This means a loss of efficiency as we have shown in Fig. 17. Just as in the case of wings, these deleterious effects can be delayed by the use of specially designed thin blade sections, sweepback, etc. A few years ago it was thought that compressibility would limit the flight speed of propeller-driven aircraft to top speeds of about 450 mph. It now appears that this limit can be pushed up appreciably and one should not be surprised at propeller-driven planes, powered by gas turbines, being designed for speeds very close to the speed of sound.

With increased speeds and larger aircraft power plants, propellers have been required to absorb more and more power. This means larger propellers and heavier propellers. Simultaneously the solidity has been increased to keep the propeller diameter down. Present-day multi-bladed designs may have solidities approaching $s = 0.2$. At much larger values, serious loss of efficiency brought about by interblade interference would be expected. It may be possible to work at slightly higher solidities by going to contrarotating propellers for, in this case, the reduced lift may be offset by the increase in efficiency due to smaller swirl losses.

The evolution from fixed-pitch to variable-pitch propellers has increased by a factor of 3 or 4 the range of J within which a given minimum efficiency can be maintained (compare curves A and B of Fig. 26). This is, however, not a sufficiently wide range to meet all operational requirements, and it has become common practice to introduce multispeed gearing between the engine and the propeller in aircraft that must fly at extremes of altitude and speed. This accomplishes the desired result but at a considerable cost in added weight, gear losses, etc. Weight of propellers, gears, spinner housing, pitch-change mechanism, etc., may, in certain cases, run as high as 0.30 lb/hp.

To summarize, modern geared propellers may have design efficiencies in the neighborhood of 90 percent and good efficiencies over a 10 to 1 range of J values. Specific thrusts are usually low (of the order of a few pounds per pound of air per second) and the velocity change through the propeller disc is small; static thrust and low-speed performance are excellent. Propellers can now be operated at good efficiencies up to flight speeds of 500 to 550 mph. It is expected that this limit will be increased with improved high-speed designs. Propeller diameters are approaching an upper limit at around 20 ft. Solidities of contrarotating propellers are approaching an upper limit at values from 0.20 to 0.30.

7. Thermal Jets. The high-speed exhaust jets of turbojet power plants, ramjets, and rockets are produced by the expansion of heated gases under pressure. The enthalpy of the working substance is partially converted into kinetic energy of the jet. The fraction converted, which we shall designate by f, is determined primarily by the expansion ratio. Since the enthalpy relative to absolute zero is directly proportional to the absolute temperature (except for specific-heat changes), the kinetic-energy output for a given expansion ratio is almost directly proportional to the absolute temperature of the working medium before expansion.

Figure 27 shows the dependence of the conversion factor for air on the expansion ratio ψ. The quantity plotted is actually the average fractional change of enthalpy for equally spaced initial temperatures from 1000 to 4500°R. This average should therefore be applicable, with only small errors, to any power plant producing propulsive thrust by the expansion of heated air through a nozzle. To fix orders of magnitude and to show how this curve may be used, we note that the average absolute enthalpy H over the same temperature range is given by

$$H = 0.26T \tag{41}$$

(The absolute enthalpy H is equal to the enthalpy h as given in Table 1 plus the enthalpy difference from absolute zero to 60°F.) Suppose we consider air at 2000°R expanded through a pressure ratio of 10 without losses. We have $H = 520$ Btu/lb, and the fraction of this enthalpy converted into kinetic energy, from Fig. 27, is 0.46, so that we can write

$$\frac{1}{2g} V_j^2 = JfH \tag{42}$$

or

$$V_j = \sqrt{2gJfH} = 224 \sqrt{fH}$$

$$= 224 \sqrt{0.46 \times 520} = 3,460 \text{ fps}$$

The thermal energy remaining in the jet is $(1 - 0.46)520 = 280$ Btu/lb or a leaving temperature of $280/0.26 = 1080°\text{R}$, or we can say that the temperature after expansion will be $(1 - 0.46)2,000 = 1080°\text{R}$.

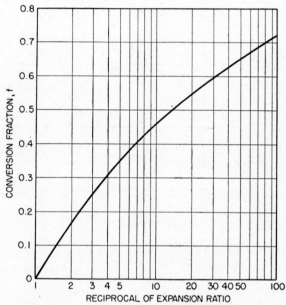

FIG. 27. Fraction of a jet's thermal energy converted to kinetic energy in an expansion through the pressure ratio ψ.

In this example the expansion was considered to be 100 percent efficient. For an expansion efficiency η_n defined by

$$\frac{1}{2gJ} V_j^2 = \eta_n fH$$

the residual or leaving thermal energy is $(1 - \eta_n f)H$, and the jet temperature $(1 - \eta_n f)T$.

In the above numerical example, the jet velocity $V_j = 3,460$ is greater than the velocity of sound, V_s, at $1080°\text{R}$. Thus the flow in the downstream part of the expansion nozzle is supersonic. It is easy to show from Eq. (42) and the relation connecting the speed of sound with T that supersonic velocities will be reached within the jet nozzle for

values of
$$f\eta_n > 0.15$$

or   (43)

$$\psi^{-1} > \frac{1.85}{\eta_n} \qquad \text{approximate}$$

Thus, if more than 15 percent of the absolute enthalpy of stationary
heated air is converted into kinetic energy without loss, supersonic speeds
will result.   Under such conditions there is always the possibility of
shock phonomema occurring with consequent partial loss of thrust.

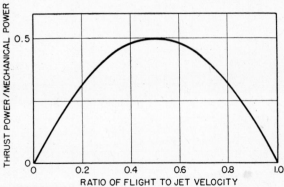

Fig. 28.   Ratio of thrust power to mechanical power of a jet as a function of flight/jet
velocity ratio.

For expansion through the same pressure ratio ψ in an engine moving
forward with a flight speed V, the following relations hold:

$$\eta_n f H = \frac{1}{2gJ} V_j^2 \tag{44}$$

$$\frac{FV}{JH} = 2\eta_n f \frac{V}{V_j}\left(1 - \frac{V}{V_j}\right) \tag{45}$$

$$\frac{P_j}{JH} = 1 - \frac{FV}{JH} \tag{46}$$

where P_j is the total power loss in the jet or the sum of the wake kinetic
and thermal power losses.   If it is desired to separate these two losses,
this may be done by using the additional equation

$$\frac{P_L}{JH} = \eta_n f \left(1 - \frac{V}{V_j}\right)^2 \tag{47}$$

Equation (45) is of particular interest.   It says that of the fraction
$\eta_n f$ of H converted into kinetic energy a part $(2V/V_j)(1 - V/V_j)$ becomes
useful thrust power.   This quantity, positive from $V = 0$ to $V = V_j$,

has a maximum equal to $\frac{1}{2}$ for $V/V_j = \frac{1}{2}$. That is, for flight speeds equal to one-half the jet velocity, one-half of the mechanical energy developed in the nozzle can be utilized for propulsion. Figure 28 shows $(2V/V_j)(1 - V/V_j)$ as a function of the ratio V/V_j.

To complete the description of a particular engine, we must determine ψ and specify how much heat is added to the compressed air, etc. For example, in the ramjet engine, ψ is determined by the ram pressure rise

$$\psi^{-1} = \psi_r^{-1} = \frac{p_r}{p_0}$$

where p_r is the pressure at the end of the ram diffuser and p_0 the ambient pressure. For 100 percent ram recovery

$$\psi_r^{-\frac{k-1}{k}} = 1 + \frac{k-1}{2} M^2 \tag{48}$$

$$f = 1 - \psi^{\frac{k-1}{k}} = \frac{(k-1)}{2} M^2 \left[1 + \frac{(k-1)}{2} M^2\right]^{-1} \tag{49}$$

also

$$H = H_0 + h_r + h_f$$

where H_0 = absolute enthalpy of the ambient air
h_r = the ram enthalpy rise
h_f = the increase of enthalpy due to the burning of fuel in the ramjet combustion chamber

$$H_0 + h_r = H_0 \left[1 + \frac{(k-1)}{2} M^2\right] \tag{50}$$

We can use the preceding material to derive the over-all efficiency

$$\eta = \frac{FV}{Jh_f} \tag{51}$$

for a ramjet (100 percent component efficiencies throughout and operating in such a way that $V_j = 2V$, which we have seen is the condition of optimum ratio of thrust energy to kinetic energy production).

$$\frac{FV}{JH} = \frac{1}{2}f = \frac{1}{4}(k-1)M^2 \frac{1}{1 + \frac{1}{2}(k-1)M^2} \tag{52}$$

$$\frac{FV}{Jh_f} = \frac{1}{(2-k)(k+1)} \frac{\frac{1}{2}(k-1)M^2}{1 + \frac{1}{2}(k-1)M^2}$$

For $k = 1.36$ (corresponding to $c_p = 0.26$)

$$\eta = \frac{FV}{Jh_f} = \frac{0.117M^2}{1 + 0.18M^2} \tag{53}$$

Figure 29 shows the efficiency of this idealized ramjet engine vs. flight Mach number M. At $M = 2$ the over-all efficiency for thrust power is of the same order of magnitude as the best shaft efficiencies for internal-combustion engines. Even when we allow for reasonable internal losses such as imperfect ram recovery, friction, etc., the ramjet or athodyd gives promise of good efficiencies at speeds corresponding to $M = 2$ or greater.

The brief and somewhat idealized theory presented here can be applied with some necessary modifications to the turbojet engine. In this case,

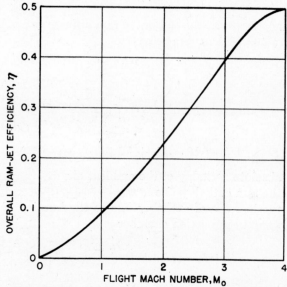

FIG. 29.   Over-all efficiency of a ramjet as a function of flight Mach number.

the pressure ratio is the product of the corrected ram pressure ratio of Eq. (48) and the compressor ratio. Then, too, account must be taken of the fact that some of the maximum enthalpy H converted into mechanical power must be converted into shaft power by the turbine and used to drive the compressor. Details of such cycle calculations are deferred until Chap. 8.

The results we have obtained do not apply directly to rocket engines because the products of combustion are different thermodynamically from air and the entire propellant charge is carried by the rocket. For rockets, the expansion ratio is high, the flame temperature is high, and consequently the energy released per pound of propellants burned is extremely large. This means high jet velocity and low thrust power efficiency, unless the flight speed is correspondingly large.

CHAPTER 3

GAS FLOWS

8. Compressible-gas Flows. All gases are compressible, and, although approximate calculations may be made for flows at low velocities by treating a gas as an incompressible fluid, high-velocity flows require that compressibility be taken into account. The gases dealt with in aircraft-gas-turbine cycles, *i.e.*, air and air mixed with products of combustion,

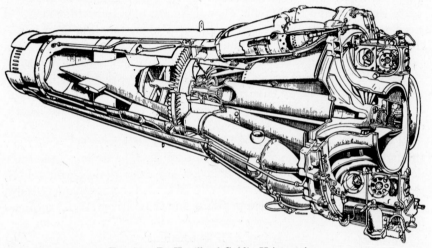

FIG. 30. De Havilland Goblin II jet engine.

may be treated as perfect gases through only a limited range of temperature. For example, a 30 percent change in temperature may result in approximately a 1 percent change in k. Therefore the factoring out of the adiabatic constant k in the derivation of an equation introduces an error when k in one place is for a temperature state differing widely from another state, and its k, in the same derivation. Practically all gas flow equations suffer from this difficulty in their derivations, and are accurate only to the extent that the gas in question behaves as a perfect gas with constant specific heats. For example, Eq. (61) derived later in this chapter for the flow of gases through ducts, may yield mass flow results in error by as much as several percent depending upon which value of k is selected in the flow process. A more accurate calculation can be made for air by using the enthalpy charts in the Appendix and calculating the

41

flow process step by step, but even this entails some assumptions and initial estimates that may introduce errors.

However, to introduce corrections for the changes in gas constants in the derivation of flow equations would, in most instances, yield not simplified equations but detailed steps in calculations to satisfy continuity laws. Therefore, small inaccuracies are generally accepted for the sake of simplicity. In the following discussions of gas flows, perfect gases are assumed unless otherwise noted, and the illustrations are for air at standard conditions with $k = 1.4$, except where enthalpy charts for air are used in the calculation of curves.

Gas flows occur in three distinctly different ways, as subsonic flow, as supersonic flow without shock, and as supersonic flow with shock. Different treatments are usually required for different kinds of flow.

9. Subsonic and Supersonic Flow in Ducts. An important factor in gas flow calculations is the stream-filament approximation used in the following treatment of flows in ducts. This is an assumption that at all points of a flow cross section all similar flow variables are of the same value, and transverse deviations from the duct axis are negligible in their effects upon energy changes. This is a reasonable first approximation for ducts and nozzles that change in area very slowly with length, and it greatly simplifies calculations.

The law of conservation of mass requires that as much fluid flow through one cross section of a duct as through another section of the same duct for steady flow conditions. Thus, at any cross section, where A, V, ρ, P, and p are, respectively, cross-sectional area of the flow, flow velocity, gas density, total or stagnation pressure, and the static pressure, the mass flow

$$W_a = A\rho V = \text{constant} \tag{54}$$

Conservation of energy requires, where there is no heat transfer, that for unit mass of fluid flow undergoing a reversible change

$$\frac{V^2}{2} + \int_{p_0}^{p} \frac{dp}{\rho} = \text{constant} \tag{55}$$

where the first member is the kinetic energy and the second represents the static heat or enthalpy referred to an initial static pressure state p_0. Differentiating Eqs. (54) and (55) yields

$$\frac{d\rho}{\rho} + \frac{dV}{V} + \frac{dA}{A} = 0 \tag{56}$$

and

$$V\,dV + \frac{dp}{\rho} = 0 \tag{57}$$

The velocity of sound in a perfect gas is $a = \sqrt{gkRV}$, and in the case of gases for which the relationship between p and ρ in adiabatic change is $p\rho^{-k} = $ constant,

$$\frac{dp}{d\rho} = k\frac{p}{\rho} = gkRT$$

(when ρ is in slugs/cu ft) and $a^2 = dp/d\rho$. Introducing this relationship into Eq. (57), we have

$$V\,dV + a^2\frac{d\rho}{\rho} = 0$$

and combining with Eq. (56) and eliminating $d\rho/\rho$ gives

$$\frac{dA}{A} = \frac{V\,dV}{a^2} - \frac{dV}{V} = \frac{dV}{V}\left(\frac{V^2}{a^2} - 1\right)$$

$$\frac{dA}{A} = \frac{dV}{V}(M^2 - 1) \tag{58}$$

Equation (58) defines the conditions for converging and diverging flows in loss-free nozzles and ducts as follows. For subsonic flows, the speed of flow increases through a converging nozzle of decreasing cross-sectional area, and flow velocity decreases in a duct or nozzle of increasing cross-sectional area. For supersonic flows at M greater than 1.0, the opposite situation exists, with flow velocity decreasing in ducts of decreasing cross-sectional area, and with flow velocity increasing in ducts of increasing area.

In a constant-area duct or flow passage where there is no friction loss, no transfer of heat to or from the duct walls, and no shock wave, there is uniform steady flow throughout the length of the duct without changes in pressure or velocity. Even in the case of a standing shock wave in the duct, the distance through the shock front is quite small, and normal flow relations are observed on either side of the shock for the local temperature and pressure conditions existing there. Ordinarily, a shock wave would not be expected to stand in the straight section of a duct; it would move to either the entrance or exit region of the straight section to a more stable location. Therefore, a straight, uniform, frictionless duct exhibits the same flow conditions at all points in its length if no heat is added to or extracted from the steady flow and if end effects near the entrance and exit are excluded.

The flow of gas from a zero-velocity reservoir through a duct or nozzle can be derived in a form useful in many gas flow problems. Flow in ducts and nozzles is never entirely frictionless however, and it is necessary to introduce a nozzle efficiency factor η_n. Velocity is equal to the square root of twice the kinetic energy

$$V_1 = \sqrt{2gJ\eta_n c_p T_0 (1 - \psi^{\frac{k-1}{k}})} \tag{59}$$

where V_1 is the velocity at cross-section station 1, T_0 is the temperature in the reservoir, and ψ is the ratio of static pressure p_1 at station 1 to the static pressure in the reservoir, which is also the total reservoir pressure P_0.

Also, $\rho_1 = p_1/Rt_1$ from the perfect-gas law. The ratio of static temperature at station 1 to the temperature in the reservoir is obtained from the relation

$$\frac{t_1}{T_0} = 1 - \eta_n + \eta_n \psi^{\frac{k-1}{k}} \tag{60}$$

Introducing the above value of ρ_1 and Eq. (59) into Eq. (54),

$$W_a = A_1 \rho_1 V_1 = A_1 \frac{p_1}{Rt_1} \sqrt{2gJ\eta_n c_p T_0 (1 - \psi^{\frac{k-1}{k}})}$$

$$= A_1 \frac{P_0}{Rt_1} \psi \sqrt{2gJ\eta_n c_p T_0 (1 - \psi^{\frac{k-1}{k}})}$$

$$= A_1 \rho_0 \frac{T_0}{t_1} \psi \sqrt{2gJ\eta_n R \frac{c_p}{c_p - c_v} T_0 (1 - \psi^{\frac{k-1}{k}})}$$

$$= A_1 \rho_0 \frac{T_0}{t_1} \psi \sqrt{\frac{2\eta_n}{k - 1} gkJRT_0 (1 - \psi^{\frac{k-1}{k}})}$$

Since the R introduced in the above derivation was in Btu instead of foot-pounds, J provides the necessary conversion factor to yield the velocity of sound in air $a_0 = \sqrt{gkJR_{Btu}T_0}$, and if ρ_0 is in slugs per cubic foot instead of in pounds per cubic foot,

$$W_a = A_1 g \rho_0 a_0 \frac{T_0}{t_1} \psi \sqrt{\frac{2\eta_n}{k - 1} (1 - \psi^{\frac{k-1}{k}})}$$

Introducing Eq. (60) into the above and inverting

$$\frac{A_1}{W_a} g \rho_0 a_0 = \sqrt{\frac{k - 1}{2\eta_n}} \left(\frac{1 - \eta_n + \eta_n \psi^{\frac{k-1}{k}}}{\psi \sqrt{1 - \psi^{\frac{k-1}{k}}}} \right)$$

$$= \sqrt{\frac{k - 1}{2\eta_n}} \left(\frac{1 - \eta_n}{\sqrt{\psi^2 - \psi^{\frac{3k-1}{k}}}} + \frac{\eta_n}{\sqrt{\psi^{\frac{2}{k}} - \psi^{\frac{k+1}{k}}}} \right) \tag{61}$$

If the nozzle efficiency $\eta_n = 1.0$, Eq. (61) reduces to the familiar gas flow relation for a perfect, loss-free nozzle

$$\left(\frac{W_a}{A_1 g \rho_0 a_0}\right)^2 \frac{k-1}{2} = \psi^{\frac{2}{k}} - \psi^{\frac{k+1}{k}} \tag{62}$$

Equation (61) is satisfactory for expanding flow with gas leaving a reservoir at pressure P_0 and falling through a pressure ratio ψ with nozzle efficiency η_n; the process is reversible when $\eta_n = 1.0$, so that the equation is then satisfied for both directions of gas flow, out of or into the reservoir.

However, retarded flows at duct efficiencies lower than $\eta_n = 1.0$ are not satisfied by Eq. (61). The equation for retarded flow requires a different expression for temperature ratios and velocity energy than that for the case of expanding flow. The enthalpy change in the retarded-flow case is

$$h = \frac{t_1 c_p}{\eta_n} [\psi^{-\frac{k-1}{k}} - 1] = T_0 c_p \frac{\psi^{-\frac{k-1}{k}} - 1}{\eta_n - 1 + \psi^{-\frac{k-1}{k}}}$$

where

$$\frac{T_0}{t_1} = \frac{\eta_n - 1 + \psi^{-\frac{k-1}{k}}}{\eta_n} \tag{63}$$

$$V_1 = \sqrt{2gJh} = \sqrt{2gJc_p T_0 \frac{\psi^{-\frac{k-1}{k}}}{\eta_n - 1 + \psi^{-\frac{k-1}{k}}}} \tag{64}$$

$$W_a = \rho_1 A_1 V_1 = A_1 \frac{P_1}{Rt_1} \sqrt{2gJc_p T_0 \frac{\psi^{-\frac{k-1}{k}}}{\eta_n - 1 + \psi^{-\frac{k-1}{k}}}}$$

$$= A_1 g \rho_0 a_0 \frac{T_0}{t_1} \psi \sqrt{\frac{2}{k-1} \frac{\psi^{-\frac{k-1}{k}} - 1}{\eta_n - 1 + \psi^{-\frac{k-1}{k}}}}$$

$$= \frac{A_1 g \rho_0 a_0}{\eta_n} \sqrt{\frac{2}{k-1} [(\psi^{\frac{k+1}{k}} - \psi^2)(\eta_n - 1) + (\psi^{\frac{2}{k}} - \psi^{\frac{k+1}{k}})]}$$

$$\frac{A_1}{W_a} g \rho_0 a_0 = \frac{\eta_n \sqrt{\frac{k-1}{2}}}{\sqrt{(1 - \eta_n)(\psi^2 - \psi^{\frac{k+1}{k}}) + (\psi^{\frac{2}{k}} - \psi^{\frac{k+1}{k}})}} \tag{65}$$

Equations (61) and (65) for air are plotted in Fig. 31 with the quantity $A_1 g \rho_0 a_0 / W_a$ as the ordinate and the pressure ratio $\psi = p_1/P_0$ as the abscissa. W_a is in pounds per second. The pressure ratio is double-valued for any given value of the A_1/W_a ratio except for the minimum-area condition; the limitations of Eq. (58) apply to the loss-free duct, and an expanding supersonic flow out of a reservoir must first go through a critical minimum nozzle area before the duct or nozzle expands for supersonic flows.   A converging-diverging nozzle of this type is known as a DeLaval nozzle.   Retarded flows for $\eta_n = 1.0$ also obey Eq. (58), and a supersonic flow that is to be retarded through pressure rise to a

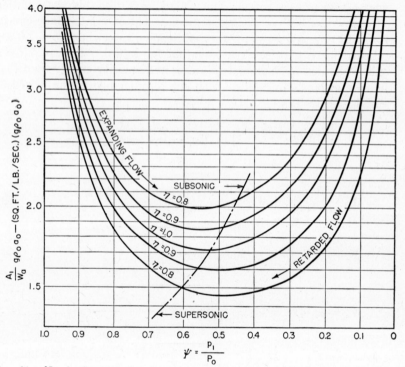

Fig. 31.   Nozzle flow function, for air, plotted against nozzle/reservoir pressure ratio.

subsonic flow must flow first through a converging diffuser section ahead of the throat or critical section, and can then further retard at subsonic velocities in a diverging diffuser section.

If gas is flowing from a state of rest in the reservoir, where the static pressure is the total pressure P_0 with density ρ_0, the absolute velocity of gas flow upon expanding without loss to a new value of static pressure p_1 and density ρ_1 is

$$V_1^2 = \frac{2k}{k-1}\frac{p_0}{\rho_0}\left[1-\left(\frac{p_1}{P_0}\right)^{\frac{k-1}{k}}\right] \tag{66}$$

Equation (58) indicates that the flow velocity in the throat of a DeLaval nozzle is acoustic, or $M = 1$. The same requirement exists in Eq. (62). Differentiating A_1 in Eq. (62) with respect to ψ, and making $dA_1/d\psi$ equal to zero,

$$\psi_{\text{crit}}^{\frac{k-1}{k}} = \frac{2}{k+1}$$

Introducing this relation into Eq. (66) above,

$$V_1^2 = \frac{2k}{k-1}\frac{P_0}{\rho_0}\left(1 - \frac{2}{k+1}\right) = \frac{2k}{k+1}\frac{P_0}{\rho_0} = k\frac{P_0}{\rho_0}\psi^{\frac{k-1}{k}} = k\frac{p_1}{\rho_1} = a_1^2$$

The above identity holds for both expanding and retarded flows for the case of a reversible or no-loss flow with $\eta_n = 1.0$. However, in actual nozzles or ducts where friction losses occur, part of the flow energy is changed to heat energy, and sonic flow at $M = 1.0$ does not occur until after the flow has passed the throat or minimum-area section of the nozzle. This is true for both expanding and retarded flows.

The absolute maximum flow velocity is attained when the gas is expanded into a vacuum, and static temperature and static pressure are both zero. The whole of the intrinsic energy of the gas is converted to velocity energy, and

$$V_{\text{max}}^2 = \frac{2k}{k-1}\frac{P_0}{\rho_0}$$

Since $a_0^2 = kP_0/\rho_0$, the maximum flow velocity after expanding into a vacuum is

$$V_{\text{max}} = a_0\sqrt{\frac{2}{k-1}}$$

For air with $k = 1.4$, V_{max} is equal to 2.236 times the acoustic velocity in the reservoir before expansion begins. The static temperature after expansion to maximum velocity in a vacuum is zero, so that M is infinite.

Velocity at any pressure ratio may be calculated from Eqs. (59) and (64), or it may be obtained more accurately by using enthalpy tables for the gas in question and converting the resultant energy change to velocity change. For flows with η_n less than unity, the efficiency factor must be properly applied to the enthalpy data obtained from the table. In the case of an expanding flow, the ideal enthalpy h from the table is multiplied by the efficiency of the duct or nozzle, η_n, to obtain the actual enthalpy change, and the resultant velocity change is $\Delta V = \sqrt{2gJ\eta_n h}$. The static temperature decrease is also influenced by the efficiency and is given by $-\Delta t = \eta_n hc_p$. In the case of retarded flow, the required velocity change for a given pressure-ratio change is increased by low efficiency and $-\Delta V = \sqrt{2gJh/\eta_n}$; the static temperature increase is also the change associated with the actual enthalpy decrease rather than the ideal, and is $\Delta t = h c_p / \eta_n$. Since the temperature conditions in the duct are known from these calculations, a_1 is also known, and the Mach number of the flow for any pressure ratio is readily calculated from the tables.

Equation (59) for expanding flow also yields M_1 by dividing through by $a_1 = \sqrt{gkJRt_1}$ and introducing the value of t_1/T_0 from Eq. (60).

$$M_1 = \frac{V_1}{a_1} = \sqrt{\frac{2gJ\eta_n c_p t_1 (1 - \psi^{\frac{k-1}{k}})}{gkJR_{\text{Btu}} t_1 (1 - \eta_n + \eta_n \psi^{\frac{k-1}{k}})}}$$

$$M_{1,\text{exp}} = \sqrt{\frac{2}{k-1} \frac{\eta_n (1 - \psi^{\frac{k-1}{k}})}{1 - \eta_n + \eta_n \psi^{\frac{k-1}{k}}}} \qquad (67)$$

Similarly, the flow Mach number in the retarded-flow case is obtained from Eqs. (63) and (64),

$$M_1 = \frac{V_1}{a_1} = \sqrt{\frac{2gJc_p t_1 (\eta_n - 1 + \psi^{-\frac{k-1}{k}})(\psi^{-\frac{k-1}{k}} - 1)}{gkJR_{\text{Btu}} t_1 \eta_n (\eta_n - 1 + \psi^{-\frac{k-1}{k}})}}$$

$$M_{1,\text{ret}} = \sqrt{\frac{2}{k-1} \frac{\psi^{-\frac{k-1}{k}} - 1}{\eta_n}} \qquad (68)$$

In Fig. 32, the data of Fig. 31 are extended to flows for very small pressure changes, and the flow Mach numbers are also shown for different flow efficiencies. In Fig. 33, flow Mach numbers corresponding to the pressure ratios of Fig. 31 are shown, as well as the static temperature ratios for the same flows. The data for Figs. 31, 32, and 33 were taken from the enthalpy charts in the Appendix for air at 500°R total temperature. For air at 2000°R total temperature, the area/flow ratios are changed by only a negligible amount in Figs. 31 and 32; in Fig. 33 the flow Mach numbers should be increased by approximately 2 percent when total temperature is increased from 500° to 2000°R. The temperature-ratio changes are then larger by approximately 10 percent of the Δt from the chart. Therefore, at $\eta_n = 1.0$ and $\psi = 0.6$, the area factor is 1.74 for both 500°R and 2000°R total temperature, the flow Mach number at 500°R is 0.887, and 2 percent greater or 0.906 at 2000°R. The temperature ratio is $t_1/T_0 = 0.864$ at 500°R, and at 2000°R is

$$0.864 + 0.1(1 - 0.864) = 0.878 \text{ approximately}$$

(the correct value is 0.880). The foregoing correction factors are reasonably accurate for values of ψ between 1.0 and 0.3.

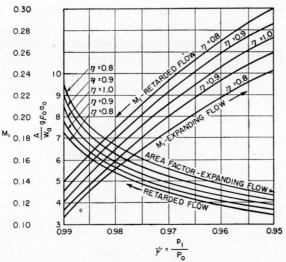

FIG. 32. Nozzle flow function, for air, for pressure ratios approaching unity.

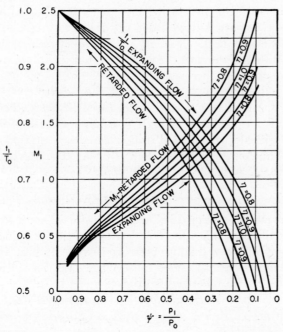

FIG. 33. Temperature ratios and flow Mach numbers for expanding and retarded flows.

Many of the air flow problems in ducts or nozzles free of shock may be solved through the use of Figs. 31, 32, and 33. For example, in one expanding-flow case, the flow Mach number is known to be 0.15 at a particular station 1 where the area is 1.32 sq ft, and the nozzle converges continuously and smoothly to an area of 0.392 sq ft at station 2. With an estimated nozzle efficiency of 0.9, find the flow Mach number at the area 0.392 sq ft and the static pressure ratio between the two stations. From Fig. 32, the flow factor at $A = 1.32$ is $Ag\rho_0 a_0/W_a = 6.6$, and ψ is 0.982. Now the ratio of areas at the two stations is $0.392/1.32 = 0.297$, and the area factor for the downstream station will therefore be

$$0.297 \times 6.6 = 1.96$$

From Fig. 31, the area factor 1.96 corresponds to a ψ of 0.7 at $A = 0.392$, so that the static pressure ratio between the two stations is

$$\frac{0.7}{0.982} = 0.713$$

At $\psi = 0.7$ in Fig. 33, the flow Mach number is 0.685. Since temperature ratios are also shown on Fig. 33, the mass flow is easily calculated if the total temperature or the static temperature at either station is known; absolute velocities are known from the temperatures and flow Mach numbers; the change in flow velocity is known between stations, and the momentum thrust of the flow through the nozzle is known from $W_a \Delta V/g$ with W_a in pounds flow per second.

If, in the above example, the area at the smaller downstream cross section were specified as 0.25 sq ft instead of 0.392 sq ft, then the flow at station 1 could not possibly lead to $M = 0.15$ for a nozzle efficiency of 0.9. The ratio of critical throat area at station 2 to area at station 1 for $\eta_n = 0.9$ from Figs. 31 and 32 would be $1.85/6.6 = 0.28$. The smallest permissible throat area for $M = 0.15$ at station 1 would then be

$$0.28 \times 1.32 = 0.37 \text{ sq ft}$$

Reducing the area at station 2 below this value does not increase the flow velocity, but merely chokes the flow back to a smaller value by limiting the conversion of reservoir static pressure to velocity head in the throat, so that a smaller static pressure fall occurs. With a station 2 area of 0.25 sq ft, the area ratio between stations 2 and 1 is 0.189; ψ at the throat is 0.55 for $\eta_n = 0.9$; Mach number at the throat is 0.915. The area factor at station 1 with area of 1.32 sq ft is $1.85/0.189 = 9.78$, which on Fig. 32 corresponds to a flow Mach number of approximately 0.11 (slightly off the chart) and a ψ of 0.991 (also off the chart). The static pressure ratio between stations 2 and 1 is then $0.55/0.991 = 0.555$.

Assuming that this nozzle exhausts to the atmosphere at the minimum-area section at a ratio of atmospheric to reservoir pressure of $\psi > 0.55$, the above example no longer applies, and station 2 conditions then correspond to this higher ψ on Fig. 31, with corresponding flow Mach number at the throat or exit and with conditions at station 1 corrected accordingly.

If, on the other hand, a larger static pressure difference exists between the reservoir and the atmosphere than is required for critical or choking flow conditions and ψ_2 is smaller than 0.55, there are several possibilities.

It will be noted that for $\eta_n = 0.9$ in expanding flow, sonic velocity is reached for $\psi_2 = 0.49$. If the nozzle is simply terminated at station 2 and the air exhausts to atmospheric conditions, between $\psi_2 = 0.55$ and $\psi_2 = 0.49$, subsonic flows result at the nozzle exit with further expansion beyond the exit. However, the maximum possible momentum change does not take place within the nozzle, and therefore the momentum thrust of the flow through the nozzle is somewhat less than if the throat section were followed by a slightly divergent section, to meet the requirements of the area-factor curve of Fig. 31 for complete expansion to atmospheric pressure. A static pressure difference between the flow static pressure and atmospheric pressure, effective across the entire exit area of the nozzle, serves in part to compensate for the loss of momentum thrust.

Similarly, if the nozzle is terminated at the throat and the expansion pressure ratio ψ is less than 0.49, then supersonic exhaust velocities will occur slightly beyond the end of the nozzle, usually accompanied by shock waves of intensities measured by the pressure ratio. As in the case of the subsonic exhaust beyond the minimum-area pressure ratio, momentum thrust is lost but partially compensated for by the static pressure excess across the nozzle exit.

It is possible, however, to design a divergent section to follow the throat section if the expansion ratio ψ is small enough to result in supersonic flows. The DeLaval nozzle of Fig. 34 is such a nozzle, and with careful design is practically shock-free in the supersonic section at the lower supersonic Mach numbers. If the expanding areas of the nozzle cross sections in the divergent section follow the requirements of Fig. 31, and if the final exit area matches the total available ψ as well as matching the critical throat area, the maximum exit velocity will be developed and maximum momentum thrust will result. If the nozzle is cut off too short at too small an exit area, velocity and momentum losses will result, accompanied by shock. If the divergent section opens up to too large an exit area, flow separation may take place accompanied by shock waves that restore the static pressure to atmospheric or higher than atmospheric pressure, with a consequent loss in thrust.

Retarded flows are handled in the same manner as expanding flows. The flow Mach number at a given cross section of the nozzle determines flow conditions at all other nozzle cross sections. The same restrictions that apply to choking flows at the nozzle throat for supersonic and near supersonic expanding flows also apply to similar retarded flows. When area ratios between entrance and throat section of the supersonic-retarded-flow nozzle are known and when the nozzle efficiency is also known, the pressure-ratio requirement for the critical flow condition is

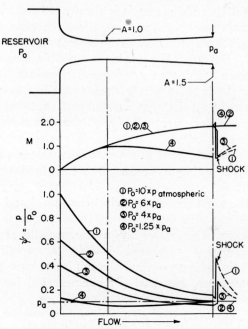

FIG. 34. Ideal flows in open DeLaval nozzle.

known, and the static pressure recovery at any following subsonic diffuser section is known from Fig. 31.

Subsonic retarded or diffusing flows are handled entirely in the subsonic area of Fig. 31, and only the diffusing- or divergent-flow section is used to convert velocity energy to pressure head. Of course, entirely subsonic flows can take place in converging-diverging ducts or in diverging-converging ducts, but throttling is the only practical effect in flows without heat transfer.

The efficiency of a duct or nozzle in converting pressure energy to velocity energy, or the opposite, depends primarily upon the shape of the nozzle and the type of flow through it. It is relatively easy to design an expanding-flow nozzle for subsonic exit velocities with an efficiency of over 90 percent. A common figure for such nozzles is 95 percent. Under carefully controlled conditions, accelerated-flow nozzles have been tested with efficiencies between 98 and 99 percent. A converging nozzle for accelerated flow can be short with a rather rapid rate of cross-sectional-area decrease with length, and the efficiency will still be high. The section of the DeLaval nozzle in Fig. 34 between the reservoir and the throat is a good example of a convergent subsonic nozzle. Even with only a slightly rounded entry from the reservoir to the nozzle proper, there is practically no flow constriction or separation at the entry section, and high efficiencies are obtained at 98 to 99 percent of ideal mass flows. If a square edge is left at the junction of the nozzle and the reservoir, the flow will, of course, tend to separate from the nozzle wall immediately adjacent to the reservoir, and a flow contraction coefficient as low as 0.8, similar to the contraction coefficient for low-velocity flows in hydraulics, may then be a measure of the flow reduction. Ordinarily, this type of inefficient opening for air flows is not used in aerodynamics unless turbulence in the flow is desired.

Retarded or divergent flows at subsonic velocities are entirely different however, and it is quite difficult to design even simple diffusing-flow passages with efficiencies higher than 0.85 except for the lower entry Mach numbers. Diffusers are frequently designated by the number of degrees taper on the diffuser walls; this is in some respects an unsatisfactory designation, since it gives no indication of the actual rate of area increase unless the cross section is also specified. For example, a circular diffuser with a 3-deg taper on the wall will expand from 0.74 to 1.1 sq ft area in a length of 2 ft; the expected diffuser efficiency would be of the order of $\eta_n = 0.73$, while the diffusion effectiveness would be about 0.71 for flow entry Mach numbers between 0.5 and 0.9. The diffusion effectiveness is the pressure-recovery effectiveness, or the ratio of actual static pressure increase to the ideal static pressure increase, $\Delta p_{actual}/\Delta p_{ideal}$. A better way to express the taper of this diffuser for estimating efficiency would be the average increase in number of diameters of the cross-sectional area per unit length of nozzle, or in the above case

$$\frac{1.18 - 0.96}{2} = 0.11$$

A similar circular-section diffuser with approximately the same ratio of entry area to exit area but of considerably greater length, so that the ratio of average diameter increase per unit length is 0.06 instead of 0.11, would be expected to have an efficiency of $\eta_n = 0.85$ or better and a diffusion effectiveness of about 0.83 or 0.84, provided that a straight nonturbulent entry flow is obtained. Giving this diffuser an even smaller taper and greater length to achieve the same diffusion and pressure recovery would, however, probably not result in a significant further increase in efficiency for air flows, since wall-friction effects contribute to efficiency losses, as do turbulence and flow-separation losses. The taper of a diffusing passage then becomes a compromise between a long diffuser with large viscous friction losses and low turbulence, and a short flow with low friction losses and a high order of flow separation and turbulence.

A nozzle for accelerated or expanding flow, with the same area ratios, could easily have a diameter change/length ratio of -0.5 with much higher nozzle efficiency than the above long diffuser. The reason for this lies in the nature and direction of the friction forces that the duct walls exert on the flow boundary layer. In Fig. 35 a section of a nozzle wall is shown and lines of equal static pressure are plotted more or less

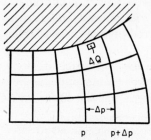

Fig. 35. Flow conditions near curved boundary surface.

vertically, while flow streamlines are drawn generally horizontally for subsonic flow conditions. In a subsonic flow increasing in area to the right, the static pressure increases from left to right, regardless of the direction of gas flow. Consider then a small element of gas volume ΔQ in the boundary layer near the duct wall. The static pressure gradient increases from left to right, so that the static pressure on the right-hand end of this element of volume is greater than the static pressure on the left end of the element. There is, therefore, an accelerating force on the element ΔQ tending to move it to the left. Now if the general flow direction is to the right, as in a diffusing or retarded flow, any flow friction between the duct wall and the boundary layer of gas, enclosing the small element, will tend to decrease its velocity to the right still further, and eventually ΔQ may lose all its kinetic energy in overcoming static pressure rise and boundary-layer friction. While the boundary layer has been slowed down greatly due to friction, the main body of gas flowing in the duct has retained a higher average velocity with smaller friction losses and therefore has maintained the static pressure rise shown from left to right for the expanded-flow area. This static pressure differential exerts itself on the stalled boundary layer and accelerates elements of it to the left in a direction contrary to the general flow direction. This backflow starts up flow eddies, which can completely ruin the flow pattern in a poorly designed diffusing duct. Since the flow-reversal accelerating force per unit element of stalled boundary-layer volume is proportional to $\Delta p/\Delta L$, the slower the rate of area change with length, the smaller the rate of static pressure change and the smaller the flow-reversal tendency. Hence the higher efficiency of long diffusers.

In the case of expanding or accelerated flow, however, while the boundary-layer friction forces tend to slow down the flow in the boundary layer, the static pressure differential along the nozzle wall still tends to accelerate the stalled boundary-layer elements to the left, in the direction of the main flow. Thus, while friction forces result in energy losses in an expanding-flow nozzle, they do not add to flow difficulties in the cumulative manner experienced in diffusers. Static pressure forces in an accelerated-flow nozzle tend to reduce the ill effects of boundary-layer friction; while in the retarded or diffusing nozzle, they aggravate the effects of boundary-layer friction.

The static pressure differential acceleration of the boundary layer, which may result in flow reversals in diffusing or retarded flow, can cause local relative velocities between the boundary layer and the main flow to approach $M = 1$ at average flow velocities far below this number. Therefore, thickening of the boundary layer, flow separation, and large-scale disturbances of the flow pattern are almost inevitable at high flow velocities. Conversely, boundary-layer accelerations in the expanding-flow nozzle decrease the velocity difference between boundary layer and main flow, and therefore decrease the frictional shear forces in the boundary-layer region.

The same direction of static pressure gradient as in subsonic flows exists in supersonic flows, so that although the supersonic-accelerating-flow nozzle has a diverging or increasing flow passage area in the direction of flow, the boundary layer is still accelerated and high efficiency is possible. Retarded supersonic flows are subject to retarded- and reversed-flow boundary layers, as in the subsonic case. A supersonic diffuser that does not have shock waves entering into the diffusion process is a rarity.

10. Gas Flow with Heat Transfer. In the previous discussions of gas flows, a condition of zero heat transfer was assumed between flow stream-lines or between the flow and the duct walls. The total or impact temperature remained constant, and relatively simple solutions exist for various types of flows. When heat is added or removed from a gas flow, the total temperature changes, and velocity and volume changes also result.

If flow velocities are low in a duct of uniform cross section, a relatively simple inexact solution can be found that is sufficiently accurate for all practical purposes (when the flow Mach number does not exceed 0.2 or 0.3). When friction may be neglected, the length of the duct through which the heat is added or subtracted is unimportant, and only the entering and leaving conditions need be taken into account for steady flow in a duct of uniform cross section.

Therefore, for the simplified case, the change in total pressure from one end of the duct to the other, useful in heat-engine combustion problems, is derived as follows: Uniform mass flow requires that $\rho_1 V_1 = \rho_2 V_2$; also the total pressure head at any section is the sum of the static head plus the velocity head $P_1 = p_1 + \frac{1}{2}\rho_1 V_1^2$.

The difference in static pressure heads between two stations is equal to the momentum change between the two stations

$$p_1 - p_2 = \rho_2 V_2^2 - \rho_1 V_1^2 \tag{69}$$

The momentum total pressure change across the heat-transfer section is then

$$\Delta P = P_1 - P_2 = (p_1 + \tfrac{1}{2}\rho_1 V_1^2) - (p_2 - \tfrac{1}{2}\rho_2 V_2^2) \tag{70}$$

Substituting the value of $p_1 - p_2$ from Eq. (69) into Eq. (70),

$$\Delta P = \tfrac{1}{2}(\rho_2 V_2^2 - \rho_1 V_1^2) = \tfrac{1}{2}\rho_1 V_1^2 \left(\frac{\rho_1}{\rho_2} - 1\right) \tag{71}$$

Now if the flow velocity is low, so that the change in static pressure between stations 1 and 2 as well as the velocity component of temperature may be neglected, Eq. (71) may be rewritten

$$\Delta P = \tfrac{1}{2}\rho_1 V_1^2 \left(\frac{T_2}{T_1} - 1\right) = \frac{\rho_1 k R T_1 M_1^2}{2}\left(\frac{T_2}{T_1} - 1\right)$$

The approximate ratio of the momentum pressure change ΔP to the total pressure at the inlet is then

$$\frac{\Delta P}{P_1} = \frac{k M_1^2}{2}\left(\frac{T_2}{T_1} - 1\right) \tag{72}$$

The addition of heat, either by chemical reaction or by transfer through the duct walls, then results in a drop in total pressure in the direction of flow ($\Delta P = P_1 - P_2$). Conversely, cooling the flow results in an increase in total pressure. The value of $\Delta P/P_1$ from Eq. (72) is smaller than the true value.

For higher flow Mach numbers, where full account is taken of the compressibility effects in the gas flow, exact solutions of the flow parameters are as follows: The momentum equation for the pressure change required by the acceleration (resulting from the volume change) is

$$\rho V\, dV = -dp \tag{73}$$

Flow in a constant-area duct requires that the product ρV = constant, so that ρV in Eq. (73) may be so treated and integrated

$$\rho V \int_{V_1}^{V_2} dV = -\int_{p_1}^{p_2} dp$$

$$\rho_2 V_2^2 - \rho_1 V_1^2 = -p_2 + p_1 \tag{74}$$

Since $\rho V^2 = pkM^2$ if ρ is in slugs, Eq. (74) is then

$$kp_1 M_1^2 - kp_2 M_2^2 = p_2 - p_1$$

Therefore

$$\frac{p_1}{p_2} = \frac{1 + kM_2^2}{1 + kM_1^2} \tag{75}$$

The mass flow rate per unit area through a section of a duct is

$$\frac{W_a}{A} = \rho V = \frac{p}{Rt} aM = \frac{p\sqrt{gk}}{\sqrt{Rt}} M$$

$$= pM \sqrt{\frac{gk}{RT}} \sqrt{1 + \frac{k-1}{2} M^2}$$

$$\frac{W_a}{pA} \sqrt{\frac{R}{gk}} = M \sqrt{\frac{1 + [(k-1)/2]M^2}{T}} \tag{76}$$

Since $(W_a/A)\sqrt{(R/gk)}$ is constant for steady flow, Eqs. (75) and (76) may be combined

$$\frac{p_1}{p_2} = \frac{M_2}{M_1} \sqrt{\frac{T_1(1 + [(k-1)/2]M_2^2)}{T_2(1 + [(k-1)/2]M_1^2)}} = \frac{1 + kM_2^2}{1 + kM_1^2}$$

$$\frac{T_2}{T_1} = \frac{1 + [(k-1)/2]M_2^2}{1 + [(k-1)/2]M_1^2} \left[\frac{M_2(1 + kM_1^2)}{M_1(1 + kM_2^2)}\right]^2 \tag{77}$$

The variation of M_2 with the temperature ratio T_2/T_1 from Eq. (77) for different values of M_1 is plotted on Fig. 36. At low values of flow velocity before heating or cooling, quite large changes in total heat may take place with only small effects upon the flow. However, at high subsonic flow velocities, and especially at $M_1 > 1.0$, small changes in total temperature have comparatively large effects upon the flow.

Addition of heat results in a change of flow Mach number toward the sonic flow condition, or $M_2 = 1.0$, whether the entering flow is subsonic or supersonic. For subsonic flows near the acoustic velocity and for supersonic flows up to very high values, only a small change in heat is required for a relatively large change in flow Mach number. For example, a flow with M_1 as high as $M_1 = 1,000$, would require only slightly more than a 2:1 total temperature change to reduce M_2 to 1.0.

Conversely, heat subtraction or cooling in the supersonic region results in a rapid increase in flow Mach number. Cooling of a subsonic flow results in a decrease in flow Mach number. Cooling of a sonic flow can result in either acceleration or deceleration; the practical factors of viscosity and thermal conductivity, which were neglected in the derivation of Eq. (77), combined with the pressure conditions in the duct downstream, will determine the direction of flow change.

It is impossible, through the continuous addition of heat in a duct of uniform cross section, to raise the flow Mach number beyond 1.0. Heating followed by cooling is necessary in order to raise a subsonic flow through the sonic condition into a state of supersonic flow.

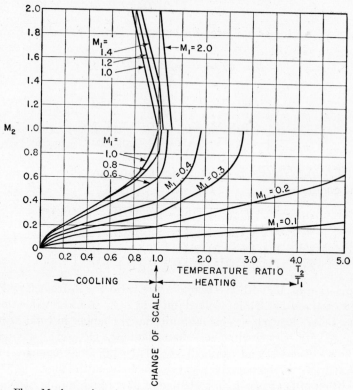

Fig. 36. Flow Mach numbers in a constant-area air flow with heating or cooling; M_1, entering Mach number; M_2, leaving Mach number.

If the flow area of the duct changes as the total heat of the flow is changed, it is possible for a flow Mach number to pass into the supersonic region, but this is in spite of the addition of heat, not because of it. An increase in flow area offsets an increase in heat as far as flow Mach number is concerned, and a decrease in area has the opposite effect of cooling a gas flow.

$$\frac{dM^2}{M^2} = \frac{1 + kM^2}{1 - M^2}\left(\frac{dT}{T} - \frac{dA}{A}\right) \tag{78}$$

The change in entropy of a steady flow of compressible fluid in a duct of constant cross section can be written

$$\Delta S = c_p \log_e \left[\frac{t_2}{t_1} \left(\frac{p_1}{p_2} \right)^{\frac{k-1}{k}} \right]$$

$$= c_p \log_e \frac{M_2^2 (1 + kM_1^2)^{\frac{k+1}{k}}}{M_1^2 (1 + kM_2^2)^{\frac{k+1}{k}}} \tag{79}$$

The entropy is found to have a maximum, and only one maximum, in terms of M_2 when $M_2 = 1.0$. Therefore, the further addition of heat at $M_2 = 1.0$ is impossible. This might indicate that the flow is incapable of absorbing more heat after $M_2 = 1.0$. Actually, a choking flow condition occurs similar to the flow in the critical or throat section of a DeLaval nozzle. When M_2 approaches 1.0, the pressure, density, and velocity conditions upstream readjust to permit $M_2 = 1.0$ with the final increment of heat addition in the duct, in a manner analogous to the adjustment of compressible adiabatic flow through a nozzle of varying cross section. The maximum possible flow through the duct then corresponds to the conditions of Eq. (78) when $M = 1.0$ and T is the total temperature after all heat additions have been made. Thermal choking is not usually encountered in gas turbines, but it is of considerable importance in rockets and ramjet engines or athodyds, and possibly when fuel is burned in the tail pipe of a turbojet engine.

At the same time that the flow Mach number is changing with the addition of heat, the other properties of the flow are undergoing change. Since M_1, M_2, T_1, and T_2 are known from Eq. (79), it is possible to calculate flow velocity, static and total pressures, static temperature, and gas density.

$$\frac{p_2}{p_1} = \frac{1 + kM_1^2}{1 + kM_2^2} \tag{80}$$

$$\frac{t_2}{t_1} = \left[\frac{M_2(1 + kM_1^2)}{M_1(1 + kM_2^2)} \right]^2 \tag{81}$$

$$\frac{\rho_2}{\rho_1} = \frac{1 + kM_2^2}{1 + kM_1^2} \left(\frac{M_1^2}{M_2^2} \right) \tag{82}$$

$$\frac{P_2}{P_1} = \left(\frac{1 + \dfrac{k-1}{2} M_2^2}{1 + \dfrac{k-1}{2} M_1^2} \right)^{\frac{k}{k-1}} \left(\frac{1 + kM_1^2}{1 + kM_2^2} \right) \tag{83}$$

$$\frac{V_2}{V_1} = \frac{\rho_1}{\rho_2} = \frac{1 + kM_1^2}{1 + kM_2^2} \left(\frac{M_2^2}{M_1^2} \right) \tag{84}$$

A somewhat more commonly used relation for P_2 and P_1 is the expression for the ratio of total pressure change to the initial total pressure

$$\frac{\Delta P}{P_1} = \frac{P_1 - P_2}{P_1} = 1 - \frac{P_2}{P_1} = 1 - \left(\frac{1 + \dfrac{k-1}{2} M_2^2}{1 + \dfrac{k-1}{2} M_1^2}\right)^{\frac{k}{k-1}} \frac{1 + kM_1^2}{1 + kM_2^2} \quad (85)$$

The functions of Eqs. (80), (81), (82), (83), and (84) are plotted against T_2/T_1 in Fig. 37 for $M_1 = 0.2$. The same quantities are plotted on

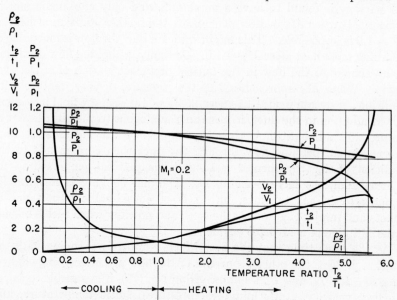

FIG. 37. Ratios of state variables in constant-area air flows with heating or cooling for initial flow Mach number $M_1 = 0.2$.

Fig. 38 for a higher subsonic Mach number at entry $M_1 = 0.4$, and in Fig. 39 for supersonic flow with $M_1 = 1.4$.

Static pressure, total pressure, and density decrease continuously with the addition of heat to a subsonic flow. The flow velocity increases with heat addition in the subsonic-flow case, and the static temperature also increases until $M_2 = 1/\sqrt{k}$. After the flow velocity reaches this value, the static temperature decreases with further heat additions, until $M_2 = 1.0$ and thermal choking takes place. This apparently anomalous action of static-temperature fall with the addition of heat takes place through a very limited range of heat addition within which the flow velocity increases approximately 16 percent, to the sonic velocity. The quantity of heat added to the flow in this range is insufficient to provide the necessary increase in kinetic energy due to the velocity change. Continuity, mass, and energy conservation requirements then result in an additional increment of mechanical energy through expansion and a drop in static temperature. The sharp drop in static pressure that

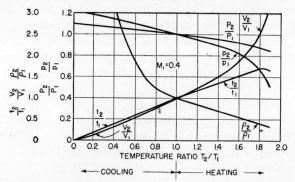

FIG. 38. Ratios of state variables in constant-area air flows with heating or cooling for initial flow Mach number $M_1 = 0.4$.

accompanies the velocity and static temperature changes in the region $1.0 > M_2 > 1/\sqrt{k}$ makes the nature of these effects evident.

When the flow is supersonic, total pressure and velocity decrease with the addition of heat, while static pressure, static temperature, and density increase. It is apparent that velocity energy is being changed to

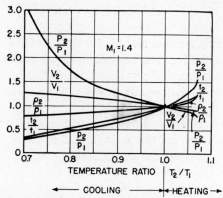

FIG. 39. Ratios of state variables in constant-area air flows with heating or cooling for initial flow Mach number $M_1 = 1.4$.

static-pressure energy. Cooling the flow instead of heating reverses these effects.

The loss of total pressure with heat addition is a consequence of greatest moment when fuel is burned in the combustion chamber of a gas turbine. The drop in total pressure from Fig. 37 for the case of

$M_1 = 0.2$ and $M_2 = 0.4$ with a temperature ratio of $3:1$ (beyond the upper limit in present conventional gas-turbine cycles) is 7 percent. The approximation of Eq. (72) indicates a total pressure loss of 5.6 percent. When $M_1 = 0.2$ and the temperature ratio is $2:1$, M_2 is equal to 0.3, approximately, and the total pressure loss is 3.5 percent; Eq. (72) yields 2.8 percent loss (a result lower than the actual loss even at $M_1 = 0.2$). This total pressure loss, usually referred to as momentum pressure loss, represents a decrease in available energy in the gas flow as it approaches a turbine inlet or jet nozzle and is therefore an important quantity.

11. Gas Flow with Boundary Friction. No gas flow is entirely free of friction losses. The losses commonly assigned to friction in flow through ducts usually include some turbulent losses as well as those due to the viscous shear forces acting along the duct walls. The friction factor f, which appears in the common coefficient $4fL/D$, has been determined experimentally for a great many different flow conditions in ducts. It is in general agreement with theory, decreasing with increasing Reynolds number of the flow but relatively independent of Mach number in subsonic flows (when the Reynolds number is held constant), except that lower values are reported for supersonic flows. Characteristic values of f for incompressible flows at various Reynolds numbers are expressed in the Kármán-Nikuradse relation

$$\frac{1}{\sqrt{4f}} = -0.8 + 2 \log_{10} (\text{RN} \sqrt{4f})$$

where RN is Reynolds number and f is the friction factor for smooth-wall ducts. The values of f for compressible air flows are in close agreement with those for incompressible flows below Mach 1.0. At $\text{RN} = 5 \times 10^4$, f is equal to 0.005; at $\text{RN} = 10^5$, $f = 0.0044$; and at $\text{RN} = 2 \times 10^5$, $f = 0.0039$.

A relation between duct and flow parameters can be written in terms of the friction coefficient for the duct, but it is an unwieldy expression that does not lend itself to the ready solution of flow problems. The general results can, however, be plotted on a chart in a convenient form for comparatively rapid solutions of many flow problems. This method requires the use of the restriction factor K of the pipe or duct.

The restriction factor of a duct or opening is the ratio of the mass flow of air or gas through the opening to the maximum mass flow possible at the same total pressure and total temperature. The maximum flow possible in a duct is obtained when $M = 1.0$ (usually the smallest cross-sectional area of the duct is taken for the passage if it is not of uniform section with length). The mass flow through an area A was expressed in Eq. (76) in terms of total temperature, flow Mach number, and the static pressure; by introducing the relation between total pressure, static pressure, and M, Eq. (76) may be rewritten as

$$W_a = APM \sqrt{\frac{gk}{RT}} \left(1 + \frac{k-1}{2} M^2\right)^{\frac{1+k}{2-2k}} \tag{86}$$

If M is made equal to 1.0 in Eq. (86), and if $k = 1.4$, while P and T are written as corrected total pressure and temperature, then

$$W_{a,\text{max}} = 49.3A \frac{\delta}{\sqrt{\theta}} \qquad \text{lb/sec}$$

The restriction factor at the duct exit is

$$K_2 = \frac{W_a}{49.3A_2} \frac{\sqrt{\theta}}{\delta} \tag{87}$$

where W_a = total actual mass flow, lb of air per sec

A_2 = area of section, sq ft

δ = ratio of total absolute pressure at exit section of duct to standard sea-level atmospheric pressure (14.7 psi or 2,117 psf)

θ = ratio of total temperature of flow to standard sea-level atmospheric temperature (520°R)

The total pressure ratio through the duct, P_1/P_2, is plotted in Fig. 40 against flow expressed as the restriction factor K_2 for various values of $4fL/D$, where f is the duct friction factor and L and D are length and diameter of the duct, respectively, in the same units. The value of f depends upon the Reynolds number (discussed on page 9), varying slightly with the flow velocity through the duct. The mean flow velocity is commonly used. The usual value of f encountered in inlet ducts to aircraft gas turbines is of the order of 0.005.

Through the use of Fig. 40, with flow conditions at the duct exit known, the required conditions at the duct inlet may be established from the ratio of total pressures P_1/P_2 on the plot. The loss in total pressure due to friction may also be expressed as an efficiency loss and made a part of the over-all efficiency factor of a complete piece of apparatus, such as a compressor or turbine, when the duct is an integral part of the device. Ordinarily, however, straight-duct flow problems are more readily solved through the use of P_1/P_2 directly.

If the duct is not round, an equivalent diameter D must be found. If D equivalent is made equal to $4m$, where m is the hydraulic radius of the duct (m = area/perimeter), reasonably satisfactory results will be obtained. When the duct includes turns, bends, and obstructions such as screens, an equivalent value for f must be selected based upon experiments or published data for such deviations from a straight duct.[1]

Flow friction in a duct converts directed energy of flow and pressure to random heat energy and thus results in an entropy increase of the flow. Maximum entropy occurs in a friction flow process when $M = 1.0$; therefore, duct friction tends to bring the flow to sonic velocity, accelerating the flow in the case of subsonic flows and retarding it in the case of supersonic flows. There is, therefore, a maximum length for a straight duct that can be traversed by a given flow before sonic velocity is reached and a choking condition occurs, similar to the choking flow in ducts with heat addition. This condition is reached in Fig. 40 when $K_2 = 1.0$.

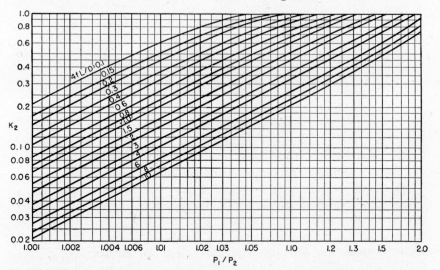

FIG. 40. Flow restriction factor K_2 for air ($k = 1.4$) at exit of constant-area duct as a function of total pressure ratio across duct for different friction factors. (*General Electric Company.*)

Friction in diffusers and nozzles is usually represented by an efficiency factor in the conventional adiabatic compression and expansion equations, but the magnitudes of friction effects may be evaluated directly in such processes. If a diffuser or nozzle is too long, friction may entirely destroy the effect, for certain flows, for which the flow passage was designed. This is particularly unfortunate in diffusing-flow passages, which must usually be relatively long to avoid flow separation. The velocity change in the flow with distance or flow-passage length may be expressed as follows, with m the hydraulic radius of the passage:

$$\frac{dV}{dL} = V\left[\frac{(fk/2m)M^2 - (1/A)(dA/dL)}{1 - M^2}\right]$$

[1] See *NACA Reports* L-208 and L-23.

If the duct is straight and dA/dL is zero, dV/dL increases when $M < 1$ and decreases when $M > 1$. In subsonic nozzles, for accelerated flow, both friction and the rate of change of area are in the same sense and result in rapid flow acceleration, especially near $M = 1.0$.

Subsonic diffusers are different, in that friction losses tend to accelerate the flow (not to be confused with the flow-reversal forces on the boundary layer due to friction), and diffusion will not occur when

$$\frac{fkM^2}{2m} > \frac{1}{A}\frac{dA}{dL}$$

This means that for a conical diffuser, the tangent of the wall angle must be equal to or greater than $fkM^2/2$ or diffusion will not take place.

The supersonic diffuser experiences deceleration from friction and also from area change, so that the wall angle may be smaller or even zero when friction is present. The supersonic accelerating nozzle, however, is limited by the same conditions as in the case of the subsonic diffuser, and too small a wall divergence angle will result in a retarded rather than an accelerated flow.

These effects of friction on nozzle and diffuser flows should make more apparent the basic reasons for the fact that sonic flows in DeLaval and reversed DeLaval nozzles occur slightly downstream from the minimum throat section when the duct efficiency is less than 1.0.

12. Ram Flow into Ducts. A problem frequently encountered in connection with aircraft in flight is the determination of air flows into a duct inlet, with the flow rate due at least in part to the ram pressure of forward flight. The shape of the duct inlet, the presence of obstructions directly ahead of or near the inlet, and the design of aircraft structures around and behind the duct exert major effects upon the flow into the duct.

However, if a duct inlet is relatively clear of interference from nearby aircraft structure and presents an entry to the airstream that does not result in large stagnation areas around the opening, such as would result from a relatively small opening in the nose of a very blunt body, ram efficiency in the flow external to the duct is usually very close to 100 percent. This condition of efficient free stream flow up to the actual inlet can and frequently does exist at the same time that internal duct losses and external drag losses result in low over-all efficiency.

A simple case is that of ram inlet flow into a straight duct with friction loss. A flow characteristic can be calculated for the duct or determined experimentally to yield a restriction factor, which may be plotted against pressure ratio, as in Fig. 40; one line on the chart would ordinarily represent the characteristics of a given duct. Such a duct is shown schematically in Fig. 41 with the inlet at station 1 facing into the relative wind of forward flight. Also shown are the air-flow streamlines ahead of the entry. These are projected sufficiently far ahead of the duct entry that they may be assumed to be essentially parallel and undisturbed at station 0.

The flight speed is M_0, so that the relative wind at station 0 is M_0, the atmospheric static pressure is p_0, ambient static temperature t_0, and the total pressure and total temperature are connected to the static values through M_0. It will also be observed that T, the total temperature, is constant with the value T_0 at all stations if there is no heat addition or subtraction through the duct walls. The static pressure at the duct exit is also the atmospheric static pressure p_0, since, in this case, all flows are assumed to be subsonic.

It is apparent that flow conditions at the duct entry may be connected to conditions at both station 0 and the duct exit through several variables.

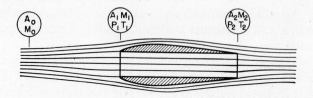

$$\longrightarrow$$
FIG. 41.   Ram flow through open duct.

For the duct itself, the flow restriction factor K_1 at the inlet is found by experiment or calculation as a function of P_1/P_2. If K_2 is known from Fig. 40, K_1 is obtained through the relation $K_1 = K_2(A_2/A_1)(P_2/P_1)$.

The restriction factor may also be expressed in terms of Mach number and of the ratio P/p at the particular flow section in question. K is the ratio of the right-hand side of Eq. (86) to the same function with M made equal to 1.0.

$$K = \frac{M\{1 + [(k-1)/2]M^2\}^{\frac{1+k}{2-2k}}}{\{1 + [(k-1)/2]\}^{\frac{1+k}{2-2k}}} \tag{88}$$

If the flow is expressed in terms of the ratio P/p of total pressure to static pressure instead of in terms of M, as in Eq. (88), the restriction factor may be rewritten

$$K = \frac{\sqrt{[2/(k-1)][(P/p)^{-\frac{2}{k}} - (P/p)^{-\frac{1+k}{k}}]}}{\{1 + [(k-1)/2]\}^{\frac{1+k}{2-2k}}} \tag{89}$$

K is plotted against P/p in Fig. 42, and a scale is also shown connecting M with K and the pressure ratio.

With K_1 and K_2 known, the pressure ratios P_1/p_1 and P_2/p_0 can be found from Fig. 42 or calculated from Eq. (89). The ratio P_1/p_0 is then found from $P_1/p_0 = (P_2/p_0)(P_1/P_2)$ where P_1/P_2 is obtained from Fig. 40. The flow restriction factor K_1 is plotted against the pressure ratio P_1/p_0 in Fig. 43 for a representative range of values of $4fL/D$.

If very high free-stream diffusion efficiency is assumed ahead of the duct inlet, there is negligible loss of total pressure head at any point in

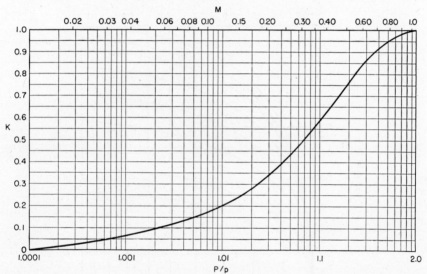

Fig. 42. Relationship of flow restriction factor to flow Mach number and total/static pressure ratio.

the free stream flow. The ratio P_1/p_0 for the free stream flow is then constant at any point in the flow for a given flight Mach number M_0 and is connected to M_0 through the familiar adiabatic relation of total to static pressure. This makes it possible to put a scale for M_0 directly on Fig. 42 along with P_1/p_0.

With a given duct of known $4fL/D$, the inlet flow restriction factor is taken from Fig. 43 for any given subsonic flight Mach number by entering at the required M_0, going along the corresponding P_1/p_0 value to the restriction-factor curve for the duct of given $4fL/D$, and finding K_1 for that duct at this value of P_1/p_0. The restriction factor K_1 of the chosen duct may thus be found for each flight Mach number M_0. The actual mass flows through the duct inlet of area A_1 are then calculated by entering correction factors θ_0 and δ_0 into Eq. (87) along with the values of K_1

obtained above; θ_0 is the ratio of the total ram temperature to 520°R, and δ_0 the ratio of total ram pressure to the standard sea-level pressure.

$$\theta_0 = \frac{t_0\{1 + [(k-1)/2]M_0^2\}}{520}$$

$$\delta_0 = \frac{p_0\{1 + [(k-1)/2]M_0^2\}^{\frac{k}{k-1}}}{14.7}$$

when p_0 is in pounds per square inch.

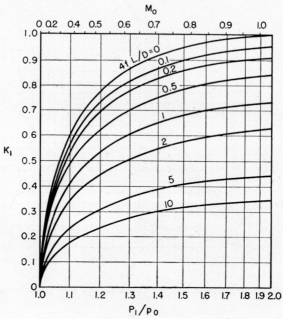

FIG. 43. Restriction factor for inlet of ram duct as a function of flight Mach number M_0 and the ratio of total inlet pressure to atmospheric static pressure for ducts with different friction factors. Ideal free-stream diffusion is assumed.

The mass flow in pounds per second is

$$W_a = 49.3 K_1 A_1 \frac{\delta_0}{\sqrt{\theta_0}}$$

$$= 76.5 K_1 A_1 \frac{p_0}{\sqrt{t_0}}\left(1 + \frac{k-1}{2}M_0^2\right)^{\frac{k+1}{2(k-1)}} \tag{90}$$

Mass flows per unit area for air at selected values of $4fL/D$ are plotted against M_0 in Fig. 44 (standard atmospheric conditions). Flows at other static temperatures and pressures are found by calculation from Eq. (90) or by multiplying the data of Fig. 44 by the correction factor

$\delta/\sqrt{\theta}$, where δ is p_0 divided by standard pressure (14.7 psia), and θ is t_0 divided by standard static temperature (520°R).

The above method of estimating ram air flows through ducts, etc., yields a good approximation to actual flows if a reasonably accurate value of $4fL/D$ can be assigned to the internal flow process and all the entrance diffusion takes place in the free stream flow. High efficiency in the free stream process is due to the fact that fixed boundary walls do not surround the diffusing flow streamlines of Fig. 41. The adjacent streamlines are moving with almost the same velocities, and consequently there is

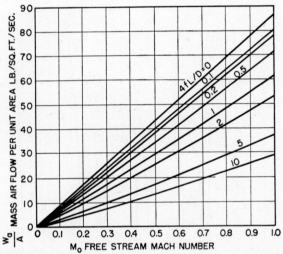

FIG. 44. Ram air flow per unit area through ducts with various friction factors as a function of free-stream Mach number.

very little viscous shear force between streamlines and a minimum of boundary-layer drag and flow reversal.

When losses in the free stream process are too large to be neglected, or when a diffuser or duct with losses also precedes the section for which restriction-factor data are available, the efficiency of that process must be taken into account. This could be the case when a substantial part of the air entering the duct is boundary-layer air, or when a long duct connects a compressor inlet with the flow entrance. The total pressure P_1 at the compressor inlet no longer corresponds to P_0, and it becomes necessary to work out an over-all restriction flow factor at A_1 in terms of the free stream flow plus any ducting that may be connected to it.

A restriction factor may be worked out for a free-stream-flow process of given efficiency by calculating the actual pressure ratios and losses for specific values of M_0 and M_1. This may be accomplished fairly readily through the use of Figs. 32 and 33, where flow Mach number is plotted against ψ, the ratio of static pressure at flow M to the total reservoir or stagnation pressure at selected values of flow efficiency. For example, flow restriction factors K may be plotted for a fixed flight Mach number M_0 against P_1/p_0. The Mach number M_1 is known from Fig. 41 for each value of K_1 (the P/p values of Fig. 41 are, however, correct only for 100 percent efficient flows). The pressure ratio $\psi_0 = p_0/P$ for M_0 is found from Fig. 32 or Fig. 33 on the proper flow efficiency curve. The ratio $\psi_1 = p_1/P$ for M_1 is found on the same efficiency curve, where P is the hypothetical reservoir pressure for the duct or flow process of given

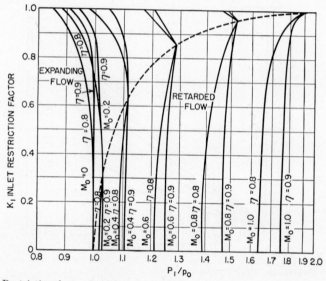

Fig. 45. Restriction factor for inlet of ram duct as a function of the ratio of total inlet pressure to atmospheric static pressure for various values of free-stream Mach number and free-stream diffusion efficiency.

efficiency. If M_1 is greater than M_0, the expanding-flow curves are used, and if M_1 is less than M_0, the retarded-flow curves are used. The ratio of static pressures p_1/p_0 is then equal to $(p_1/P)/(p_0/P) = \psi_1/\psi_0$. The actual pressure ratio P_1/p_1 at station 1 for M_1 is then found from Fig. 41, or as $1/\psi$ for $\eta = 1.0$ on Fig. 32 or 33. The desired pressure ratio P_1/p_0 at section 1 is then obtained by multiplying the above values of P_1/p_1 and p_1/p_0 together. Restriction factors are plotted on Fig. 45 for selected values of M_0 and flow efficiency. Expanding flows are shown in the area above the dashed line and retarded flows below this line. The flow conditions along this dashed line correspond to forward flight at exactly the right M_0 to equal M_1, so that the air inducted by the engine or compressor undergoes no change in state between stations 0 and 1 and there is no energy loss regardless of the stated efficiency of the free stream flow, because there is neither diffusion nor expansion.

The duct-efficiency definition used in calculating data for Figs. 32 and 33 is the ratio of the actual pressure energy change to the kinetic energy change in a retarded-flow process, and is its reciprocal in an expanding-flow process. This is a reasonably satisfactory definition for the efficiency of a variable-area duct when there is a continuous change in flow Mach number from one end of the duct to the other without reversals in the rate of change; it also fits the free-stream-flow case fairly well, although such flows are usually assumed to be 100 percent efficient. It is not a good definition for flow efficiency for uniform long ducts or for flow passages that change in area very slowly with length. Here friction is a large factor, and severe losses can occur with but minor changes in flow Mach number. There is no really satisfactory efficiency definition for this kind of duct, and a friction flow factor is the usual means of handling the problem.

However, the flow of a free-stream diffuser of less than 100 percent efficiency into a simple friction flow duct may be estimated by matching K_1 and P_1/p_0 of Figs. 43 and 45 against each other for any chosen values of $4fL/D$ and free-stream efficiency at various values of M_0. The restriction-factor curve of the specified duct can be transferred from Fig. 43 to Fig. 45 to obtain the crossing points on the M_0 lines at the specified flow efficiency.

When an inlet duct is followed by a compressor, turbine, combustion process, heat exchanger, or combinations of these elements, the simple friction factor $4fL/D$ is no longer adequate to describe the flow process. A practical solution is to calculate the inlet restriction factor in terms of P_1/p_0 for the specified operating conditions, or better yet to measure the actual flow characteristics of the device complete with all inlet ducting. The restriction factors thus found may be plotted against P_1/p_0 on Fig. 44 to determine actual flow restriction factors at all flight Mach numbers. It should be pointed out that when the mass flow is calculated from the restriction factor, Eq. (90) is accurate only for free stream flows with $\eta = 1.0$. The factor for θ_0 is correct, but δ_0 is incorrect, and P_1 should be obtained directly from Fig. 45 as the pressure ratio P_1/p_0 multiplied by the atmospheric pressure p_0. Equation (90) would then be rewritten

$$W_a = 49.3 K_1 A_1 \frac{P_1}{p_0} \frac{p_0}{14.7 \sqrt{T_0}}$$

$$= 76.5 K_1 A_1 \frac{P_1}{\sqrt{t_0}} \frac{1}{\sqrt{1 + [(k-1)/2]M_0^2}} \tag{91}$$

The flow characteristic of a gas turbine is complex and difficult to calculate accurately. However, flows of some types of jet engines and turboprop engines may be estimated in a rough way if several simplifying assumptions are made. It is assumed that constant shaft speed N can be maintained under all flight conditions that are to be investigated; the absolute shaft speed N in rpm is to be held constant, not the corrected speed N_{corr} common in dimensional analysis. This may be done in a jet engine by controlling the turbine inlet temperature or adjusting the exhaust nozzle area, or both. A turboprop engine's rpm is controlled by means of turbine inlet temperature and propeller pitch. A second assumption is that Reynolds-number variations do not influence the flow, and the third assumption is that the compressor is a rigid pump that passes a constant volume of gas through its inlet area A_2 once the speed N is fixed.

Actually, many axial-flow compressors have flow characteristics that closely approach the constant Q/N characteristic of the last assumption. Centrifugal compressors are not usually as stiff regarding flow characteristics, although through a restricted operating range, even the centrifugal compressor may be considered a constant-volume pump at constant speed without introducing extreme errors.

If the volumetric flow at the compressor inlet is constant, then the inlet velocity V_2 is also constant; this is another way of saying that flow angles relative to the impeller vanes or rotor blades do not change. We may now derive the inlet flow conditions for a constant-volume compressor.

$$\frac{Q}{A_2} = V_2 = a_2 M_2 = M_2 \sqrt{gkRt_2}$$

Introducing the relation between T_2 and t_2 for a flow of M_2,

$$\frac{Q}{A_2} = M_2 \sqrt{\frac{gkRT_2}{1 + [(k-1)/2]M_2^2}}$$

If there is no conduction of heat through the duct walls bringing the air to the compressor inlet, T_2 is the same as T_0, the ram total temperature of the atmosphere at flight speed M_0; the relation between t_0 and T_0 at M_0 is then written into the above equation.

$$\frac{Q}{A_2} = M_2 \sqrt{gkRt_0 \frac{1 + [(k-1)/2]M_0^2}{1 + [(k-1)/2]M_2^2}}$$

$$\frac{1 + [(k-1)/2]M_2^2}{M_2^2}\left(\frac{Q}{A_2}\right)^2 = a_0^2\left(1 + \frac{k-1}{2}M_0^2\right) \tag{92}$$

Equation (92) is exact for a rigid compressor, so that if the inlet flow Mach number is known at zero flight speed, or for any other value of

M_0, the inlet Mach number may be calculated for the entire range of flight speeds. This calculation has been made for several different static inlet flow conditions, and the results are plotted on Fig. 46 against M_0. For convenience in reading the chart, ΔM_2 is plotted instead of M_2, and the value of M_2 for a selected flight M_0 is found by subtracting ΔM_2 at that M_0 from the original value of M_2 at $M_0 = 0$. Restriction factors for the same compressors are plotted in the same way. It is of interest

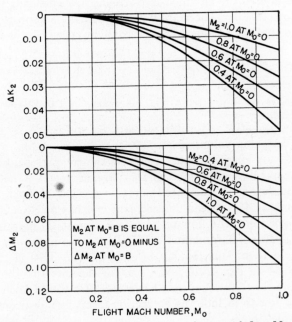

Fig. 46. Variations in compressor inlet restriction factor and flow Mach number for various static inlet conditions and flight speeds. Flow process ahead of inlet assumed loss-free.

that the inlet flow Mach number decreases with increasing flight speed, is down by approximately 2 percent at $M_0 = 0.5$, and is down by approximately 5 percent at $M_0 = 1.0$.

The flow velocity V_2 at the compressor inlet does not change with increasing M_0; the ram temperature rise increases the acoustic velocity in air at the inlet at the same rate that M_2 decreases. The static temperature t_2 at the inlet influences the density of the air flow, however, and thus the mass flow.

The largest single factor influencing compressor flow is the ram pressure rise due to flight velocity. A complete loss of ram pressure rise will result in an actual reduction in mass flow with increasing flight speed, owing to the adverse effects of ram temperature rise. An efficient pressure recovery with low duct losses may result in an increase in the mass flow of the order of 60 percent between $M_0 = 0$ and $M_0 = 1.0$.

If the compressor inlet is the actual entry point of the free stream flow in flight, the mass flow is readily computed through the use of Fig. 44 and the restriction factor K_2, either calculated or read from Fig. 45. For a given M_0 and corresponding K_2 at the inlet, a corresponding K_1 on Fig. 45 is used to find the ratios of P_1/p_0 (for the same flight Mach number M_0 and at the assumed free-stream-flow efficiency η). Usually η is very close to 1.0. The mass flow through the compressor inlet then is related to the compressor flow at zero flight speed by the equation

$$W_a = \frac{P_1}{p_0} \frac{K_2}{\sqrt{1 + [(k - 1)/2]M_0^2}} \left(\frac{W_a}{K_2}\right)_{M_0 = 0} \tag{93}$$

where P_1/p_0 is obtained from Fig. 44. If $\eta = 1.0$, P_1/p_0 is equal to $\{1 + [(k - 1)/2]M_0^2\}^{\frac{k}{k-1}}$ for all values of K_2 and is the value of P/p on Fig. 41 for matching values of M.

Frequently, a long inlet duct connects the compressor inlet with the air scoop that takes air from the free stream flow. A friction factor $4fL/D$ is measured or calculated for this section of duct, and if the upstream area is A_1 and the downstream end has an area A_2 to match the compressor inlet, the flow restriction factor at A_1 may be found by entering Fig. 40 at K_2 and finding P_1/P_2 for the appropriate value of $4fL/D$. K_1 is then equal to $K_2(A_2/A_1)(P_2/P_1)$. This is the value of K_1 that is used on Fig. 45 to find P_1/p_0 for the corresponding flight M_0 at free-stream-flow efficiency η. Equation (92) would then be revised for the mass flow to include the correction terms for the presence of friction in the inlet duct.

$$W_a = \frac{P_1}{p_0} \frac{K_1}{\sqrt{1 + [(k - 1)/2]M_0^2}} \left(\frac{W_a}{K_1}\right)_{M_0 = 0} \tag{94}$$

As an example, an hypothetical axial-flow gas-turbine jet engine with a rigid compressor inducts 150 lb of air per second on the test stand under standard atmospheric conditions at rated shaft speed. There is no inlet duct ahead of the compressor except for a rounded entry nozzle to hold entrance losses to a minimum value. The inlet flow velocity is approximately 400 fps at an inlet $M_2 = 0.37$, which corresponds to a restriction factor of $K_2 = 0.63$ for an inlet area $A_2 = 4.83$ sq ft at $M_0 = 0$ and without inlet duct. This engine is then installed in an airplane, with an inlet duct 10 ft long and 2.48 ft in diameter at the compressor inlet. Since the design speed of the aircraft is in the range of 500 mph, the inlet area of the duct A_1 is made equal to 4 sq ft with a diameter of 2.25 ft to keep structure as small as possible and still take most of the flow diffusion in the free stream. There is a screen in the duct, and the friction coefficient f is found to be 0.012, and taking the smallest area for the calculation of the friction factor, $4fL/D = 4 \times 0.012 \times 10/2.25 = 0.213$. From Fig. 40, P_1/P_2 is 1.023 when K_2 is 0.63. This means that the total pressure at the duct entrance at $M_0 = 0$ is 2.3 percent higher than the total pressure at the compressor inlet. The new mass flow is now $150/1.023 = 146.5$ lb/sec at zero flight speed; K_1 is 0.744.

From Fig. 46, we interpolate and find that for a compressor with $K_2 = 0.63$ at $M_0 = 0$, K_2 is 0.625 at $M_0 = 0.4$. From Fig. 40,

$$\frac{P_1}{P_2} = 1.023$$

as closely as the curve can be read, and

$$K_1 = K_2 \left(\frac{A_2}{A_1}\right)\left(\frac{P_2}{P_1}\right) = \left(\frac{4.83}{4}\right)\left(\frac{1}{1.023}\right) 0.625 = 0.738$$

This value of K_1 is now used in Fig. 45 to find P_1/p_0 at $M_0 = 0.4$ if free-stream efficiency η is less than 1.0, but since the duct inlet flow velocity is fairly close to the flight velocity, with only a small pressure rise due to free-stream diffusion, η is assumed to be equal to 1.0, and P_1/p_0 is 1.075 from Fig. 43 or Fig. 42.

The mass flow is then computed from Eq. (93).

$$W_a = 1.12 \frac{0.738}{\sqrt{1 + [(1.4 - 1)/2](0.4)^2}} \frac{146.5}{0.744} = 160.5 \text{ lb/sec}$$

Similar calculations are made for $M_0 = 0.8$ and $M_0 = 1.0$, and the results are plotted on Fig. 47.

The assumption of perfect free stream flow in the above example is not entirely unwarranted, since the test-stand data for the jet engine were recorded without correction for entrance losses; and to some extent these entrance losses of the order of 1 to 3 percent may well represent free-stream losses. In the case where some boundary-layer air from the wing or fuselage is added to the free-stream air going to the engine, the equivalent free-stream efficiency may be much lower. Accordingly, the mass flow for the same engine with free-stream $\eta = 0.8$ is also plotted on Fig. 47, and the flow for $\eta = 0$ is shown too, as a matter of general interest. It is necessary to use Fig. 45 to determine P_1/p_0 for $\eta = 0.8$; and of course for $\eta = 0$, $P_1/p_0 = 1.0$ at all values of M_0.

A common assumption that is frequently made in estimating air flows into gas turbines is that a stagnation point exists in the inlet ducting just ahead of the compressor inlet. The flow efficiency of the inlet system is estimated, and the stagnation total temperatures and pressures are calculated at the stagnation reservoir or plenum chamber ahead of the compressor, for that efficiency and at a number of different flight Mach numbers.   Temperature and pressure ratios are obtained from Figs. 32 and 33.

The mass flow of the engine as determined on the ground by test or by calculation is then corrected for the new inlet conditions by multiplying W_a by δ/θ where δ and θ are total pressure and total temperature ratios, respectively, of the new stagnation condition to the test or standard-condition pressure and temperature.   If the compressor speed is corrected for the new inlet conditions, the flow correction factor used is $\delta/\sqrt{\theta}$; this

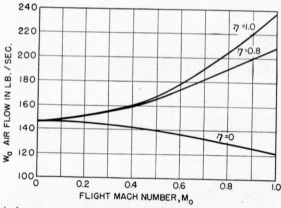

Fig. 47.   Typical compressor flow vs. flight Mach number for different over-all ram efficiencies.   The value of M_2 for $M_0 = 0$ was taken as $M_2 = 0.37$.

is discussed fully in the section on dimensional analysis.   This method of calculating flows is used for all flight altitudes and speeds below supersonic.   Actually, it is not too far from real flow conditions in many gas-turbine installations using centrifugal compressors preceded by a large plenum chamber in the intake.   The errors are small even when using this flow-estimating method for inlet ducts with straight through flow, although duct losses are often less because the undesirable diffusion and expansion in the plenum chamber are avoided.

Ram flow into ducts at supersonic speeds may be treated by the methods used above for the flow conditions following the last shock wave before entry.   Shock waves are discussed in some detail in the following sections of this chapter, and methods of determining conditions on either side of a shock are presented.   In general, supersonic inlet ducts are preceded by a plane shock wave immediately ahead of the inlet or across the mouth of the inlet.   A straightforward solution for the flow variables immediately ahead of or in the inlet itself is then obtained from the known relations across plane shock waves. The pressures, temperatures, and flow Mach number behind the shock are used as the starting point of the subsonic-flow-region calculations just described. When oblique shocks are encountered ahead of a cylindrical duct, the detailed flow solution is much more difficult and is somewhat beyond the scope of this book. However, there are some general solutions of three-dimensional oblique shocks indicated in the text. The case of two-dimensional inclined shocks such as would be approximated in long, narrow entry slots, is soluble from the data given.

13. Normal Shock Waves. A brief, elementary description of normal shock waves appeared in Chap. 1 in connection with supersonic flows around airfoils. Oblique shock waves, with the air flow entering the shock plane at other than a 90-deg or normal angle, also occur, but the plane normal shock is the simplest case and will be covered first. Equation (20) can be rewritten to yield the ratio of the flow velocity after the shock to the flow velocity before the shock as

$$\frac{V_b}{V_a} = \frac{2}{(k+1)M_a^2} + \frac{k-1}{k+1} \tag{95}$$

Since the mass flow through the shock is continuous and uniform, $\rho_a V_a = \rho_b V_b$, and Eq. (95) can be made to yield the density ratio

$$\frac{\rho_a}{\rho_b} = \frac{2}{(k+1)M_a^2} + \frac{k-1}{k+1} \tag{96}$$

Equation (22) stated the static pressure conditions after and before the shock

$$\frac{p_b}{p_a} = 1 + \frac{2k}{k+1}(M_a^2 - 1) \tag{97}$$

The perfect-gas law $p = \rho R t$ connects static temperature with both density and static pressure, so that the ratio of static temperatures across the shock is obtained by multiplying Eq. (96) by Eq. (97)

$$\frac{t_b}{t_a} = \frac{p_b}{p_a}\frac{\rho_a}{\rho_b}$$
$$\frac{t_b}{t_a} = \frac{[2kM_a^2 - (k-1)][(k-1)M_a^2 + 2]}{(k+1)^2 M_a^2} \tag{98}$$

The ratio of the velocities of sound across the shock is, of course, the square root of the static temperature ratio

$$\frac{a_b}{a_a} = \sqrt{\frac{t_b}{t_a}} \tag{99}$$

It is also easy to derive the downstream flow Mach number in relation to

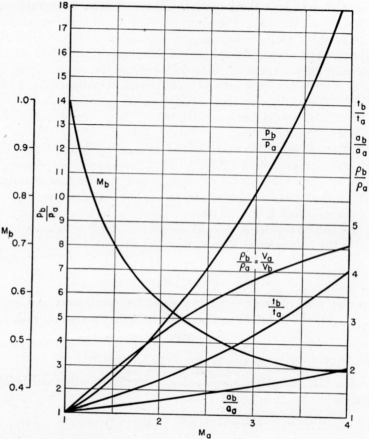

FIG. 48.   Ratios of state variables across normal stock wave in air as a function of upstream Mach number M_a.

the Mach number of the flow entering the shock, since $M = V/a$ and Eq. (95) gives the absolute velocity ratio. M_b is expressed conveniently as a squared term

$$M_b^2 = \frac{V_b^2}{a_b^2} = \frac{V_a^2}{a_b^2}\left[\frac{(k-1)M_a^2 + 2}{(k+1)M_a^2}\right]^2 = \frac{M_a^2 a_a^2}{a_b^2}\left[\frac{(k-1)M_a^2 + 2}{(k+1)M_a^2}\right]^2$$

therefore
$$M_b^2 = \frac{(k-1)M_a^2 + 2}{2kM_a^2 - (k-1)} \qquad (100)$$

The five quantities of Eqs. (95) to (99) are plotted in Fig. 48, for air with $k = 1.4$, against M_a, the Mach number of the entering flow.

The compression across a shock wave is not adiabatic. The entropy increases as the gas flows through the shock, and there is a corresponding decrease in available energy. When there is adiabatic compression, the relation

$$k \log \frac{\rho_b}{\rho_a} = \log \frac{p_b}{p_a}$$

holds. In Fig. 49, $\log (\rho_b/\rho_a)$ is plotted against $\log (p_b/p_a)$ for air; the dashed straight line is the adiabatic relation. At low values of the pressure ratio, corresponding to entry Mach numbers as low as $M_a = 1.15$, the shock curve begins to fall away from the adiabatic line. A very low intensity normal shock wave is a reasonably efficient diffuser; but as the entry Mach number grows larger, more and more of the initial kinetic energy of the gas stream is converted by the shock wave into temperature rise rather than into pressure energy. This represents an efficiency loss from an available-energy standpoint.

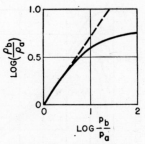

FIG. 49. Deviation of compression across shock wave from ideal isentropic. The dashed line represents the relation between p and ρ in an ideal isentropic compression.

The efficiency of a shock wave as a supersonic diffuser can be presented as the ratio of the work required for an equivalent adiabatic compression through the shock pressure ratio to the difference in kinetic energy across the shock

$$\eta_s = \frac{J c_p t_a[(p_b/p_a)^{\frac{k-1}{k}} - 1]}{(1/2g)(V_a^2 - V_b^2)}$$

This may, by the use of the previously derived shock relations, be reduced to the form

$$\eta_s = \frac{(k+1)^2 M_a^2}{(k-1)(kM_a^2+1)(M_a^2-1)} \left\{ \left[1 + \frac{2k}{k+1} (M_a^2 - 1) \right]^{\frac{k-1}{k}} - 1 \right\} \quad (101)$$

Usually, there is more interest in the efficiency of a normal shock wave followed by a subsonic diffuser. The efficiency of the subsonic diffuser is important to the process, especially at low values of M_a, and is denoted by η_n. The over-all diffusion efficiency for a normal plane shock wave plus a subsonic diffuser is the ratio of the work required for an equivalent adiabatic compression to final stagnation pressure to the total kinetic energy before the shock

$$\eta = \frac{(P_c/p_a)^{\frac{k-1}{k}} - 1}{[(k-1)/2]M_a^2}$$

where P_c/p_a is the pressure ratio derived in the Eq. (104). The efficiency is then

$$\eta = \frac{2}{k-1} M_a^{-2} \left\{ \left(1 + \eta_n \frac{1 + \frac{k-1}{2} M_a^2}{\frac{2k}{k-1} M_a^2 - 1} \right) \left[1 + \frac{2k}{k+1} (M_a^2 - 1) \right]^{\frac{k-1}{k}} - 1 \right\} \quad (102)$$

Values of η are plotted against M_a in Fig. 50.

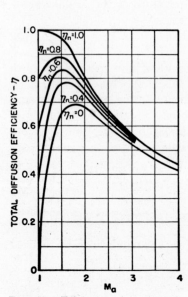

FIG. 50. Efficiency of a normal shock wave followed by subsonic diffusers of different efficiencies η_n, as a function of initial Mach number M_a.

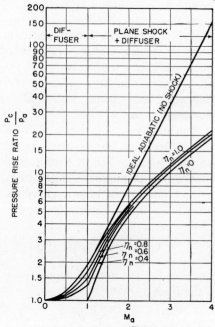

FIG. 51. Ratio of total pressure after diffusion, P_c, to static ambient pressure p_a, as a function of initial Mach number M_a.

When a plane shock wave is followed by subsonic diffusion to full stagnation pressure P_c, the ratio of final pressure to the static pressure before the shock is

$$\frac{P_c}{p_a} = \frac{P_c}{p_b} \frac{p_b}{p_a}$$

For a subsonic diffuser of efficiency η_n, the pressure recovery is written

$$\frac{P_c}{p_b} = \left(1 + \eta_n \frac{k-1}{2} M_b^2 \right)^{\frac{k}{k-1}} = \left(1 + \eta_n \frac{1 + \frac{k-1}{2} M_a^2}{\frac{2k}{k-1} M_a^2 - 1} \right)^{\frac{k}{k-1}} \quad (103)$$

The over-all pressure-recovery ratio is therefore

$$\frac{P_c}{p_a} = \left(1 + \eta_n \frac{1 + \dfrac{k-1}{2} M_a^2}{\dfrac{2k}{k-1} M_a^2 - 1}\right)^{\frac{k}{k-1}} \left[1 + \frac{2k}{k+1}(M_a^2 - 1)\right] \quad (104)$$

Values of this ratio are plotted in Fig. 51 against M_a for several subsonic diffuser efficiencies η_n. Also shown is a similar curve for a completely shock-free isentropic compression. To complete the data, ram pressure ratios have also been run out through the entire subsonic flow range of $M_a < 1$. When the diffuser efficiency $\eta_n = 1.0$, Eq. (104) reduces to

$$\frac{P_c}{p_a} = \left[\frac{2kM_a^2 - (k-1)}{k+1}\right]\left[\frac{(k+1)^2}{2} \frac{M_a^2}{2kM_a^2 - (k-1)}\right]^{\frac{k}{k-1}} \quad (105)$$

This is the formula frequently used in Pitot static tube measurements to determine supersonic free-stream Mach numbers experimentally.

Considerable confusion can result in discussing the pressure-rise ratio in inlet ducts of aircraft turbines and athodyds or ramjets if the over-all diffusion efficiency is not carefully distinguished from the pressure-recovery effectiveness. This latter quantity, which we call ram or diffusion effectiveness, is defined as the ratio of the actual pressure increase in the diffusion process to the pressure increase that would be obtained in a loss-free isentropic diffusion process without shock. In the case of a subsonic flow in a diffuser to complete stagnation pressure

$$\text{Ram effectiveness}_{\text{subsonic}} = \frac{\left(1 + \dfrac{k-1}{2} \eta_n M^2\right)^{\frac{k}{k-1}} - 1}{\left(1 + \dfrac{k-1}{2} M^2\right)^{\frac{k}{k-1}} - 1} \quad (106)$$

When the subsonic diffuser is preceded by a normal shock wave with $M_a > 1$,

$$\text{Ram effectiveness} = \frac{(P_c/p_a) - 1}{(P_a/p_a) - 1}$$

P_a/p_a is the shock-free isentropic compression ratio shown for reference purposes on Fig. 51, or the ratio of total pressure to static pressure before the shock.

Over-all ram effectiveness for a shock followed by a subsonic diffuser of efficiency η_n is

Ram effectiveness =

$$\frac{\left\{1 - \eta_n \dfrac{1 + [(k-1)/2]M_a^2}{1 - [2k/(k-1)]M_a^2}\right\}^{\frac{k}{k-1}} \left[1 + \dfrac{2k}{k-1}(M_a^2 - 1)\right] - 1}{\{1 + [(k-1)/2]M_a^2\}^{\frac{k}{k-1}} - 1} \quad (107)$$

Ram effectiveness is plotted against M_a in Fig. 52 for several values of diffuser efficiency η_n. It can be seen by comparison with Fig. 50 that although the ram effectiveness is very nearly equal to the over-all diffusion efficiency η for Mach numbers less than 0.5, for higher values of M_a there is considerable divergence. This is particularly the case for high supersonic flows with partial pressure recovery through shock.

14. Inclined or Oblique Shock Waves. Shock waves can exist in a supersonic gas flow at angles other than normal to the direction of flow. Indeed, when conditions behind the shock will permit, a normal shock usually will not occur if an oblique shock is possible in its stead.

For such inclined or oblique shocks, conservation of momentum requires that the component of velocity in the plane parallel to the shock front remain unchanged through the shock wave. This fact, coupled with the essential

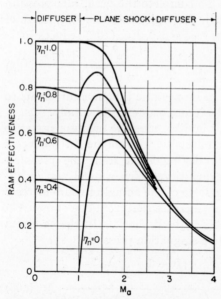

FIG. 52. Ram-pressure-recovery effectiveness of diffuser or diffuser plus normal shock wave, for various diffuser efficiencies, as a function of the initial Mach number M_a.

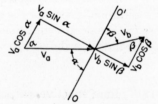

FIG. 53. Velocity vector relations across oblique shock front OO'.

discontinuity in the normal component of velocity means that the flow direction changes in passing through the shock.

Figure 53 shows the conditions that hold at an oblique shock in two-dimensional flow. The line OO' is the trace of the shock front on the plane of the figure. Velocities before and after the shock are V_a and V_b, respectively. The velocity components parallel to the shock plane are equal, as pointed out earlier, and

$$V_a \cos \alpha = V_b \cos \beta \tag{108}$$

while the velocity components $V_a \sin \alpha$ and $V_b \sin \beta$ normal to the shock front change abruptly through the shock. Equations for the oblique shock may be derived analogous to Eqs. (95) through (100) for normal shocks. They are

$$\frac{V_b}{V_a} = \frac{\sin \alpha}{\sin \beta} \left[\frac{2}{(k+1)M_a^2 \sin^2 \alpha} + \frac{k-1}{k+1} \right] \tag{109}$$

$$\frac{\rho_a}{\rho_b} = \frac{2}{(k+1)M_a^2 \sin^2 \alpha} + \frac{k-1}{k+1} \tag{110}$$

$$\frac{p_b}{p_a} = 1 + \frac{2k}{k+1}(M_a^2 \sin^2 \alpha - 1) \tag{111}$$

$$\frac{t_b}{t_a} = \frac{[2kM_a^2 \sin^2 \alpha - (k-1)][(k-1)M_a^2 \sin^2 \alpha + 2]}{(k+1)^2 M_a^2 \sin^2 \alpha} \tag{112}$$

$$\frac{a_b}{a_a} = \sqrt{\frac{t_b}{t_a}} \tag{113}$$

$$M_b^2 = \frac{1}{\sin^2 \beta} \frac{(k-1)M_a^2 \sin^2 \alpha + 2}{2kM_a^2 \sin^2 \alpha - (k-1)} \tag{114}$$

Equations (109) and (114) contain sin β. This quantity may be eliminated, however, by making use of Eq. (108). This permits us to write

$$\frac{1}{\sin \beta} = \sqrt{1 + \cot^2 \alpha \left[\frac{2}{(k+1)M_a^2 \sin^2 \alpha} + \frac{k-1}{k+1} \right]^{-2}}$$

$$\frac{V_b}{V_a} = \sqrt{\left[\frac{2}{(k+1)M_a^2 \sin^2 \alpha} + \frac{k-1}{k+1} \right]^2 \sin^2 \alpha + \cos^2 \alpha} \tag{115}$$

$$M_b^2 = \left\{ 1 + \cot^2 \alpha \left[\frac{2}{(k+1)M_a^2 \sin^2 \alpha} + \frac{k-1}{k+1} \right]^{-2} \right\}$$
$$\left[\frac{(k-1)M_a^2 \sin^2 \alpha + 2}{2kM_a^2 \sin^2 \alpha - (k-1)} \right] \tag{116}$$

The intensity of an oblique shock wave depends upon the angle as well as the entering Mach number. As in the case of a normal shock, the component of flow velocity at a right angle to the shock plane must be greater than 1.0 for a shock of finite intensity to exist. As the normal component of entering flow, $V_a \sin \alpha$, is reduced to Mach 1.0, the shock becomes vanishingly small. Therefore, the condition that must hold is

$$M_a \geq \frac{1}{\sin \alpha} \tag{117}$$

For a given M_a, the shock intensity depends upon the angle α directly. We may take as a convenient measure of shock intensity the relative loss in energy conversion across the shock front; this relative loss can be shown to be equal to $1 - \eta_s$ where η_s is derived in the same way as in Eq. (101), except that $M_a \sin \alpha$ is introduced instead of M_a. The Mach angle α_M is defined by $\alpha_M = \sin^{-1}(1/M)$. It is then possible to show that the shock intensity for angles near to α_M is proportional to $(\alpha - \alpha_M)^2$.

The Mach angle has special significance in the supersonic flow problems.　Weak shocks are frequently found in Schlieren photographs at angles very nearly equal to the Mach angle.　In certain cases strong shocks may be correlated with the envelope of a family of intersecting Mach lines.　In such a case it is possible to think of the strong shock as a superposition of many weak shocks at appropriate Mach angles.

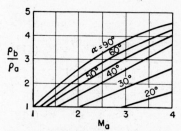

Fig. 54.　Density ratio across oblique shock as function of initial Mach number M_a for various angles of shock inclination α.

Figures 54, 55, and 56 are plots of ρ_b/ρ_a, p_b/p_a, and M_b for inclined shocks as a function of M_a for selected values of α.　Notice that in each of these figures the Mach angle limitation of Eq. (117) is clearly illustrated.　In Fig. 57 the downstream angle β is shown vs. M_a for various inclination angles α.

In Fig. 58 the angle of deflection or turning of the flow, $\theta = \alpha - \beta$, is shown.　It is interesting to note that on this figure, for every value of M_a and θ, there are two values of entering angle α.　It is found, however, that one of these solutions is dynamically more stable than the

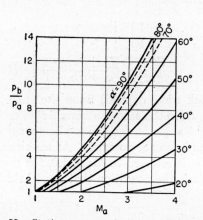

Fig. 55.　Static pressure ratio across oblique shock as function of initial Mach number M_a for various angles of shock inclination α.　Dashed curves represent solutions that, in free space, are dynamically less stable than solutions for smaller inclination angles α.

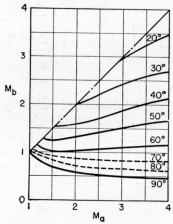

Fig. 56.　Final Mach number after shock, M_b, vs. initial Mach number M_a for various inclination angles α.

other.　The less stable solutions are shown by dashed lines in Figs. 55 to 58.

At values of M_a from 1.5 to ∞, the entrance angle for maximum turning of flow direction is approximately $\alpha = 65°$, so that most of the region from the $\alpha = 60°$ line to the $\alpha = 90°$ line on Fig. 58 corresponds to the lower dynamic stability solutions mentioned above. Therefore, most of the shock waves found in practice will have entrance angles of less than 60 deg. Ordinarily a plane disturbance parallel to the shock is required

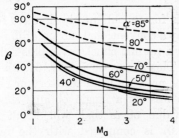

FIG. 57. Downstream angle β vs. initial Mach number M_a for various values of α.

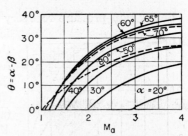

FIG. 58. Flow turning angle θ as a function of the initial Mach number M_a for several values of the inclination angle α.

to produce and maintain a plane shock wave at $\alpha = 90°$. Such a disturbance might exist over a limited area ahead of a flat-nosed projectile or across the entrance of a duct at supersonic flow velocities.

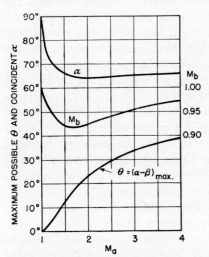

FIG. 59. Maximum possible θ and corresponding values of α and M_b as a function of the initial Mach number M_a.

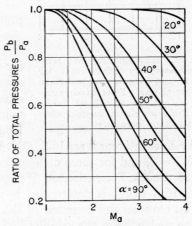

FIG. 60. Total pressure ratio across inclined shock.

The maximum possible flow turning angle for air through an oblique shock occurs at $M_a = \infty$, and θ is equal to 45.6 deg. The corresponding α is 67.8 deg, and the downstream Mach number is $M_b = 1.0$. Figure 59 shows the maximum flow turning angle θ_{max} as a function of M_a; the values of M_b and α coincident with these maxima are also shown.

The ratios of total pressures before and after oblique shocks are shown in Fig. 60.   These are derived from Eq. (111) and the relation

$$\left(\frac{P}{p}\right)^{\frac{k-1}{k}} = 1 + \frac{k-1}{2} M^2 \qquad (118)$$

Better ram pressure recovery results for an oblique shock wave followed by a conventional subsonic diffuser than for a normal shock wave plus a diffuser.   This shows up in Fig. 61, where the total pressure head recovery or ram effectiveness for a single oblique shock (at a value of α that will result in $M_b = 1.0$) is compared with the ram effectiveness of a normal or plane shock.   Ram efficiency as well as ram recovery effectiveness, as defined earlier, are used to facilitate the comparison.   In order to have the results apply most directly to the shock waves, subsonic diffusion was assumed to be loss-free in both cases.

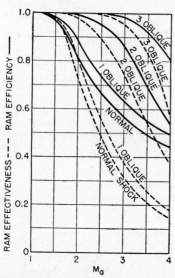

Fig. 61.   Ram efficiency and ram-pressure-recovery effectiveness for normal and for one, two, and three oblique shocks.   Final Mach number $M_b = 1.0$ after oblique shocks and angles are chosen to yield minimum entropy increase.

Flows at high supersonic speeds may profitably be subjected to several oblique shocks before entering a subsonic diffuser.   This is also shown in Fig. 61 for two and for three oblique shocks.   These shocks are so positioned that the total entropy change is a minimum and the flow Mach number following the last shock is unity.   Under these conditions, ram efficiency and ram effectiveness are both above 90 percent for two oblique shocks up to $M_a = 2$, and for three oblique shocks up to $M_a = 3$.

15. Shock Formation on Wedges and Cones.   Shock formation in front of a wedge is determined by the incident Mach number and the angles between the direction of the approaching flow and the two faces of the wedge.   For the symmetrical case, where the wedge axis coincides with the direction of the incident flow, these two angles are equal.   If M_a in Fig. 59 is large enough to yield a possible flow turning angle θ equal to or greater than θ_w, the semiangle of the wedge, the shock will attach itself to the point or apex of the wedge at such an angle that the flow behind the shock moves parallel to the wedge face (see Fig. 62).   As pointed out in connection with Fig. 59, the maximum turning angle for oblique shocks in flow of air occurs for $M_a = \infty$ and is equal to 45.6 deg under standard conditions. Thus the bluntest wedge that can have an attached shock has an included angle of twice this value or just over 90 deg.

For a given incident flow M_a, and a given wedge, the determination of the shock condition proceeds as follows. For the given Mach number M_a, determine whether or not the maximum possible turning angle is larger than θ_w from Fig. 58 or 59. If so, the shock will be attached, and the incident angle can be read from Fig. 58 by setting $\theta = \theta_w$. With

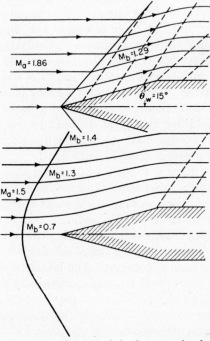

Fig. 62. Attached and detached shock waves ahead of wedges.

M_a and θ known, ρ_b, p_b, M_b, etc., can be determined from Figs. 54 to 57. If M_b is also supersonic, as is frequently the case, additional downstream shocks may be found. These may be located and fixed in position by irregularities on the wedge surface. Such shocks are frequently very weak and inclined at an angle closely approaching the Mach angle, indicated by the dashed lines in Fig. 62.

If the wedge is not symmetrical with respect to flow direction, flow conditions on either side may be determined separately and independently for the appropriate angles between wedge faces and the flow, as long as neither wedge-face angle is greater than the maximum possible flow turning angle for the incident M_a.

If for a given entry Mach number, the maximum possible θ is smaller than θ_w, the shock wave will be detached and at some distance in front of the vertex of the wedge. The smaller M_a, the greater is the distance. A vanishingly small shock occurs at an infinite distance for $M_a = 1$. The lower sketch of Fig. 62 shows a detached shock wave for $M_a = 1.5$ in front of a wedge of 15-deg semivertex angle. The maximum turning angle for $M_a = 1.5$, from Fig. 59, is approximately 12 deg. Immediately in front of the wedge apex, the shock is normal to the incident flow. Behind the shock wave here, the fluid is moving at low velocities and high pressures. To the side in either direction, the shock becomes oblique and of smaller intensity, until at large distances the shock approaches the Mach angle α_M in inclination and becomes vanishingly small in intensity.

The Mach angle for $M_a = 1.5$ is approximately 42 deg. Thus as we move outward along the shock front, all angles of incidence are encountered from 90 to 42 deg. Maximum flow turning of about 12 deg occurs for $\alpha = 60°$. The deflection is zero for 90-deg incidence and again for the Mach angle of 42 deg at a great distance to one side. The precise location and shape of a detached shock wave have not yet been satisfactorily predicted for a specified set of conditions.

Since all wedges have a finite thickness, the flow behind the shock eventually turns a corner and alters the pressure and velocity conditions. An attached inclined shock wave at the apex of a wedge does not, therefore, continue out to infinity with undiminished intensity. Actually, curvature of the shock front exists, and even with very thick wedges, the shock-front inclination approaches the Mach angle at a relatively short distance to one side from the wedge. The intensity of the shock diminishes, and the flow moves past the wedge essentially undisturbed.

Theoretical analysis of supersonic flow past cones requires cylindrically symmetrical solutions of the three-dimensional flow equations. Although the cylindrical symmetry reduces the mathematical problem to a two-dimensional one, the solutions are considerably more complicated than for two-dimensional flow past wedges. For a limited number of included cone angles,[1] solutions have been worked out in excellent agreement with wind-tunnel and other experimental results. The general procedure for finding such solutions has been to solve the fluid flow equations for the region downstream from the shock and then to find a shock wave that would convert the uniform motion ahead of the shock into the desired solution. Figure 63 shows a particular solution for a cone of 20-deg semivertex angle. The curved streamlines are typical of three-dimensional flow, as are the curved dashed lines representing disturbances or

[1] TAYLOR, G. I., and J. W. MACCOLL, Proc. Roy. Soc. A, vol. 139, p. 278, 1933.

wavelets originating on the surface of the cone. Also shown on the same figure is a sketch of a detached shock wave for a projectile in flight.

16. Shockless Supersonic Flows around Corners and over Curved Surfaces. Supersonic flows can take place around corners and curved surfaces under favorable conditions without high-intensity shock. The flow process is then adiabatic, but obeys the limitations that apply in general to supersonic flows. If a supersonic flow issues from a jet nozzle at a flow static pressure equal to the static pressure of the atmosphere into which the nozzle discharges, the flow emerges with direction virtually unchanged until entrainment of the atmosphere at the jet boundary results in flow dis-

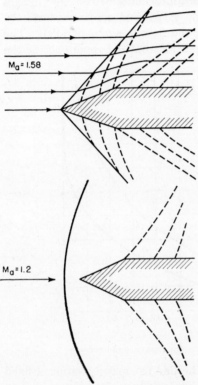

Fig. 63. Attached and detached shock waves ahead of cones. Note curved Mach lines.

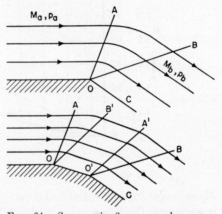

Fig. 64. Supersonic flow around corners.

persion. However, if the same jet flow exhausts to an atmosphere at a lower static pressure than exists in the flow at the nozzle exit, a sudden expansion takes place as the gas leaves the nozzle. In simple cases where a two-dimensional analysis is reasonably close to the actual flow, a ready solution for the flow problem exists. This type of expanding flow may also occur on the downstream side of turbine nozzles, with a resultant change in flow direction between the nozzle and the moving-blade row. The effect is large in partial-admission steam turbines but small in full-admission turbines with nozzle rings composed of airfoil shapes.

Exact solutions for steady two-dimensional supersonic flows of a stream of gas past a corner have been found.   The flow of such a stream is shown in Fig. 64 where a uniform parallel flow along a surface reaches a corner O.   Beyond O, the streamlines are no longer parallel, and the flow expands to the static pressure beyond the corner.   Since the flow is supersonic, or at least $M_a = 1.0$, in the approaching stream, the changes must all occur past the Mach line OA.   Expansion continues until the radial line OB is reached, after which the flow is again parallel.   The position of OB is determined by the condition that the angle BOC be the

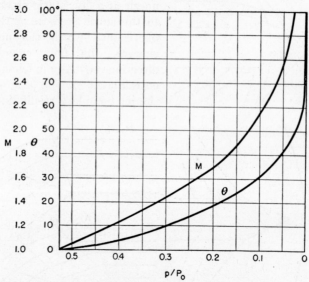

Fig. 65.   Data for solution of supersonic flows around corners.

Mach angle for the expanded flow.   The line OC may be either a fixed boundary or the free surface of the fully expanded jet in static equilibrium with the surrounding atmosphere.   The lines OA, OB, and OC do not indicate conditions of shock, but only the geometrical configuration of the flow.

It is found that the expansion that occurs depends only upon the angle through which the flow turns and the entering Mach number M_a. In Fig. 65 data are plotted that permit interpretation of supersonic flows around corners of an angle α. M and θ are plotted as functions of the ratio of static to stagnation or total pressure.   These curves are used as follows.   For each value of flow Mach number, there is an associated angle θ and a value of $\psi = p/P$.   This θ is the angle through which the flow would have turned if M_a had been equal to 1.0 at the corner and if the final static pressure around the corner had permitted complete expansion to the new value of M. Now if the flow approaching the corner is already supersonic ($M_a > 1.0$), then some supersonic expansion has taken place before the flow reached the corner, and the ability of the flow to expand through the angle θ_a corresponding to M_a is already exhausted. Therefore, if the Mach number after expanding around the corner is M_b at a pressure ratio value of ψ_b and an associated angle function θ_b, the actual flow turning angle is $\alpha = \theta_b - \theta_a$.

To find M_b for air when M_a and α are known, enter Fig. 65 at $M = M_a$ and read off the corresponding values of θ_a and p_a/P. To this value of θ_a add the angle α, and for the resulting angle $\theta_b = \theta_a + \alpha$ read off M_b and p_b/P. The maximum possible value of α is $\theta_b = 130.6°$ when θ_a is zero for $M_a = 1.0$, and p_b/P is zero with expansion to a vacuum. Therefore, if θ_b is required to be greater than 130.6 deg in the addition of θ_a and α, the flow will not turn through α but will fall short of that figure. If the static pressure of the atmosphere or in the reservoir beyond the corner imposes a smaller value of θ_b than is required by the angles of the solid surfaces at the corner, the flow will separate from the surface as a free jet after leaving the corner, expanded to the new static pressure p_b.

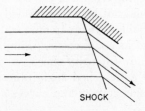

SHOCK

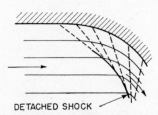

DETACHED SHOCK

Fig. 66. Supersonic flow at inside corners and at concave surfaces.

Expansion of a supersonic flow over a smoothly curved surface may be treated by considering the curved surface as a succession of corners connected by flat areas. Provided that high-intensity shock waves are not formed to upset adiabatic expansion conditions in the neighborhood of the surface, the solution obtained for expanding flow around a corner is applicable here also if the total angle through which the flow is turned around the curved surface is treated like the turning angle around a corner.

The above paragraphs have discussed the expansion of a supersonic flow around corners and curves. Ideally, this is a reversible process, and a diffusing flow would follow the same streamlines in the opposite direction; actually, conditions are usually unfavorable for a diffusing supersonic flow, and the flow breaks down with severe shock waves. Thus, a diffusing flow around a sharp outside corner would be quite impractical; while if a gently curved surface were substituted for the corner, there is a possibility that the diffusion might take place without severe shock.

When supersonic flows must follow inside corners or concave surfaces, there are some rather definite limitations on the contour of the surface. If a curved surface were fitted to one of the streamlines flowing around the corner in Fig. 64, no disturbance would be expected other than that due to boundary-layer friction and surface roughness or discontinuities. However, if the corner were removed, it would be necessary for the flow to readjust itself, and this would almost certainly take place with the occurrence of a shock wave. A sharp inside corner would generate a shock wave originating in the corner with flow direction changed according to the flow-angle relations established for inclined shock waves. If the included angle of the corner were too small, so that the required turning could not be accomplished across an inclined shock wave, then the shock would move upstream and flow in the corner might be subsonic or multiple shocks could occur. Similar flows in smoothly curved corners can result in low-intensity shocks or Mach lines that converge and become tangent to a detached high-intensity shock. Examples of such flows around inside corners and curves are shown in Fig. 66.

CHAPTER 4

AIRCRAFT-GAS-TURBINE COMPRESSORS

17. Introduction. The gas-turbine compressor takes air from the inlet duct and compresses it to the desired pressure ratio at the combustion-chamber inlet. Compressors of low efficiency limit the power output of an engine and have a serious effect upon over-all efficiency. A reduction in compressor efficiency of 1 percent may require a 3 percent or greater increase in fuel to maintain constant power output.

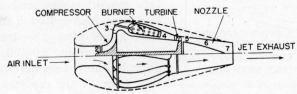

FIG. 67. Schematic illustration of jet engine with centrifugal compressor and can combustors.

Compression of air in gas-turbine engines is accomplished at such high flow rates that heat losses through the walls of the compressor are negligible compared to the work of compression (usually less than 0.1 percent). Accordingly, the compression is essentially adiabatic.

In an ideal (loss-free) adiabatic process, the work of compression is

$$c_p t_2 \left[\left(\frac{p_3}{p_2} \right)^{\frac{k-1}{k}} - 1 \right] \quad \text{Btu/lb}$$

where the indicated subscripts are those shown in Fig. 67. Ordinarily, compressors are rated in terms of total pressures and temperatures so that these quantities will appear in the general treatment that follows.

Compressor efficiency η_c is defined as the ratio of the ideal work of compression, given above, to the shaft input, so that we may write for the actual work input

$$h_c = \frac{c_p T_2}{\eta_c} \left[\left(\frac{P_3}{P_2} \right)^{\frac{k-1}{k}} - 1 \right] \tag{119}$$

Frictional and turbulent flow compressor losses remain as heat in the compressor exhaust. This permits us to write, alternatively,

$$h_c = c_p (T_3 - T_2) \tag{120}$$

93

Solving for η_c from Eqs. (119) and (120), we find

$$\eta_c = \frac{(P_3/P_2)^{\frac{k-1}{k}} - 1}{(T_3/T_2) - 1} \tag{121}$$

The efficiency of the compressor is known, neglecting heat-conduction losses, if the total pressure ratio is known and if the inlet and exit total temperatures are known. The total pressure heads at inlet and exhaust can be measured with a high degree of accuracy, but unfortunately this is not true of the temperature measurements, particularly at the hot or exit end of the compressor. Accurate temperature measurements in a high-velocity gas stream are difficult to obtain without interfering with flows to the extent that delivery characteristics are affected. Temperature measurements tend to be low because of heat-radiation and conduction losses from the temperature-sensitive element, as well as to the difficulty in developing full stagnation temperature conditions around the entire envelope of the bulb or thermocouple.

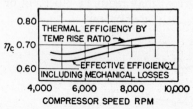

Fig. 68. Comparison of temperature-ratio efficiency and actual shaft efficiency of BMW compressor.

The errors in temperature measurement, leading to low values of temperature at the compressor exhaust, added to bearing friction and conduction heat losses from the compressor, result in indicated efficiencies by temperature rise that are usually from 2 to 5 points higher than actual or shaft efficiencies. It is therefore important that the method of estimating the efficiency of a compressor or other flow process be specified, and that appropriate corrections be made before using temperature efficiencies in cycle calculations. The difference between shaft efficiencies and temperature-ratio efficiencies for a particular axial-flow compressor is shown in Fig. 68.[1]

The pressure ratio of a multistage compressor is the product of the pressure ratios of the individual stages. The over-all efficiency cannot be arrived at so easily. Because of the losses, the temperature rise in each stage is higher than the isentropic temperature rise for loss-free compression; each succeeding stage receives air at successively higher temperatures than would be the case with 100 percent efficient compression. This is a preheat effect, which increases the work to be done by later stages of the compressor and results in a lower over-all efficiency

---

[1] LUNDQUIST, W. G., and R. W. COLE, Performance Characteristics of the BMW003 Turbojet Engine and a Comparison with the Jumo 004, *SAE Preprint*, April, 1946.

than that of individual stages. Thus, it has the opposite effect on efficiency of the familiar reheat process in turbines.

For a compressor with equal stage efficiencies and pressure ratios and a finite number of stages, the over-all compressor efficiency is related to the total pressure ratio and the individual stage efficiencies by

$$\eta_c = \frac{(P_3/P_2)^{\frac{k-1}{k}} - 1}{\left[1 + \frac{(P_3/P_2)^{\frac{k-1}{xk}} - 1}{\eta_s} \right]^x - 1}$$

where η_s is the individual stage efficiency and x is the total number of stages.

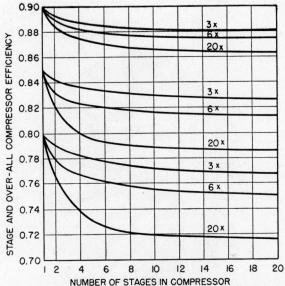

FIG. 69. Over-all compressor efficiency vs. number of stages for various compression ratios. Individual stage efficiencies correspond to compressor efficiency for 1 stage.

The variation of η_c with the number of stages for a number of different total pressure ratios and stage efficiencies is shown in Fig. 69; the stage efficiencies correspond to the efficiency shown for single-stage operation. It is significant that multistage compressors with high stage efficiencies suffer comparatively little by compounding, while compressors with low stage efficiencies suffer much greater losses in adiabatic efficiency. The preheat factor, or the ratio of over-all compressor efficiency to stage efficiency, can be plotted from the data of Fig. 69, and preheat factors for 2-, 6-, and 20-stage compressors with stage efficiencies of 85 percent are plotted against compression ratio in Fig. 70.

The theory of compressors is satisfactory only from an over-all standpoint. That the theory is incomplete is indicated by the fact that the theoretical losses based upon detailed design information are generally

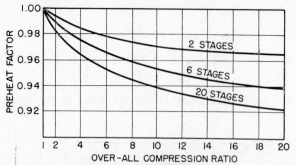

Fig. 70.   Preheat factors for multistage compressors with 85 percent stage efficiencies.

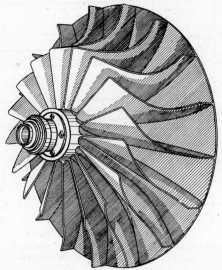

Fig. 71.   Single-entry centrifugal-compressor impeller.

much smaller than the actual losses. As a result, compressor designers use theory only as a starting point and then proceed as indicated by their own experience and the accumulated knowledge of other designers in accurately estimating the performance of a new design.

Compressors for aircraft gas turbines may be of centrifugal or of axial-flow type. The centrifugal compressor has the advantages of design simplicity and lower cost, while the axial-flow compressor has the advantages of smaller diameter and higher peak efficiency. Axial-flow compressors are generally multiple-stage units. Centrifugal compressors, on the other hand, may be either single-stage or multiple-stage with single-entry or dual-entry impellers.

18. Centrifugal Compressors. The single-stage centrifugal type with single-entry impeller is, by far, the simplest kind of gas-turbine compressor, and its performance characteristics are useful in estimating the performance of multiple-stage units. A typical single-entry impeller is shown in Fig. 71. Such a compressor consists of the impeller in its housing and a diffuser. The necessity for a diffuser accounts, in large measure, for the greater over-all diameters of centrifugal units over those of axial-flow compressors (the general air flow rates of either dual-entry centrifugal or axial-flow compressors may be approximately the same for rotors of equal tip diameters). The fluid flow leaving the impeller is almost radial with respect to the impeller. This flow is nearly tangential to the rotor periphery, however, owing to the velocity ratio there, and must be collected in an annulus. It is then turned, in individual stacks or in the diffuser, through an angle of at least

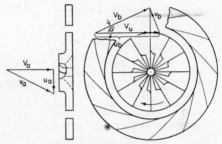

Fig. 72. Entrance and exit velocity diagrams for centrifugal impeller.

90 deg to reach the next stage or the combustion chamber. Since turning a high-velocity air flow in a short radius results in a large pressure drop, the annulus and diffuser must be relatively large to reduce the flow velocity efficiently.

A centrifugal impeller and diffuser are shown schematically in Fig. 72. Velocity vectors are indicated for the entering and leaving conditions at the impeller. It should be noted that the entrance direction at the impeller eye is essentially axial, while the exit flow is in the radial plane normal to the inlet direction.

The maintenance of ideal frictionless flow through the impeller requires an energy addition per pound of air that accounts for the change in kinetic energy, the gain in energy due to centrifugal forces, and the change in energy due to diffusion in the rotor passages. The conventional relation is

$$E = \frac{1}{2g} [(V_b^2 - V_a^2) + (u_b^2 - u_a^2) + (v_a^2 - v_b^2)] \tag{122}$$

where $(1/2g)(V_b^2 - V_a^2)$ is the increase in kinetic energy, $(1/2g)(u_b^2 - u_a^2)$ is the work done in moving a unit mass of air from radius r_a, where centrifugal force is u_a^2/gr_a, to radius r_b, where the force is u_b^2/gr_b, and $(1/2g)(v_a^2 - v_b^2)$ is the energy change due to static pressure rise in a rotor in which the cross-sectional area of the flow changes to cause a decrease in the relative velocities from inlet to outlet.

From the trigonometric relations of the vector diagrams at inlet and outlet points, and by introducing V_u, the tangential component of the velocity V, the identity $uV_u = \frac{1}{2}(V^2 + u^2 - v^2)$ can be introduced into Eq. (122) to obtain

$$E = \frac{1}{g}\left(u_b V_{ub} - u_a V_{ua}\right) \tag{123}$$

With a straight axial inlet to the impeller, the tangential component V_{ua} of V_a is zero. In an ideal radial-flow rotor, the tangential component V_{ub} of V_b is equal to u_b, so that

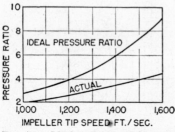

FIG. 73. Ideal and practical compression ratios for single-stage centrifugal air compressor vs. impeller tip speed.

$$E = \frac{u_b^2}{g} \tag{124}$$

Therefore, in the ideal case, the energy added to the air flowing through the compressor is just twice the kinetic energy $u_b^2/2g$ corresponding to the rotor tip velocity; and if the radial component u_b of the leaving velocity is small relative to V_b, half of the work input appears as static pressure rise and half as kinetic energy.

The total pressure rise through the compressor, then, is obtained by setting

$$\frac{u_b^2}{gJ} = c_p T_2 \left[\left(\frac{P_3}{P_2}\right)^{\frac{k-1}{k}} - 1\right]$$

or

$$\frac{P_3}{P_2} = \left(\frac{u_b^2}{Jgc_p T_2} + 1\right)^{\frac{k}{k-1}} \tag{125}$$

It should be emphasized that the pressure ratio given by this equation is valid only under the assumption of no losses.

Pressure ratios obtained with a number of representative centrifugal compressors under standard atmospheric conditions at rated flows were used to plot the curve in Fig. 73. The ideal curve of pressure ratio against impeller tip speed from Eq. (125) is also shown. Practical pressure ratios achieved depend upon the size of the compressor. The curve in Fig. 73 is for impellers of the order of 24 in. (2.0 ft) in diameter. Smaller impellers are less efficient as a rule and do not develop as high pressure ratios and efficiencies as do the larger impellers. The slip factor at the rim of the impeller, V_u/u, in the compressors of Fig. 73 is of the order of 0.9.

Another expression that is sometimes used in compressor design work is the pressure coefficient. This is the ratio of the adiabatic work [Eq. (119)] required to compress air to the observed pressure, to the energy the air would have if it left the impeller rim at zero slip [Eq. (124)]. The pressure coefficient C_p may be written

$$C_p = \frac{J g c_p T_2 [(P_3/P_2)^{\frac{k-1}{k}} - 1]}{u_b^2}$$

It is easy to show that this expression may be written

$$C_p = \frac{(P_3/P_2)^{\frac{k-1}{k}} - 1}{(k-1)(u_b/a_0)^2} \tag{126}$$

where u_b/a_0 is the ratio of the impeller tip velocity to the velocity of sound in the still air ahead of the compressor entrance, since $T_2 = T_0$. The ratio u_b/a_0 has been called the compressor Mach number by some authors; this terminology will not be adopted here, because it seems desirable to reserve the name Mach number for describing conditions at one point.

The external requirements for a compressor are usually given in terms of flow and pressure rise. The pressure rise in a centrifugal compressor has been shown to be directly connected with the impeller tip speed, and if a value can be assigned to the pressure coefficient, the required u_b/a_0 and therefore the impeller tip speed are known. The pressure coefficient depends upon the specific flow, and in general, pressure coefficients for centrifugal compressors fall below 0.70. An average value might be 0.67 for compressors with impellers of the order of 30 in. in diameter, with lower coefficients for smaller impellers. Advances in design technique will result in higher pressure coefficients. There is an upper limit to the pressure ratio available from a single-stage centrifugal compressor; this limit depends on the maximum u_b/a_0 that may be used without encountering excessive losses at the impeller rim or exceeding mechanical limits. If a higher ratio is required, it will be necessary to use a multiple-stage compressor.

The specific flow rate of the compressor is determined chiefly by the air-swallowing capacity at the inlet or eye of the impeller. Assuming that the absolute velocity of the air flow at the compressor inlet is in an axial direction and uniform across the entrance, the mass flow rate from Eq. (86) is

$$W_a = \sqrt{\frac{gk}{R}} \, \frac{P_2}{\sqrt{T_2}} \, M_a \left(1 + \frac{k-1}{2} M_a^2\right)^{\frac{1+k}{2-2k}} \times \tfrac{1}{4}\pi D^2 (e^2 - h^2) \tag{127}$$

where e is the ratio of the outside diameter of the impeller eye to the impeller diameter D, and h is the ratio of the hub diameter or inside diameter to D. Thus $\frac{1}{4}\pi D^2(e^2 - h^2)$ is the effective entry area for the flow. Maximum flow velocity relative to the impeller blades and, therefore, maximum local Mach number occur at the outer diameter of the impeller eye. Here the relative velocity v_e is the resultant of the axial velocity of the entering air and the vane velocity at the maximum diameter of the entry

$$v_e = \sqrt{V_a^2 + e^2 u_b^2} \tag{128}$$

or in terms of local Mach numbers

$$M_e = \sqrt{M_a^2 + e^2 \left(\frac{u_b}{a_2}\right)^2}$$

$$M_c = \sqrt{M_a^2 + e^2 \left(\frac{u_b}{a_0}\right)^2 \left(1 + \frac{k-1}{2} M_a^2\right)} \tag{129}$$

and

$$M_a = \sqrt{\frac{M_e^2 - e^2 \left(\frac{u_b}{a_0}\right)^2}{1 + \frac{k-1}{2} e^2 \left(\frac{u_b}{a_0}\right)^2}} \tag{130}$$

where a_0 is the velocity of sound in the still atmosphere ahead of the compressor inlet. The value of M_a in Eq. (130) can then be introduced into Eq. (127), which is rewritten to yield the mass flow rate per unit area of impeller inlet in terms of the limiting relative Mach number M_e at the outside diameter of the impeller eye and the factor eu_b/a_0. The total temperature and pressure, corresponding to the atmospheric stagnation values ahead of the inlet, are written in the corrected form as ratios θ and δ, to standard conditions. The mass flow rate per unit area in pounds per square foot per second is

$$\frac{W_a}{A} = 85.3 \frac{\delta}{\sqrt{\theta}} \sqrt{\frac{M_e^2 - e^2 \left(\frac{u_b}{a_0}\right)^2}{1 + \frac{k-1}{2} e^2 \left(\frac{u_b}{a_0}\right)^2} \left[1 + \frac{k-1}{2} \frac{M_e^2 - e^2 \left(\frac{u_b}{a_0}\right)^2}{1 + \frac{k-1}{2} e^2 \left(\frac{u_b}{a_0}\right)^2}\right]^{\frac{1+k}{1-k}}}$$

$$\frac{W_a}{A} = 85.3 \frac{\delta}{\sqrt{\theta}} \sqrt{\left[M_e^2 - e^2 \left(\frac{u_b}{a_0}\right)^2\right] \frac{\left(1 + \frac{k-1}{2} M_e^2\right)^{\frac{1+k}{1-k}}}{\left[1 + \frac{k-1}{2} e^2 \left(\frac{u_b}{a_0}\right)^2\right]^{\frac{2}{1-k}}}} \tag{131}$$

Since u_b/a_0 is determined by the required pressure ratio for a given compressor, the remaining variables consist of the eye diameter, the

impeller shaft speed, and the relative Mach number M_e. In early reciprocating-engine supercharger practice, M_e was limited to values of less
than 0.75. It now appears that careful attention to inlet vane design
and the use of a large number of vanes makes it possible to go to values
of M_e as high as 0.90 without serious loss in efficiency. As a result of
the Mach-number limitation at the impeller inlet tips, there is an optimum eye diameter for maximum flow. Exceeding this diameter neces-

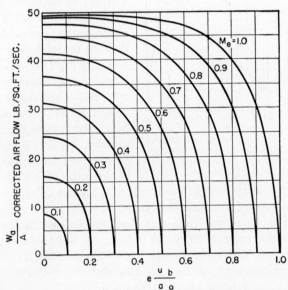

FIG. 74.   Mass air flow per unit impeller entry area.   Single-sided impeller under standard
conditions.

sitates a reduction in the axial flow velocity in the inlet, which
is accompanied by a rapid drop in flow rate.

In Fig. 74 the flow rate under standard atmospheric conditions as
given by Eq. (131) is represented. Here mass flow per unit area of the
actual entry is represented vs. eu_b/a_0 for several values of M_e. In
Fig. 75 a different situation is presented. Mass flow per square foot of
total impeller disc area is plotted against e. The inlet tip Mach number
is given the limiting value $M_e = 0.9$, the hub diameter is given the fixed
value $h = 0.2$, and the standard atmosphere flow per unit impeller cross-
sectional area is then plotted as a function of e for several values of u_b/a_0.

$$\frac{W_a}{(\pi/4)D^2} = 85.3(e^2 - h^2)\sqrt{\left[0.9^2 - e^2\left(\frac{u_b}{a_0}\right)^2\right]\frac{\left[1 + 0.2e^2\left(\frac{u_b}{a_0}\right)^2\right]^5}{(1 + 0.2 \times 0.9^2)^6}} \quad (132)$$

All the preceding equations for flow should be multiplied by 2 for double-entry impellers.

Figures 74 and 75 indicate a serious design restriction in the flow velocity of the inlet annulus directly ahead of the impeller eye. The maximum flow through the annulus is the flow for critical pressure ratio across the entrance, and the design flow must, necessarily, be considerably

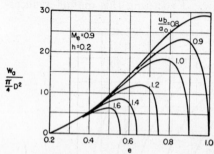

less than this to keep duct losses and M_e to reasonable figures and to provide for possible compressor overspeed requirements. The limitations on inlet flow velocity imposed by Eq. (132) when the design is near the optimum impeller-inlet-eye ratio ordinarily hold inlet velocities to reasonable figures; Mach numbers in the annulus are, thereby, kept well under 0.5 with flow restriction factors in the inlet of the order of 0.65 or less.

Fig. 75.   Mass air flow per square foot of total impeller disc area plotted against centrifugal-impeller eye diameter/tip diameter ratio.

Another quantity useful in compressor design is Q/nD^3, necessary in applying the laws of dynamic similarity, where Q is the volumetric flow rate in cubic feet per unit time, n is shaft revolutions in the same time unit, and D is the impeller diameter in feet. If Reynolds-number effects can be neglected, and they usually are small in centrifugal-compressor design problems except at low rotating speeds, geometrically similar compressors should have identical char-

acteristics when the Q/nD^3 of one compressor is equal to the Q/nD^3 of the other. The pressure ratios that compressors can reach with but negligible losses in efficiency can therefore be correlated with this quantity; Fig. 76 shows some commonly established upper and lower working limits of Q/nD^3 plotted against compression ratio for single-stage, single-sided centrifugal impellers.

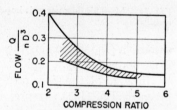

Fig. 76. Practical upper and lower limits for dimensionless volumetric flow factor vs. compression ratio.

Using the preceding methods and the data available from Figs. 73, 74, and 76, impeller speed, tip diameter, and eye or annulus diameter can be selected to meet the required external characteristics of the compressor. These dimensions may require modification as design and test work progress, but they will at least provide a starting point based upon experience with other compressors that have proved to have satisfactory performance characteristics.

The axial width of impeller blades at the exit of the impeller is determined by the volume flow rat at the impeller tip and the discharge angle β (see Fig. 72). The volume of flow leaving the mpeller is dependent upon the mass flow and the density at the impeller exit, which latter depends upon the efficiency of the diffusion process through the impeller. It is necessary to assume an efficiency value for this flow process in preliminary calculations that is consistent with the expected over-all efficiency. The total circumferential cross-sectional area at the impeller exit is then

$$A_b = \frac{W_a}{\rho_b V_u \tan \beta}$$

where V_u is the tangential component of velocity of the leaving gas, and β is the impeller discharge angle. Discharge angles usually stay within the limits of 12 to 24 deg. Low values of β result in excessively high blades and higher rates of diffusion in the flow through the impeller than are consistent with good efficiency; high values of β result in high Mach numbers relative to the stationary diffuser vanes and reduce the flow range.

The selection of actual blade shapes is still a matter of skill and experience if high-efficiency performance is to be expected. The liberal use of scale models is most helpful and reduces the margin of ignorance to size effects. The necessity for giving the proper direction to the leading edge of the blade relative to the approaching air, the avoidance of short-radius turning of the air flow, reasonable pressure distributions along the blade, and gradual changes in cross-sectional areas of the flow passages are obvious. The number of blades required for maximum efficiency and the thickness and shaping of the blade edges require the application of experience.

The designer of centrifugal impellers has been severely limited in the past because of mechanical-strength problems and the difficulty of machining any but simple blade contours. The typical impeller shown in Fig. 71 was formerly machined with straight radial blades out of a blank or forging of a lightweight alloy. The curvature of the leading edges was then produced by bending the blades over forms in a special fixture; methods of machining the complete impeller have since been adopted. Other impellers have been made in two parts, the outer disc having straight radial blades and the entering end having been machined out of a forged blank; the finished halves are then doweled together. The machining of the half with doubly curved blades on a machine developed for the purpose has permitted the use of better blade shapes with longer diffusing passages through the impeller so that a 13-in.-

diameter impeller made in this way has performance characteristics comparable to those of a contemporary impeller of Fig. 73 of at least twice that diameter.

At the expense of additional weight and complication and the danger of icing difficulties under unfavorable conditions, stationary guide vanes can be installed in the annulus ahead of the impeller inlet to impart a spin or prewhirl to the entering air column. This prewhirl reduces the Mach number relative to the impeller eye and should result in increased efficiency. The velocity diagrams shown in Fig. 77 illustrate the effect of prewhirl on impeller inlet Mach number. By keeping the same limit on Mach number, the annulus or eye diameter can be increased and the flow correspondingly increased beyond that indicated in Eq. (131). Prewhirl can be quite important when it is difficult to shape the leading edges of the impeller blades sufficiently by bending to provide correct approach angles.

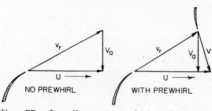

Fig. 77. Impeller entry velocity diagrams with and without prewhirl.

The design of the diffuser is as important to the over-all performance of the centrifugal compressor as is the design of the impeller. Since approximately half the energy of the air at the impeller tip is velocity energy, the diffuser usually is required to convert most of this velocity head to pressure head. It is very difficult to design a simple conical diffuser passage with an efficiency greater than 85 percent, even under the most favorable conditions. Therefore, the relatively complicated centrifugal-compressor diffuser, which must turn the air flow through a minimum angle of 90 deg and reduce the velocity to a few hundred feet per second in a few inches of passage length, imposes a difficult problem. The designer can count on losing at least 7 or 8 percent of the shaft input energy in the diffuser, and usually considerably more than this.

The details of a diffuser section preceding an annular combustion chamber, or another stage of compression, may be quite different from the diffuser ahead of can-type combustion chambers. The can-type combustion chambers require individual compressor exhaust stacks, one for each can, while the annular combustion chamber or the inlet of another compressor stage can be supplied either through a number of individual parallel passages or from a simple annular flow passage.

In either case, there is usually a vaneless space or vortex chamber into which the impeller discharges. This is desirable, since air may leave the impeller at supersonic velocities relative to the diffuser walls; with normal impeller efficiency, this may occur at impeller tip speeds above 1,300 to 1,400 fps or at total pressure ratios in excess of **3.2** to **3.8**. The flow from the impeller tip is almost tangential, and the whirl velocity in the vortex chamber or annulus is approximately inversely proportional to the radius (owing to the conservation of angular momentum, $r^2(d\omega/dt)$ = constant). Supersonic diffusion occurs without shock in the vortex or vaneless diffuser space, and velocities become subsonic before reaching the diffuser vane tips (see Fig. 78).

The number of diffuser vanes and the clearance between vane tips and impeller rim have a considerable influence upon the external characteristics of the compressor. In general, increasing the number of vanes either in impeller or diffuser defines the air flows more rigidly. Within

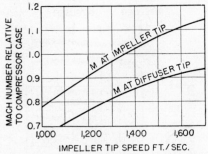

Fig. 78. Typical flow Mach numbers in the vaneless diffuser space of compressor with 21-in.-diameter impeller.

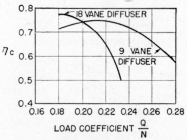

Fig. 79. Effect of number of diffuser vanes upon efficiency of one compressor.

limits, the efficiency may be increased, but the operating range is correspondingly decreased. That is, the curves of efficiency against delivery and pressure ratio tend to be sharper with higher maxima, as in Fig. 79. Attempts to replace diffuser vanes with cascaded airfoils have also resulted in a reduced width of operating range. Increasing the clearance between the impeller tip and diffuser vane tips has the effect of widening the operating range, usually accompanied by a small loss in peak efficiency.

Diffusers for use with can-type combustion chambers usually have one diffuser vane per chamber, although supplementary vanes may be used to assist in turning the air flow around corners. Some representative diffuser vane configurations are sketched in Fig. 80.

The progressive rises in static pressure through the flow passages of a typical dual-entry centrifugal compressor are shown in Fig. 81. These curves are plotted for the flow conditions existing in a jet engine running at various shaft speeds.

Diffuser design is primarily a matter of observing the general restrictions placed upon other high-efficiency flow processes: no abrupt changes in passage areas, no short-radius changes in flow direction at high

velocities, and careful attention to detail in selecting size, shape, and angle
of attack of guide vanes.   The cross-sectional flow area at the exit of the
vortex chamber and point of entry to the diffuser guide vanes may vary
from a third greater to twice as large as the impeller exit area.   The passage areas then expand from the minimum or throat area at the guide vane
entrances until the exit is reached with a total area of about twice that of
their effective entrance areas.   The length of the diffuser passage is
determined by the slope of the area-expansion curve, often equivalent to

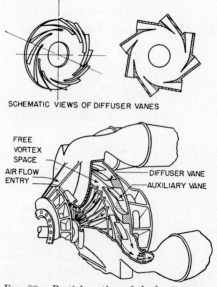

SCHEMATIC VIEWS OF DIFFUSER VANES

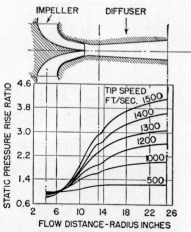

FIG. 80.   Partial section of dual-entry centrifugal compressor with individual can-type
combustors.   Vane-type diffuser with corner-
turning vanes in the elbow of the combustor
duct.

FIG. 81.   Static-pressure-rise ratio
through compressor flow passages of
typical double-entry centrifugal compressor. (*From L. J. Cheshire, Proc.
IME, vol.* 153, *pp.* 409–512, 1945.)

a conical diffuser with an included-angle slope of approximately 6 deg.
By shaping the diffuser vanes and by proper design of the outlet cones of
diffusers intended for use with can combustors, any schedule of divergence
selected by the designer can be fitted.   The principal limitation here is
space, since long diffusion passages may require excessive space for aircraft applications.

The efficiency and flow of a given compressor depend upon entrance
conditions, impeller speed, and the pressure ratio against which the compressor is required to work.   Usually the data is plotted with mass flow
as the abscissa and pressure ratio as the ordinate.   Lines of equal corrected compressor speed are then plotted with lines of constant efficiency
superimposed.   Figure 82 is typical of single-stage centrifugal com-

pressors in use in jet engines. The dashed surge line indicates limiting conditions of flow and pressure ratio beyond which the angles of attack of impeller vanes, diffuser vanes, or both, are too great and stall occurs. Attempted operation above the surge line results in unstable flows with local flow reversals and pressure oscillations that may become very large, particularly when the compressor is coupled to a turbine and combustion chamber. The slight step in the surge line of Fig. 82 may be due to the occurrence of stall at different places in the compressor for different flow conditions.

The design of the compressor must be such that the "operating line" shown on Fig. 82 lies within the range of stable and efficient compressor

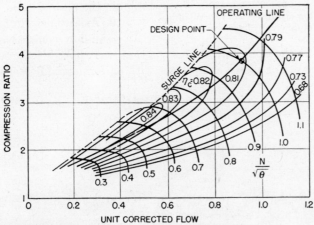

Fig. 82. Pressure-flow characteristic of high-efficiency centrifugal compressor with constant efficiency contours shown.

operation. The operating line is the line connecting the points of stable equilibrium at various speeds for which the air-swallowing characteristic of a turbine matches the delivery-pressure–flow characteristic of the compressor and at a combustor temperature at which turbine and compressor shaft powers match. There is ordinarily one operating line on the corrected performance plot for a jet engine with a fixed-area exhaust nozzle and at a selected flight speed or ram pressure ratio. For jet engines with adjustable exhaust nozzles and for gas turbines driving controllable-pitch propellers, there are families of curves for the operating lines.

In order to get a clearer idea of the flow characteristic of the compressor of Fig. 82, corrected mass flows are plotted against corrected rpm for different values of pressure ratio in Fig. 83. The effects of changes in pressure requirements upon flow at a given compressor speed are easier to visualize than in the preceding illustration.

Pressure ratios higher than 3 or 4 are not ordinarily obtained at high efficiency in single-stage centrifugal compressors, although some experimental compressors have yielded ratios as high as 6 with fair efficiency. The limitation is impeller tip speed as determined from mechanical and flow considerations. Higher pressure ratios than these are obtainable by operating centrifugal compressors in series, using as many stages as are required to obtain the desired ratio.

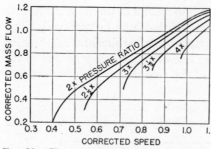

Fig. 83.   Flow-speed relation for centrifugal compressor at different compression ratios.

19. Axial-flow Compressors. An axial-flow compressor can be subjected to the same sort of analysis that was applied to the centrifugal compressor. For such a compressor with uniform axial flow, considering

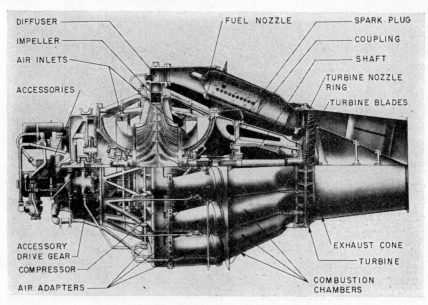

Fig. 84.   General Electric I-40 turbojet engine with dual-entry centrifugal compressor—cutaway view. (*Aviation magazine.*)

conditions only at the mean radius of the rotor blades, the energy transferred by the rotor can be written

$$E = \frac{u}{g}\left(V_{2u} - V_{1u}\right) \qquad \text{ft-lb/(lb)(sec)} \qquad (133)$$

where $V_{2u} - V_{1u}$ is the change in whirl or tangential component of the flow velocity produced by the rotor. If the stator-blade curvatures are such that air enters the rotor in an axial direction without whirl, V_{1u} is equal to zero. Ideally, the rotor-blade curvature can also be increased so that the relative discharge velocity of the rotor is purely axial, and it is then apparent that the tangential component V_{2u} is identical with the rotor velocity u. The energy-transfer equation is then rewritten $E = u^2/g$, identical with Eq. (124) for the centrifugal compressor.

If the above stipulations were adhered to, theoretically a single-stage axial-flow compressor could be built with as high a pressure ratio as a single-stage centrifugal compressor. Practically, this is not possible because of the fluid flow limitations that do not appear in formulas. Single-stage compression ratios are more often limited to values of the order of 1.2 rather than the 4 to 6 obtainable from centrifugal compressors. This is due partly to the difficulty of turning air through the required large angle in a single-stage rotor. At the same time the rotor must act as a diffusing passage in the flow process for maximum-pressure-rise designs, and the length of passage or distance across the rotor is much too short to permit a large pressure change to take place efficiently. Further, since the blade speed on the inlet side of the rotor is the same as the blade speed on the outlet side in the axial-flow rotor, a limiting speed condition exists at the entering edges of rotor blades in the axial design. This is different from the centrifugal compressor in which air enters the impeller at the eye, where blade velocities are low with respect to impeller tip speed. Axial-compressor-blade tip speeds must be lower than in the centrifugal compressor to avoid severe shock losses at the inlet edges of the rotor blades.

A practical limitation is recognized in the amount of "lift" that can be obtained across a single stage consisting of one row of rotating blading. Attempting to exceed this limiting value of lift or pressure ratio results in a stalled airfoil, or in this case a stalled compressor stage. The characteristics of axial-flow compressors are more sharply peaked when plotted against flow or pressure than are those of centrifugal compressors, although higher peak efficiencies are usually obtainable in the axial-flow design.

Equation (133) indicates that the energy imparted to the air flow by the rotor is proportional to the change in whirl or tangential component of flow velocity through the rotor. A study of the turning of air flows in airfoil cascades, then, provides a starting point for axial-flow compressor design. Vector diagrams of flow paths through compressor-blade rows are useful. Angles are usually measured from the axis of the machine, as in Fig. 85.

For purposes of simplification, a two-dimensional flow path is assumed. Air enters with velocity V_1 and angle α and leaves with velocity V_2 and angle β.

The change in energy across the blade row is

$$E = \frac{1}{2g}(V_2^2 - V_1^2 + v_1^2 - v_2^2) \qquad \text{ft-lb/lb} \qquad (134)$$

where $(1/2g)(V_2^2 - V_1^2)$ is the energy due to the change in absolute velocity, and $(1/2g)(v_1^2 - v_2^2)$ is the energy of compression in the diffusing passage through the rotor-blade row. This is the same as Eq. (122) for the centrifugal compressor except that the term for the centrifugal flow forces does not appear in a compressor with true axial flow.

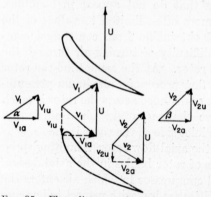

From momentum relations, the change in total pressure across the moving-blade row is

$$\Delta P = \rho(V_{2a} \tan \alpha - V_{1a} \tan \beta)u \qquad (135)$$

Equation (135) is actually correct only for incompressible flows but may be used with but small error for single stages of axial-flow compressors. The total pressure change ΔP across the moving-blade row

FIG. 85. Flow diagrams through moving-blade row of axial-flow compressor.

includes both static and velocity pressure increases. The velocity pressure increase is

$$\frac{\rho}{2}(V_2^2 - V_1^2) = \frac{\rho}{2}(V_{2a}^2 \tan^2 \beta + V_{2a}^2 - V_{1a}^2 \tan^2 \alpha - V_{1a}^2)$$

which reduces to $(\rho/2)V_a^2(\tan^2 \beta - \tan^2 \alpha)$ when V_{1a} is equal to V_{2a} and the axial flow velocity V_a is uniform on either side of the blade row. The static pressure component is

$$\Delta p = \frac{\rho}{2}(v_1^2 - v_2^2) \qquad (136)$$

The relative values of velocity and static pressure components depend upon entering and leaving flow velocities and angles.

The kinetic energy of the flow leaving the rotating-blade row is usually translated, at least partially, into a pressure rise. In the axial-flow compressor, this is done by passing the flow through a stationary-blade row. Turning the air flow from the relatively large entering angle β (leaving the rotating row) to a smaller leaving angle α (usually the same α as in entering the rotating row) is equivalent to flow through a diffusing nozzle. The cross-sectional flow area available at the entrance of the stationary-blade row or cascade is roughly proportional to cos β, and the effective leaving area is proportional to cos α, so that the diffuser ratio or ratio of leaving area to entering area is cos α/cos β. The same type of flow usually is found in the rotor blades, except that the flow angles relative to the moving-blade row must be used instead of α and β.

Since turning the flow through a large angle is the equivalent of a large diffuser-area ratio, the turning angle $\beta - \alpha$ is necessarily small in

Fig. 86.   Rotor of 6-stage symmetrical-design axial-flow compressor.   Compression ratio, 2.8, tip diameter 17.7 in., 17,000 rpm.   (*Westinghouse Electric Corporation.*)

order to avoid large diffuser losses in the short flow distance through the blade row.   Only small pressure ratios are normally possible in a single blade row.   Early development work on axial-flow compressors with rotor blades moving at supersonic velocities indicates that higher pressure ratios may be obtained in a single stage in the future.

The force that the blading must exert on the flow to turn it from β to α is separated into two components, the tangential force and the axial force.   From momentum, the tangential force per unit axial flow area is

$$F_u = \rho V_a^2 (\tan \beta - \tan \alpha) \tag{137}$$

when the axial component of flow velocity is uniform.   The force in the

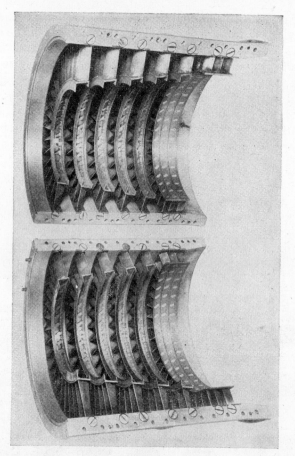

FIG. 87.   Stator for compressor rotor of Fig. 86.   Note three rows of straightening vanes at exit end.   (*Westinghouse Electric Corporation.*)

axial direction is the pressure-rise force

$$F_a = \tfrac{1}{2}\eta\rho V_a^2(\tan^2 \beta - \tan^2 \alpha) \qquad (138)$$

where η is the diffuser efficiency of the cascade.   The resultant force is

$$F_r = V_a^2\rho(\tan \beta - \tan \alpha)\sqrt{1 + \frac{\eta}{2}(\tan \beta + \tan \alpha)^2}$$

at the direction

$$90° + \tan^{-1}\left[\frac{\eta}{2}(\tan \beta + \tan \alpha)\right]$$

This resultant force is the lift force of the cascade of airfoils.

Although many single airfoils have C_D/C_L ratios as low as 0.01 for large aspect ratios, there are usually reasons related to structural strength, requirements on camber, etc., that prevent their use in axial-flow compressors. About the best that can be done in practice is to use a profile that has about twice as large a drag/lift ratio or $C_D/C_L = 0.02$. With this value of C_D/C_L, the deflection angle of the flow will be less than the ideal turning angle by $\tan^{-1} 0.02$ or $50.6'$. The flow direction will then be related to the efficiency by

$$\tan^{-1}\left(\frac{\tan \beta + \tan \alpha}{2}\right) - 50.6' = \tan^{-1} \eta \left(\frac{\tan \beta + \tan \alpha}{2}\right)$$

If this equation is solved for the efficiency η for different values of $\frac{1}{2}(\tan \beta + \tan \alpha)$, it will be seen that η has a maximum value of 0.96 when the mean flow angle $\tan^{-1}[\frac{1}{2}(\tan \beta + \tan \alpha)]$ is very close to 45 deg. This calculated efficiency decreases as the mean flow angle departs from 45 deg, slowly at first and then rapidly as the mean flow angle approaches 0 or 90 deg (compare with Fig. 25).

The value 0.96 for η calculated for a 45-deg cascade with a drag/lift ratio of 0.02 is a great deal higher than is achieved in axial-compressor practice. This can be traced to the fact that an actual three-dimensional compressor model differs from the two-dimensional cascades just discussed in several important respects.

These effects result in the losses in the actual compressor being several times as great as the losses for an infinite cascade. These additional losses have been studied rather thoroughly, so we know approximately how much loss to expect from casing-wall friction, tip clearance, trailing vortexes, etc. The equation above, with the effective value of $\tan^{-1}(C_D/C_L)$ substituted for the angle $50.6'$, gives a fairly good description of the efficiency in its dependence on the flow angles.

There are certain conditions of equilibrium that are established under steady flow conditions in an axial-flow compressor. First, the pressure rise across the compressor must be constant from hub to tip. This may not be strictly true for individual stages but is generally desirable. This condition may be expressed as

$$\eta u(V_{2a} \tan \beta - V_{1a} \tan \alpha) = \text{constant} \tag{139}$$

independent of r when η, u, V_a, β, and α may all vary with r. Second, the centrifugal force due to tangential whirl at every radial distance must be balanced by a static pressure gradient

$$\Delta p = \frac{\rho V_u^2}{2r} \Delta r \tag{140}$$

When axial velocity is held constant throughout the compressor and when the first condition of constant total pressure rise is met, the product

rV_u is constant, and the compressor design is the constant-circulation type.

The preliminary design of a constant-circulation cascade for a compressor stage proceeds in an orderly manner when the entering and leaving flow angles are known at the mean diameter. Velocity triangles at other radii are constructed, keeping the product of rV_u constant. The conditions of Eq. (139) are observed, where $u(\tan \beta - \tan \alpha)$ is a constant, assuming η fixed for a constant-circulation compressor. The deflection or turning angles in both rotor and stator are known from $\beta_1 - \alpha_1$ and $\beta_2 - \alpha_2$, as well as the relative flow angles in rotor and stator from the velocity triangles. Since the relative flow angles, and therefore the turning angles, are known for either blade row at any chosen radius or blade height, the actual blade form to be used can be selected from cascade data for blades with varying cambers and angles of incidence. Blade-setting angles, blade forms, and camber angles are then established.

Figure 88 shows the principal dimensions and angles in an airfoil cascade. The flows indicated are absolute for stationary-blade rows and relative for moving-blade rows; camber of the airfoil is shown as an angle $\theta = \beta' - \alpha'$ instead of the distance y usually used in aircraft wing shape descriptions. $\beta' - \beta$ is the incident angle at the leading edge of the blade, corresponding to

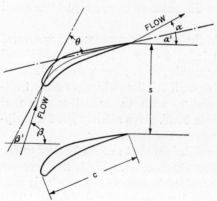

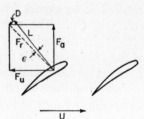

Fig. 88. Notation for principal dimensions and angles in an airfoil cascade.

Fig. 89. Vector diagram of forces acting on blade in rotating row.

angle of attack in the simple airfoil. $\alpha - \alpha'$ is the deviation angle of the flow leaving the trailing edge of the blade; α' is sometimes designated as the blade-setting angle.

The deflection angle or turning angle of the flow is $\beta - \alpha$, and may approach θ, the camber angle, in very closely pitched blade rows. The chord c is the width of the blade, and the pitch s is shown. Figure 89 shows the forces acting on a blade section in a rotating row; ϵ, the gliding angle, is $\tan^{-1} (C_D/C_L)$.

Aspect-ratio effects are usually quite large in axial-flow compressors, since mechanical-strength considerations may limit blade lengths to aspect-ratio values of the order of 2. Longer blades are sometimes designed with thick sections near the hub to keep centrifugal and bending stresses within limits; poor cascade performance near the hub is accepted in order to gain the advantage of a higher aspect ratio. At the best there is serious tip-clearance leakage, and usually no effort is made to fair blade ends into shroud rings, when shroud rings are used. Tip clearances are appreciable when compared with average blade height at the tip, and over-all efficiency may be reduced by the order of 2 percent when the tip clearance is increased from 1 percent of blade length to 2 percent of blade length. Reducing tip clearance under the 1 percent factor may yield a limiting benefit of 1 percent rise in efficiency. Aspect-ratio and end effects are less important when the turning angle of the flow is small.

Conventional axial-flow compressors almost always operate at Reynolds numbers above 250,000 and frequently above 1,000,000 with respect to the blade chord. Efficiency begins to fall off at Reynolds numbers below 400,000 as a rule, and if the compressor is operated at values below 100,000, efficiency drops rapidly. Mach number is a limiting factor at the other end of the scale; when local Mach numbers approach 1.0, serious energy losses result. Practically, this means that the rotor tip Mach number of an axial-flow compressor usually cannot exceed 0.7 or 0.8 before efficiency begins to drop. An isometric diagram of adiabatic efficiency of an axial-flow compressor is shown plotted against both Reynolds number and Mach number in Fig. 90.

The air-swallowing capacity of an axial-flow compressor with straight flow inlet can be estimated from Fig. 74 for centrifugal compressors by making the ratio of eye diameter to tip diameter unity. Permissible tip velocities can be increased considerably by placing prewhirl vanes ahead of the first row of rotating blades, and flow may thereby be increased without exceeding limiting Mach numbers.

A high degree of turning is usually achieved through the medium of a cambered blade form. Flow through an uncambered-blade row with small turning of the fluid flow in general means little change in flow area; there is negligible diffuser action, and principally whirl energy is added in the rotor-blade row; the compression-energy term $(1/2g)(v_1^2 - v_2^2)$ of Eq. (134) is very small.

If blade paths are designed for the lowest relative Mach numbers throughout the compressor for a given flow in a given inlet duct or compressor entry, it will be found that the fluid undergoes about the same amount of turning in the rotor-blade rows as in stator-blade rows.

A compressor in which diffusion takes place in both rotating- and stationary-blade rows in approximately equal amounts is known as a symmetric compressor, and the static pressure rise is uniform through both rotor and stator blades. Theoretically, a symmetric compressor should yield the maximum pressure rise per stage and result in the shortest compressor axially for a given pressure ratio. Rotor and stator blades may be mirror images of each other.

A compressor with only turning and but negligible diffusion in the rotor blades must depend upon the stator rows to act as diffusers; and conversely, in other designs, diffusion may be almost complete in the rotor. In both cases, the amount of static pressure rise per stage is less than that

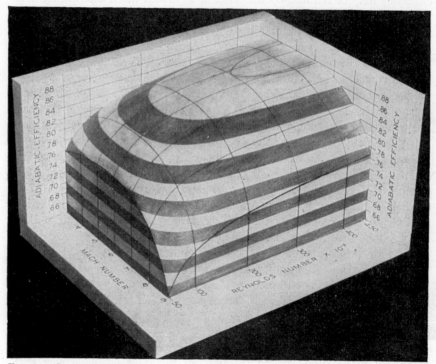

Fig. 90. Isometric diagram of adiabatic efficiency of an axial-flow compressor plotted against Reynolds and Mach numbers. (*Ponamareff, Westinghouse Eng., March,* 1947.)

available per stage in the symmetric design because of Mach-number limitations. Such compressors are known as antisymmetric or non-symmetric types. Another classification of compressor types is obtained by specifying whether the compressor is a reaction or impulse compressor. The percentage of the stage static pressure rise that occurs in the rotor defines the percent reaction; a symmetric compressor with 50 percent pressure rise in the rotor is a 50 percent reaction compressor, while an impulse nonsymmetric compressor with 10 percent static pressure rise in the rotor would be 10 percent reaction or 90 percent impulse.

Experimental evidence to date indicates that for a given over-all compression ratio, a nonsymmetric compressor (about 10 percent impulse or 90 percent reaction) has slightly higher efficiency than the symmetric design. More stages are required to achieve the required total pressure ratio owing to speed limitations, and the compressor is larger and heavier; the authors suspect that a symmetric design of the same number of stages, over-all compression ratio, and physical length would show about the same or better efficiency than the nonsymmetric design. Some European

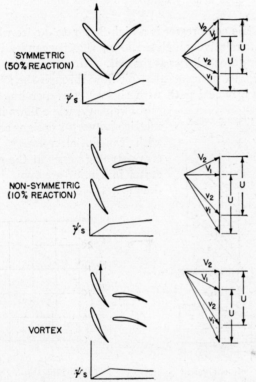

Fig. 91. Velocity diagrams for three types of axial-flow compressors. Typical pressure rises plotted under blade diagrams.

and British design experience has been just the opposite of that in the United States.

Still a third type of blade path is known as vortex blading. In the symmetric compressor, there are prewhirl vanes ahead of the first row of rotor blades, and flow enters and leaves both rotor and stator blades with whirl energy; in the nonsymmetric design, flow enters the rotor blades axially and leaves with whirl; and in vortex blading, air enters rotor blades with whirl and leaves substantially axially. Therefore the stator blades are required to provide some velocity acceleration to add entering whirl velocity for the succeeding row of rotor blades, and there is a slight static pressure drop through the stator rows.   The tangential or whirl velocity is usually made inversely proportional to the radius of rotation, as is the case with constant-circulation blading.   This type of whirl-velocity distribution is also known as a free vortex; hence the name vortex blading.   The three types of compressor-blade paths and their static pressure rises are shown schematically in Fig. 91.   Efficiency of the vortex compressor is usually comparable with that of the nonsymmetric compressor.

The symmetric compressor is a high-flow-rate device when worked to the limit, and its relatively high axial flow velocity can lead to substantial leaving losses or diffuser losses at the exit.   An examination of the velocity diagrams of Fig. 91 indicates that air flow through the symmetric compressor follows a helical path with zigzags corresponding to changes in whirl velocity, while flows in the nonsymmetric and vortex designs are largely axial with tangential velocity zigzags.   The straightening vanes at the exit end of the stator in Fig. 87 are typical of symmetric design.

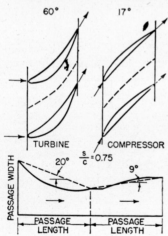

Fig. 92. Widths of equivalent flow passages through turbine- and compressor-blade rows. (*A. B. Howell, Proc. IME, vol.* 153, *pp.* 409–512, 1945.)

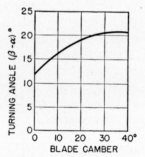

Fig. 93. Flow turning angle vs. blade camber for pitch/chord ratio equal to 1.0 and blade-setting angle of 30 deg. (*A. B. Howell, Proc. IME, vol.* 153, *pp.* 409–512, 1945.)

The amount of turning in a blade row of an axial-flow compressor is much less than that customarily found in a turbine-blade row.   Where the turning in a turbine-blade row may be of the order of 60 to 130 deg, the fluid flow deflection in the compressor-blade row is apt to average 15 to 20 deg, perhaps 6 to 20 deg at the blade tip, 10 to 24 deg at the mean diameter, and 20 to 30 deg at the root.   The width of equivalent flow passage through the turbine blades may change through a ratio of 2:1

or more, while that of the compressor row would be nearer 1.4:1 or less, as indicated in Fig. 92. In Fig. 93 the amount of turning or fluid deflection is shown plotted against camber angle θ in degrees for a typical compressor-blade section with a pitch/chord ratio = 1.0 and a blade-setting angle of 30 deg.

The blade forms chosen for a given compressor are a matter of selection by the designer based upon cascade tests, previous experience, and calculation. A skilled designer can usually predict compressor performance characteristics with a surprising degree of accuracy if he is provided with sufficient cascade-test data for the airfoil shapes in question. Guessing at cascade characteristics is unprofitable, and actual tests are required. Frequently it is possible to design a blade with the correct form, taper, length, twist, and camber for a particular stage, and then by judicious cropping of length of the blank make it do for a number of neighboring stages without serious loss of efficiency. This practice leads to quick results in development work and possibly to lower manufacturing costs, but not necessarily to optimum efficiencies. Advances in blade-fabricating techniques may tend to make this practice obsolete.

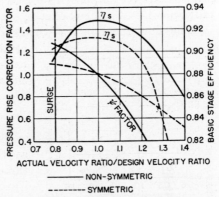

Fig. 94. Axial-flow-compressor pressure-rise correction and basic stage efficiency for off-design conditions.

It may also be necessary to sacrifice something in the drag/lift ratio of the blade form selected in order to obtain a blade that will accept off-design flows without too great a penalty in efficiency losses. A change in volumetric flow without a corresponding change in rotational speed will result in a shift of the velocity ratio or the ratio of the mean axial flow velocity to the mean peripheral rotor-blade velocity, where the mean diameter is defined as the product of the tip diameter and $\sqrt{(1 + h^2)/2}$. A shift in velocity ratio calls for a change in blade-angle setting, and since this is normally impractical in service, the blades must be able to accept flows at varying angles of incidence or attack without stalling or serious loss of efficiency. A 20 percent change in velocity ratio may result in a stall or a 3 to 4 percent drop in efficiency accompanied by a much larger change in the pressure-rise ratio (see Fig. 94). A well-rounded leading edge may not give a blade the lowest possible drag/lift ratio, but it frequently holds up efficiency at off-design operating conditions better than does a blade with a sharp leading edge and lower drag at the design point.

The pitch/chord ratio of a blade row is important both to pressure ratio of the stage and to stage efficiency. Figure 95 shows the effect of varying the pitch/chord ratio at the mean diameter of one typical compressor stage. The choice of h, the hub diameter/tip diameter ratio, influences pitch selection, since a very small hub leads to blades that are pitched much too closely near the hub if spacing at the tips is not to be too great. Hub/tip ratios greater than $h = 0.7$, on the other hand, may lead to excessive efficiency losses, owing to the relatively greater influence of friction losses and end effects.

The flow function $F = Q/nD^3$ discussed earlier in connection with centrifugal compressors is equally applicable to axial-flow compressors, and since $\pi nD = U$, it may also be written

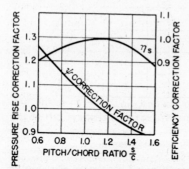

FIG. 95. Axial-flow-compressor pressure-rise and efficiency correction factors vs. pitch/chord ratio for a typical design.

$$F = \frac{Q}{0.29UD^2} \qquad (141)$$

Since the volumetric flow Q decreases as the gas is compressed in passing through the compressor, the axial velocity may be reduced progressively in successive stages, or the blade length may be reduced by going to a larger hub/tip ratio, or the designer may employ a combination of the two. Holding the hub diameter of the compressor rotor constant and decreasing blade height requires a smaller change in hub/tip ratio and generally leads to higher efficiency than holding tip diameter constant and increasing hub diameter; all combinations of the two are used in practice as design requirements are modified by tip-leakage areas, etc. The possible stage pressure rise is greatest in the constant-tip-diameter design, since absolute blade velocities are higher than in the constant-hub-diameter design, and required blade lift coefficients are lower for a given pressure rise.

A rough size calculation for an axial-flow compressor can be made from the data presented here, although it is not the intention of this volume to present detailed design methods or data. With total pressure and temperature at the inlet known, the static pressure and static temperature are calculated from the design value of axial velocity V_a at the inlet, and the required flow cross section is then established from V_a and the specified inlet flow rate. It is necessary to assume a value of efficiency η_c for the compressor and to calculate the exit total temperature from

Eq. (121). After the axial flow velocity at the exit has been selected, the exit static pressure, static temperature, flow, Q_{exit}, and required exit cross-sectional area may be established. Selection of the inlet and exit hub/tip ratios then establishes the inlet and exit tip and hub diameters, and the principal dimensions of the compressor are fixed except for speed N, the length of the compressor, and the number of stages. The speed N is chosen with due regard to maximum permissible tip Mach number at the entrance to the first row of rotating blades. Since the fluid density increases with flow through the compressor, the blade width can usually be decreased progressively through the compressor, leading to a shorter compressor.

Principal dimensions for three axial-flow compressors, each designed for 30 lb of air per second at 70°F inlet temperature (24,000 cfm) and with a compression ratio of 4:1 are shown in the following tabulation. The tip Mach number of the vortex compressor is low, and an increase in speed would be permissible; Mach numbers of the other two designs are near the limit for efficient over-all design.

Approximate pressure-rise ratios per stage that may be expected for symmetric-, nonsymmetric-, and vortex-flow compressor designs are shown plotted against rotor tip speed in Fig. 96. The total stage pressure

DATA ON TYPICAL AXIAL-FLOW COMPRESSORS*

	Compressor		
	Symmetric	Nonsymmetric	Vortex
Speed, rpm	15,750	8,750	5,000
Number of stages	10	18	22
Stage pressure ratio	1.149	1.080	1.062
First stage			
Tip diameter, in	16	19	24.5
Hub diameter, in	10	11.5	15.25
Blade length, in	3	3.75	4.63
Tip velocity, fps	1,100	725	535
Axial flow velocity, fps	525	335	200
Tip Mach number	0.72	0.72	0.58
Last stage			
Tip diameter, in	16	19	24.5
Hub diameter, in	14	16	21.25
Blade length, in	1.0	1.5	1.63
Tip velocity, fps	1,100	725	535
Axial flow velocity, fps	475	275	195

* PONAMAREFF, *Westinghouse Eng.*, March, 1947.

ratio appears to be more dependent upon rotor tip speed than upon the type of blade design for blade paths of comparable efficiencies. Maximum tip speeds are limited by local Mach numbers and the velocity triangles of the various blade-path designs. With prewhirl before the first rotor stage, the symmetric compressor can operate with tip speeds of 1,300 fps or higher. However, the nonsymmetric and vortex designs may be limited to tip speeds of the order of 800 fps and 600 fps because of axial entry, or actual contra-prewhirl in the case of vortex blading. The data of Fig. 96 are not representative of all blade-path designs, however. The symmetric 6-stage rotor of Fig. 86 is worked to the limit for reasonably high efficiency, and delivers air at a design compression ratio of 1.185 per stage.

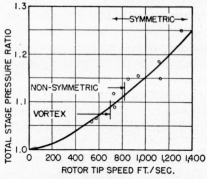

FIG. 96. Approximate stage pressure ratios for symmetric-, nonsymmetric-, and vortex-flow compressor designs plotted against rotor tip speed.

It should be remembered that high relative tip Mach numbers (in excess of 0.7) are likely to lead to serious decreases in stage efficiency. The first stage Mach number may be higher, however, in order to keep diameter as small as possible for the required flow, perhaps as high as 0.75, since the Mach number decreases quite rapidly in succeeding stages. This is due to temperature increase, decreases in axial velocity, reduced tip diameter, or combinations of these factors. The use of prewhirl vanes reduces losses for a given air flow, but also cuts down the pressure rise. Tip Mach number is

$$M_{\text{tip}} = \frac{\sqrt{(U - V_u)^2 + V_a^2}}{49.2 \sqrt{t}} \qquad (142)$$

The available stage pressure ratio can also be calculated from aerodynamic data for the blade row or cascade, provided that the proper corrections that must be applied to individual airfoil characteristics are known. The lift force or resultant of the forces on a blade row given in Eqs. (137) and (138) is the pounds of lift required per unit axial flow area. Using flow data at the mean diameter of the blade row as a first approximation, the mean relative velocity is taken as the relative velocity at half of the total turning angle

$$v_r = V_a \sqrt{1 + \frac{\eta}{2} (\tan \beta + \tan \alpha)^2} \qquad (143)$$

The lift coefficient from aerodynamic relations is

$$C_L = \frac{2L}{\rho v_r^2 A} \tag{144}$$

where L is the lift per unit area of flow, and where A is the total blade area per unit of axial cross-sectional flow area through the row, or c/s.

$$
\begin{aligned}
C_L &= \frac{2s V_a^2 \rho (\tan \beta - \tan \alpha) \sqrt{1 + (\eta/2)(\tan \beta + \tan \alpha)^2}}{c\rho V_a^2 \{1 + [(\eta/2)(\tan \beta + \tan \alpha)]^2\}} \\
&= \frac{s}{c} \frac{2(\tan \beta - \tan \alpha)}{\sqrt{1 + (\eta/2)(\tan \beta + \tan \alpha)^2}}
\end{aligned} \tag{145}
$$

where s/c is the pitch/chord ratio of the blade row.

Since Eq. (135) gives the total pressure change across the moving-blade row as

$$\Delta P = \rho V_a (\tan \beta - \tan \alpha) u$$

this can also be expressed by using Eq. (145) as

$$\Delta P = \frac{\rho V_a u C_L c}{2s} \sqrt{1 + \left[\frac{\eta}{2}(\tan \beta - \tan \alpha)\right]^2} \tag{146}$$

The maximum value of C_L that can be obtained for blades in a cascade is considerably lower than the lift coefficients that apply to single airfoils, although the drag/lift ratio of the single airfoil is increased only slightly in a cascade when end effects are excluded. Lift coefficients are slightly less for the same angles of attack when the angle of attack in the cascade is taken with respect to the mean flow line. Actually the angle of incidence on the leading edge of the cascade airfoil may exceed this assumed angle of attack by a large margin, and the blade stalls earlier than does an individual airfoil. Figure 97 shows a typical relation between lift-drag plots for an individual airfoil and a blade in an infinite cascade. End effects further reduce the effective lift coefficient of a blade in a grid or cascade. Figure 98 shows the effect of pitch/chord ratio on cascade lift coefficients as well as the effects of the flow outlet or blade-setting angle for an average airfoil; a high blade-setting angle brings the adjacent blade surfaces closer together, and is equivalent to a decrease in the s/c ratio.

Off-design characteristics of a compressor can be calculated if the effects of individual variations have previously been determined from model testing of individual stages and complete compressors. A few of these correction factors appear in the accompanying diagrams. Comprehensive data is beyond the scope of this book.

The external characteristics of axial-flow compressors are generally represented by the plot of Fig. 99. Peak efficiencies may be somewhat higher than for centrifugal compressors, with off-design efficiency dropping away from the peak value faster than in the case of the centrifugal

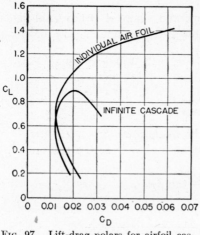

FIG. 97. Lift-drag polars for airfoil cascade and isolated airfoil.

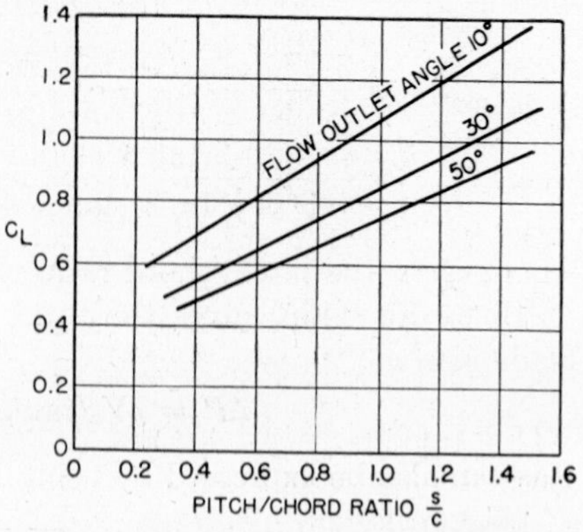

FIG. 98. Effect of pitch/chord ratio on cascade lift coefficients of typical blade section at different outlet flow or blade-setting angles.

compressor. The sensitivity of flow rate to changes in compression ratio is also less than for the centrifugal compressor (compare Fig. 100 with Fig. 83).

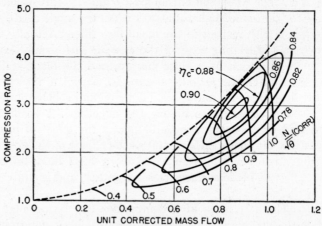

FIG. 99. External flow characteristic of typical axial-flow compressor.

Figure 101 shows the characteristics of another higher pressure compressor. This is an early British design with 14 stages rated 50 lb of air flow per second under standard conditions at a conservative 8,000 rpm with a maximum rotor diameter over the blade tips of 1.71 ft. The blade-path design was symmetric with 50 percent reaction. The efficiency of this early compressor is about the same as that indicated in Fig.

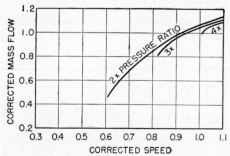

FIG. 100.   Flow-speed relation of axial-flow compressor at different compression ratios.

102 for another compressor with 21 stages and a 10 percent impulse rotor; it was excellent for a 5:1-ratio compressor at the time when designed.

Present design practice will permit the construction of axial-flow compressors with shaft efficiencies at the design point of 90 percent or better

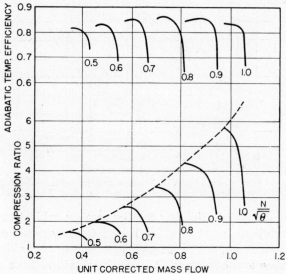

FIG. 101.   External flow characteristic of 14-stage symmetric axial-flow compressor. Design compression ratio is 5:1.

for the lower pressure ratios.   However, in order to get the last 2 or 3 percent improvement in working efficiency, it is necessary to run at low Mach numbers and relatively low mass flow rates per square foot of frontal area.   The specific weight of the compressor increases rapidly with reduced speed. The value of small frontal area and low weight must be balanced against the penalty of lowered engine efficiency. This can be done properly only by comparing the two engine designs as each would be applied to an airplane for a given mission. The over-all performance characteristics of the aircraft with the different engine installations then provide a sound basis for selection of the best engine for the job.

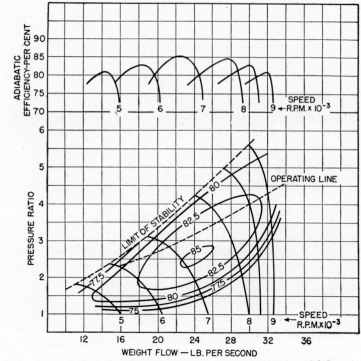

Fig. 102.   External flow characteristic of 21-stage nonsymmetric axial-flow compressor with 10 percent impulse rotor. (*Ponamareff, Westinghouse Eng., March,* 1947.)

The design details of axial-flow compressors are subject to an infinite number of variations, most of which have relatively minor effects individually upon efficiency but in the aggregate account for wide variations in characteristics and efficiency. One designer will achieve a 5:1 compression ratio with 21 stages, and another will do it with 9 stages. Early German designs used 90 percent reaction rotors, and stator blades were little more than vanes made of curved sheet metal; partly as a result of this practice, their compressor efficiencies were from 5 to 10 percent lower than contemporary British and United States designs. In order to improve efficiency, German designers went to 70 percent reaction with airfoil stator sections, and when their work stopped in 1945, 50 percent reaction blading was being studied.

Various combinations of axial-flow and centrifugal compressors are possible; axial-flow inducer stages ahead of a centrifugal stage have been studied; a semicentrifugal entrance to an axial-flow compressor permits a smaller hub and greater air-swallowing capacity. The exit end of the compressor may also require a diffuser in order to slow axial leaving velocity to the point where the air can be accepted by the combustion chambers. Straightening vanes in the exit flow are also a normal requirement, and coarse screens have been placed across the flow to decrease large-scale turbulence and improve flow to the burners. Such a screen may be seen between the compressor and the axial-flow burner of the jet engine shown in Fig. 114; the compression ratio of this engine is approximately 4:1 with the high rotor tip speed of almost 1,300 fps, and symmetric stages.

Mechanical construction details change from one design to the next, but a few limiting conditions carry through from one design to another. Low-speed compressors are frequently constructed with drum-type rotors. The blades are inserted in a continuous drum or in rings that are flanged to fit one against the other; the entire assembly may then be pulled up tight and held together with a through bolt or stay bolt. This is satisfactory as long as speeds are low and centrifugal stresses are moderate. It has the further advantage that blades can be held in place in experimental compressors by means of threaded studs and nuts through the ring or drum surface, thus making it possible to change blade-setting angles easily. For high-speed compressors, however, it becomes necessary to go to disc-type construction with blades fitted into flanges that are machined from a solid-center forging with disclike extensions, or into discs assembled on a shaft. The high-speed, high-flow symmetric compressors use disc construction, while vortex and nonsymmetric compressors may use either disc or drum construction (see Figs. 103, 107, and 157).

Axial-compressor rotor blades are usually made of a stainless or semi-stainless steel, although blading of light alloys and some of the better structural plastic materials have been experimented with. As long as the adiabatic temperature rise does not adversely affect the strength of the light-alloy blades, it is permissible to use them. Plastic blades, such as glass-reinforced phenolic laminates, in general are too much subject to creep distortion and erosion of leading edges to permit their use. Since rotor blades are very seldom shrouded, it is essential to select materials with high damping coefficients. Methods of fastening the blades in the rotor disc or drum include both bulb- and tree-type roots, locked by means of grub screws, peening, or locking wires or keys.

Stator blades can usually be made of any material with moderate strength, stability, and corrosion and erosion resistance. Quite frequently they are shrouded at both ends, thus simplifying the fastening problem. Aluminum alloys and steel, including stainless, are normally

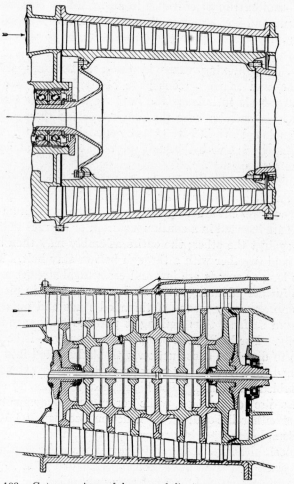

FIG. 103. Cutaway views of drum- and disc-type rotor construction.

used with or without protective coatings. Unshrouded stator blades should be made of materials with high damping coefficients.

Leakage of air at blade tips and past shroud rings is probably the largest single source of energy loss in axial-flow compressors, so that thermal expansion effects upon blade-tip and shroud clearances are of first-order importance. Temperature gradients and thermal expansion in compressors result in greater variations of blade clearance than do centrifugal-force deformations. Frequently blade tips are reduced in thickness to permit "rubs" in operation without wrecking the compressor (see Fig. 104).

Aircraft compressor casings are almost universally cast of either aluminum or magnesium alloys; magnesium alloys lead to the lightest designs, and compare favorably with aluminum in strength if generous fillets are used in all corners. Casings are frequently box-ribbed for

Fig. 104. Typical compressor blades. (*Westinghouse Electric Corporation.*)

strength and rigidity of structure; blade and shroud clearances depend upon rigid structures with stable dimensions.

Antifriction-, sleeve-, and slipper-type bearings have been used. Thrust loads may influence the bearing design to a considerable extent, and it is necessary to make special provisions for thrust bearings. In some gas turbines, the axial thrust of the compressor rotor is fairly well balanced by an opposite thrust force on the turbine rotor on the same shaft; here there is a requirement for only a light thrust bearing. When the compressor thrust is not well balanced, however, the thrust-bearing problem becomes quite serious, and excessive bearing losses may occur.

Fig. 105. Armstrong Siddeley X jet-engine compressor rotor—drum-type construction.

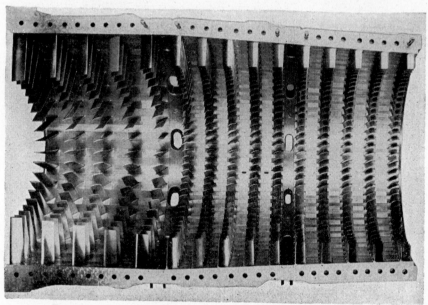

Fig. 106. Armstrong Siddeley X jet-engine compressor stator—half.

Compressor thrust loads are sometimes balanced by means of labyrinth seals located at the proper diameter on the end face of the last high-pressure disc of the rotor.   This method is also used for single-entry centrifugal impellers on the back side of the impeller.   The symmetric axial-flow

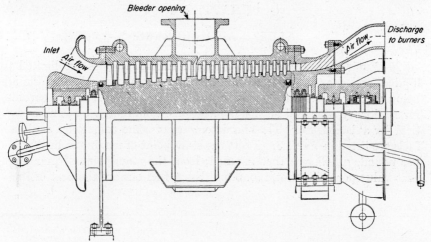

FIG. 107.   Experimental locomotive compressor with solid rotor construction.   Characteristics are shown in Fig. 102.

compressor rotor usually has a smaller end thrust than either the vortex or the low-impulse nonsymmetric design.   It would be expected to have a higher end thrust than a low-reaction nonsymmetric rotor with substantially constant axial flow velocity.

CHAPTER 5

FUELS AND BURNERS

20. Fuels. Fuels suitable for use in aircraft engines are limited to liquids, and gas turbines are no exception to this rule; while efforts are being made to devise means for burning powdered coal in gas turbines for stationary, rail, and marine applications, solid fuels are not now practical for aviation use. The characteristics of some commonly available fuels are listed in Table 3. From the standpoint of maximum heat value per pound, gasoline is the best fuel; from the standpoint of maximum heat value per cubic foot, No. 5 and No. 6 fuel oils are the best of those

TABLE 3

Fuel	Specific gravity, 60/60		Viscosity	Heat of vaporization, Btu/lb	Pour or freezing point, °F	Lower heat of combustion (60°F)	
						Btu/lb	Btu/cu ft
Aviation gasoline....	Min.	0.68	0.4 centipoise at 60°F	130	....	18,700[b]	793,000
	Max.	0.73	0.5 centipoise at 60°F	140	− 76[b]	19,000	866,000
Motor gasoline.......	Min.	0.70	0.6 centipoise at 60°F	130	....	18,800	822,000
	Max.	0.78		140	− 40*	19,100	929,000
Kerosene, No. 1 fuel oil	Min.	0.77	1.4 centistoke at 60°F	110	− 50	18,400	884,000
	Max.	0.83	1.7 centistoke at 60°F	120	0[a]	18,600	962,000
No. 2 fuel oil........	Min.	0.84	32 SSU at 100°F	100	− 30	18,200	953,000
	Max.	0.89	38 SSU at 100°F	120	10[a]	18,400	1,022,000
No. 3 fuel oil........	Min.	0.87	34 SSU at 100°F	95	− 20	17,900	972,000
	Max.	0.90	45 SSU at 100°F[a]	105	20[a]	18,100	1,015,000
No. 5 fuel oil........	Min.	0.93	50 SSU at 100°F[a]	105	− 15	17,500	1,015,000
	Max.	1.00	40 SSF at 122°F[a]	115	30	17,900	1,118,000
No. 6 fuel oil........	Min.	0.95	45 SSF at 122°F[a]	90	10	17,300	1,025,000
	Max.	1.02	300 SSF at 122°F[a]	100	60	17,500	1,113,000
Jet propulsion JP-2..	Min.	.....	0.92 centistoke at 100°F[c]	120	....	18,300	
	Max.	0.850[c]	10.0 centistokes at −40°F[c]	130	− 76[c]	18,500	981,000
Navy diesel fuel.....	Min.	0.80	35 SSU at 100°F[d]	105	− 40	18,400	918,000
	Max.	0.82	45 SSU at 100°F[d]	115	0[d]	18,600	951,000
Benzene............		0.884	0.7 centipoise at 60°F	170	42	17,500	966,000
Methyl alcohol......		0.797	1.34 centipoises at 60°F	473	−144	9,060	449,000
Ethyl alcohol........		0.794	0.65 centipoise at 60°F	368	−179	11,910	590,000

* Freezing point of motor gasoline is higher than aviation gasoline but probably not above −40°F.

Specification
[a] ASTM Tentative Specification.
[b] Army-Navy Specification AN-F-28.

Specification
[c] Army-Navy Specification AN-F-34.
[d] Navy Department Specification 7-0-2.

fuels listed. In low-speed aircraft, weight is at a premium; and in high-speed aircraft with thin wings and small fuselage, space is of equal value with weight. The choice of a best fuel for aircraft turbines must be a compromise between space and weight requirements for the necessary amount of heat needed for a flight, tempered by the peculiarities of the gas-turbine engine and the relative difficulties of storing and transporting the selected fuel, both on the ground and in the air.

Most of the fuels used for aircraft gas turbines have fairly high vapor pressures at normal temperatures. Ordinarily, gasoline will have a

Fig. 108. Rolls Royce Nene I turbojet engine, 5,000 lb ssl thrust, weight 1,550 lb. Note can-type combustors.

sufficiently high vapor pressure on a warm day that the mixture of fuel vapor and air above the liquid surface will be too "rich" to ignite and explode from a spark or an incendiary bullet. Kerosene, on the other hand, has a lower vapor pressure, and under the same atmospheric conditions, the mixture of air and fuel vapor above the surface of kerosene may well exist in explosive proportions. If the temperatures of these liquid fuels are lowered, however, the vapor-air mixtures will become leaner for the same altitude conditions. The kerosene tank may then have an air space above the liquid level too lean to be explosive, and the tank containing gasoline may become explosive. When the pressure-altitude is changed, the richness of the vapor-air mixture changes also, becoming richer at higher altitudes for the same liquid temperature. Thus, with a range of liquid temperatures going from well over 100°F to lower than −60°F and with pressures varying from sea level to the maximum altitude of the aircraft carrying the fuel tank, it is almost impossible to specify a fuel that does not have an explosive vapor above the liquid surface of the fuel under some of the possible conditions that may be encountered.

The practice is to make the optimum compromise considering the type of aircraft, the maximum altitude possible, the probable temperature range of the fuel at various altitudes for steady conditions and also after a fast climb, the specific requirements and limitations of the engine itself regarding fuel requirements, and then hope for the best.

21. The Combustion Process. The heats of combustion of the fuels in Table 3 are given as the "low" heat values of the various materials when burned in air. The low heat value of a fuel is the amount of heat that must be removed from the products of combustion to return them to their initial temperature before combustion started, but with any water in the combustion products still in the vapor state. The thermal process in gas turbines is such that no condensation of water vapor will occur in the exhaust due to the high exhaust temperatures, and therefore the heat of condensation of the water vapor in the exhaust is lost. Since the combustion of a pound of the fuels in Table 3 in air will result in from 0.7 to 1.5 lb of water vapor in the combustion products, depending upon the particular fuel, the low heat value is of the order of 1,000 Btu/lb less than the high heat value of the fuel.

The heats of combustion of hydrocarbons can be calculated from the known analysis of the fuel, but a number of methods of estimating the result have been developed that are satisfactory and are much faster when the analysis is not known with certainty. The National Bureau of Standards has published a formula for mixed hydrocarbons such as gasoline, kerosene, fuel oils, etc., based on the density or specific gravity of the fuel; the lower heat value is given by

$$H = 19,960 + 1,360(\text{sp. gr.}) - 3,780(\text{sp. gr.})^2 \qquad \text{Btu/lb} \quad (147)$$

The amount of fuel needed by the burner is measured by the required temperature rise through the burner and the incidental heat losses that occur. The total enthalpy of material entering the burner is the enthalpy of the entering air plus that of the liquid fuel. This sum must be subtracted from the enthalpy of the leaving gas, along with incidental heat losses by conduction and also the heat of vaporization of the fuel. The heat per pound of compressor air that must be furnished through the combustion of fuel is

$$h_b = \eta_b H \frac{W_f}{W_a} = h_4 - h_3 + h_{\text{loss}} + \frac{W_f}{W_a} h_{\text{latent}} + \Delta h_\lambda \frac{W_f}{W_a} \quad (148)$$

where h_3 and h_4 are the enthalpies of 1 lb of pure air at states 3 and 4, entering and leaving the combustion chamber, h_{loss} is heat lost by conduction through the walls of the combustion chamber per pound of air flow, and h_{latent} is the latent heat of vaporization of 1 lb of fuel. Ordinarily

the latent heat of vaporization of the liquid fuel is included in the determination of the heating value of the fuel, so that the h_{latent} term may be
neglected in Eq. (148). The specific heats of the liquids of Table 3 are
approximately equal to 0.5. The term Δh_λ is a correction term for the
heat required to raise the gaseous products of complete combustion of 1 lb
of fuel from the temperature of the fuel supply to the final temperature
at state 4; the combustion products are assumed to be carbon dioxide
and water vapor, and the heat calculated is *minus* the heat of the oxygen
consumed from the air on complete combustion. On the basis of heating
value of the fuel per pound of air, the Δh_λ correction is equivalent to a

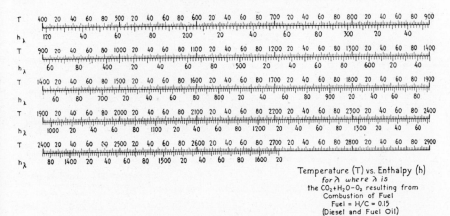

Temperature (T) vs. Enthalpy (h)
for λ where λ is
the $CO_2 + H_2O - O_2$ resulting from
Combustion of Fuel
Fuel = H/C = 0.15
(Diesel and Fuel Oil)

FIG. 109. Enthalpy correction factor for combustion products in air. (*By permission
United States Navy Department, Bureau of Ships.*)

further reduction in the lower heat value of the fuel, although of course
the actual energy is still present in the increased mass flow due to the fuel
addition. No correction has been indicated for the enthalpy of the
unburned fuel vapor that escapes combustion; the c_p of the fuel vapor is
fairly close to the effective c_p in the Δh_λ correction, and at the usual fuel/air
ratios and with normal combustion efficiency, the error would be negligible.

The value of Δh_λ depends upon the final temperature as well as the
H/C ratio of the fuel. An H/C ratio of 0.15 is a reasonable representa-
tion for diesel and fuel oils, and an H/C ratio of 0.18 is sufficiently
accurate for kerosene and gasoline. Approximate values of h_λ in the
temperature range of 500 to 2500°R are obtained from the relations

$$h_\lambda = 0.24T + 0.00014T^2 \qquad \text{Btu/lb fuel for H/C} = 0.15 \qquad (149)$$
$$h_\lambda = 0.322T + 0.000129T^2 \qquad \text{Btu/lb fuel for H/C} = 0.18 \qquad (150)$$

Accurate values of h_λ can be read from the charts of Figs. 109 and 110,
and Δh_λ equals the difference between h_λ at T_4 and h_λ at T_3.

The fuel/air ratio is

$$\frac{W_f}{W_a} = \frac{h_b}{\eta_b H} = \frac{h_4 - h_3 + h_{\text{loss}}}{\eta_b H - \Delta h_\lambda - h_{\text{latent}}} \tag{151}$$

and the total heat addition per pound of compressor air to the combustion chamber can then be expressed

$$h_b = \eta_b H \frac{h_4 - h_3 + h_{\text{loss}}}{\eta_b H - \Delta h_\lambda - h_{\text{latent}}} \tag{152}$$

Where the air supply contains moisture, the $h_4 - h_3$ terms must be corrected; Chap. 8 discusses this correction.

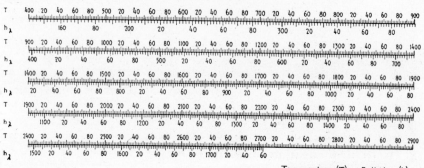

Temperature (T) vs. Enthalpy (h)
for λ where λ is
the $CO_2 + H_2O - O_2$ resulting from
Combustion of Fuel
Fuel = H/C = 0.18
(Kerosene and Gasoline)

Fig. 110. Enthalpy correction factor for combustion products in air. (*By permission United States Navy Department, Bureau of Ships.*)

Figure 111 shows burner temperature rise for 100 percent combustion at constant pressure plotted against W_f/W_a for a number of different fuels and inlet air conditions.

With low heat loss through the burner walls and with normal fuel/air ratios, the heat requirement is given approximately (usually accurately within 2 or 3 percent) by the very simple relation

$$h_b = h_4 - h_3 \tag{153}$$

Normally, heat leakage through the walls of the burner is considerably less than 1 percent of the total heat release in the combustion chamber. This low rate of heat leakage through the walls of a relatively poorly insulated combustion space may be easily understood when the rate of heat release in the combustion process is noted.   Heat releases as high as 30,000,000 Btu/(cu ft)(hr) for gas turbines should be contrasted with 250,000 Btu/(cu ft)(hr) for a Navy boiler.   The gas stays in the burner too short a time to lose an appreciable amount of heat by conduction.

The combustion efficiency η_b is the ratio of the actual enthalpy increase of the fuel plus working fluid to the ideal enthalpy increase if combustion were complete. Efficiencies of less than 0.95 are not considered very satisfactory under rated load conditions, although considerably lower efficiencies may be found at other conditions.

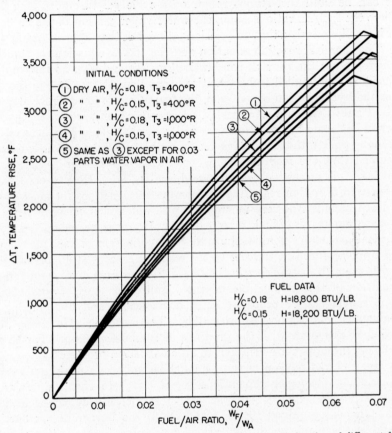

Fig. 111. Temperature rise for constant-pressure 100 percent combustion of different fuels in air plotted against fuel/air ratio.

In making accurate design calculations, it is frequently necessary to take all the combustion variables into account in order to minimize avoidable errors. This is important, for example, in matching turbine and compressor. For routine performance estimates, approximation formulas may be used with an occasional complete heat-balance check on results.

The composition of the gas leaving the burner is that of air plus 0.6 to 6 percent water vapor, 1.5 to 15 percent carbon dioxide, and less the oxygen consumed in combustion. In the event of incomplete combustion, unburned fuel, small quantities of cracked fuel vapors, carbon monoxide (usually less than 0.1 percent), solid carbon particles, and other undesirable products such as the characteristically evil-smelling aldehydes are also present. The properties of the diluted burner gases in gas turbines are sufficiently near those of air that thermodynamic data for air can be used throughout rough open-cycle gas-turbine calculations where the fuel/air ratio is small, the water vapor content of the inducted air is small, and when the compression ratio is less than approximately 4:1.

The chemical reaction equation and the energy equation for combustion represent the over-all combustion process and give no information regarding the detailed transformations that take place. Before the carbon and hydrogen can be oxidized, the fuel molecule must dissociate, and this is known to be a complicated process in which parts of the hydrocarbon molecule are oxidized in a series of chain reactions. Thus, for methane (CH_4), the simplest molecule of the paraffin series, it is usually assumed that the reaction chain consists of five different reactions in which CH_4 is successively decomposed to CH_3, CH_2, $HCHO$, etc. Such detailed information regarding the combustion reactions for most of the hydrocarbons is still very incomplete, and much of it is speculative, so that at present it is of little practical use. However, consideration of the physical aspects of combustion and the application of fluid mechanics and principles of heat transfer to the reacting gases is of importance.

Mass and heat transfers in the combustion process involve four steps: formation of the combustible mixture, ignition or start of combustion, flame movement or propagation of combustion, and final mixing of products of combustion with excess air. The last of these four steps, the mixing of excess air with the products of combustion, is peculiar to gas turbines; the others are common to all combustion processes.

The fuel and oxygen of the air must be uniformly mixed on a scale approaching molecular dimensions for a complete chemical reaction. Thus, a liquid fuel must be vaporized before such mixing can occur, and although heat is added to the fuel feed to the burner or combustion chamber, space and weight limitations may prevent the addition of sufficient heat to vaporize the liquid fuel completely before it reaches the burner. Various forms of fuel sprays are used to introduce the fuel into the mixing-chamber portion of the burner as a finely atomized mist. This fine spray is distributed quite uniformly through a relatively large region in which hot air from the compressor is also present. The increase in fuel surface from which vaporization can take place is very great with fine sprays, and vaporization is correspondingly rapid. A fuel spray nozzle discharging at the rate of 10 gal/hr will atomize about 0.6 cu in./sec, the average drop size of the discharge being between 0.003 and 0.006 in.

in diameter, and the total vaporizing surface for a 1-sec flow of fuel will be of the order of 7 sq ft.

The rate of vaporization of a cloud of fuel droplets depends upon the mean diameter of the droplets (where the mean diameter is the size of a particle having the same surface-to-volume ratio as the spray), the particle-size distribution, the vapor pressure of the liquid, the atmospheric pressure, velocity of the spray relative to the air, temperatures of both air and liquid, and the rate at which the spray droplets receive heat energy from the flame and other hot bodies by radiation. For high-pressure fuel sprays and for some other specialized types of sprays, the size distribution is such that the amount of unevaporated fuel remaining in the spray is approximately inversely proportional to the square root of the elapsed time after ejection from the nozzle. With less effective sprays, the size distribution changes, and the relative initial evaporation rate is considerably retarded. Since it has been shown that the mass rate of evaporation from the surface of a droplet is a direct function of the first power of its diameter,[1] it is of the greatest importance that sprays yielding exceedingly small droplets be utilized if maximum combustion rates are to be achieved in compact burners.

Fuel concentration in the air must be within definite limits, or the mixture will not ignite and burn with sufficient speed. The theoretical stoichiometric fuel/air weight ratio for a paraffin hydrocarbon is

$$\frac{W_f}{W_a} = \frac{14n + 2}{205.8n + 68.6} \tag{154}$$

where n is the number of carbon atoms in the molecule. For octane with 8 carbons, the theoretical ratio of fuel to air is 0.0662; and while mixture ratios between 0.25 and 0.04 can be burned, for maximum reaction speed the ratio should be approximately 0.073, and for most complete combustion the ratio should be about 0.060. Combustion of gasoline with ratios less than about 0.055 is slow and erratic, so that for smaller ratios the air flow must be separated into primary and secondary streams. The primary stream passes through the primary combustion chamber while the secondary stream by-passes the primary burning space and is later mixed with the products of combustion as they flow toward the turbine inlet nozzle ring.

Vigorous mechanical mixing of the fuel vapor with the primary air is necessary, since mixing by diffusion is far too slow a process to be of aid in forming a combustible mixture. This mechanical mixing is achieved by inducing a high order of turbulence in the primary combustion space. Primary air is admitted through large numbers of small holes in

[1] LLOYD, *Proc. IME*, vol. 153, p. 469, 1945.

the burner shell, or turbulence may be established by placing screens or deflectors in the air stream and by using counterflow of fuel and air. This turbulence must be uniform and on a small scale physically in order to ensure the fine-grained mixing necessary for rapid and uniform flame propagation. Flame propagation rates are quite critical of completeness of mixing of fuel and air, fuel/air ratio, local turbulence, and the local temperature conditions.

Final mixing of the secondary air with the primary combustion products occurs downstream from the primary combustion space, air entering through slots or holes in the burner shell in order to produce complete mixing and a homogenous gas mixture before entering the turbine.   Since the length of the entire burner is limited by severe space and weight

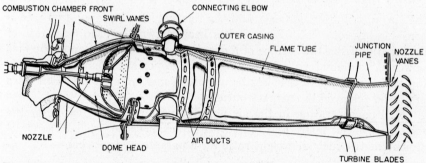

FIG. 112.   Section through De Havilland can-type combustion chamber. (*Flight magazine*.)

restrictions, and since the volume of the primary flame varies through wide limits with fuel/air ratio, air density, etc., the mixing zone overlaps the primary combustion zone.   With low fuel-flow rates and with small flame volume, mixing of excess air occurs almost immediately after the fuel nozzles; but with high fuel flows and with large flame volumes, complete mixing may not be accomplished before the flame reaches the turbine inlet nozzle ring.   While this mixing process is not so critical as that in other stages of the combustion process, chilling of the products of combustion before the chemical reactions have been completed must be avoided.

22. Burner Types.   There are two principal geometrical types of combustion chambers in use.   The can-type combustor was first used in the early British designs of jet engines and the annular or straight-through combustor was used in some later British designs and German engines, and independently in some United States designs.

A can-type combustion chamber is shown in section in Fig. 112. This is a British-designed "flowerpot" type of combustion chamber used on the De Havilland Goblin II jet engine.   Sixteen chambers are used on this engine, located around the periphery of the turbine inlet nozzle ring. Air from the compressor enters the outer dome of the combustion chamber and is there divided into primary and secondary air streams. The primary combustion air is admitted to the fuel burner through the metering annulus located in the outer dome between the air inlet tube and the inner dome; approximately one-quarter of the air to the combustion chamber passes through it. The air for primary combustion then passes through swirl vanes around the fuel-spray nozzle; a small quantity

of primary air passes around the outside of the swirl vanes through holes in the inner dome and flared cover plate, increasing turbulence in the flame.

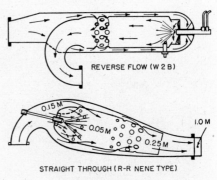

REVERSE FLOW (W 2 B)

Secondary air passes between the flame tube and the outer casing, entering the flame tube through holes in the tube. The sizes, locations, and number of holes are critical. This method of entry serves to cool the outer casing and provides controlled dilution and cooling of the combustion gases from a flame temperature of 3500°F to 1450°F at the turbine nozzle ring. A high degree of turbulence in the early combustion and cooling stages is desirable, and is obtained by

STRAIGHT THROUGH (R-R NENE TYPE)

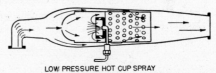

LOW PRESSURE HOT CUP SPRAY

Fig. 113. Sections of typical can-type burners. Flow Mach numbers are indicated on straight-through type.

means of the swirl vanes and air inlet through numerous small holes.

Other can combustors differ from the above only in design details. Various methods of obtaining graduated air velocities in the primary combustion space may be used, as are different methods of introducing secondary air. The basic design of an outer casing surrounding a perforated flame tube, both cooled by the flow of secondary air, remains fundamental in all current designs. A number of different designs are shown in Fig. 113. Typical air-flow Mach numbers are indicated at various stages on one of these sketches.

The annular combustion chamber is less complex than can combustors when applied to a gas turbine, but some of the mechanical problems are more severe. An annular combustion chamber is shown in perspective in the cutaway drawing of the engine in Fig. 114. The general principles followed in the can-type burner are also used in designing annular combustors. Primary air is admitted around the fuel nozzles; the fuel is burned under conditions of high flame turbulence, and secondary air is admitted through holes, slots, or louvers in the inner burner walls. A section of a simplified annular flow burner is shown in Fig. 115, and a

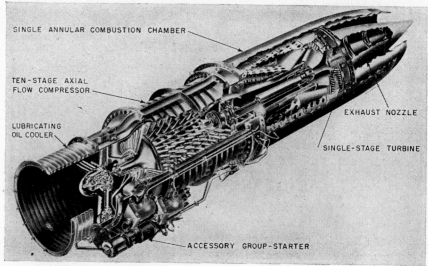

FIG. 114. Westinghouse 19XB jet engine with annular burner. Rated thrust, 1,600 lb ssl; weight, 718 lb.

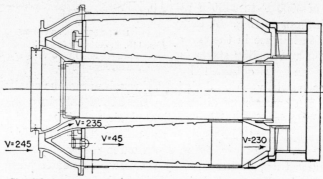

FIG. 115. Simplified axial-flow annular burner with typical gas flow velocities indicated (fps).

photograph of a typical perforated burner basket or flame tube is shown in Fig. 116. Other constructions are indicated in Fig. 117. An annular-type burner can be segmented into several parts if desired; it then approaches the can-type-burner design.

The sizes and locations of air entrance holes in the fire tube or partition separating combustion space from the outer flow passages control the degree of turbulence in the flame and the completeness of mixing of secondary air with primary air. Although nonuniformity of temperature distribution may have only small effect upon cycle efficiency, it is essential that good mixing be obtained in order to avoid undesirable stratification in the gas flow entering the turbine blading. Excessive stratification can result in local hot spots in which permissible temperature limits may be exceeded by several hundred degrees. Variations of ±5 percent of the average temperature are usual.

Fig. 116. Perforated burner basket for annular combustion chamber. (*Westinghouse Electric Corporation.*)

However, it is sometimes profitable to employ stratification in order to graduate the temperature along the length of a turbine blade so as to subject the most highly stressed portions of the blade to lower than average temperatures. An annular sheath of cold air flowing into the rotating turbine blading at the height of the blade roots can be achieved fairly readily with the annular type of combustion chamber, and with more difficulty in can-type combustors. Practically, it may make it possible to run a turbine at a somewhat higher average gas temperature than would be possible without stratification.

Several radial temperature-distribution curves across the entrance to the first row of stationary turbine blading downstream from the burner are shown in Fig. 118; these are for different burner temperatures in an annular combustion chamber in which no particular effort has been made to produce cooling at the blade roots.

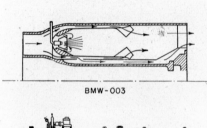

PERFORATED BASKET TYPE

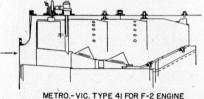

BMW-003

METRO.-VIC. TYPE 41 FOR F-2 ENGINE

FIG. 117. Typical annular combustion chambers.

Peripheral variations in temperature in an engine are due to faulty fuel-nozzle matching, airflow unbalance, boiling of fuel, and combustion-efficiency variations. Fuel-nozzle balance is affected by mechanical similarity of parts, unequal wear in operation, dirt in fuel lines, and "gravity head" across the engine. Gravity head is the fuel-manifold pressure unbalance between upper and lower fuel nozzles resulting from the column of fuel standing in the manifold corresponding to the diameter of the engine; the effect is negligible except at very low manifold pressures.

Of equal importance with design features that will ensure proper combustion and mixing of primary and secondary flows, are the problems of designing for long life. High temperatures and thermal expansion problems are sufficiently extreme to limit combustor life to only a few hours under unfavorable conditions and with indifferent designs. There are only a few general principles that can be laid down to guide the designer. The best obtainable refractory alloys that can be fabricated into the required shapes should be used; thermal expansions should be offered the least possible restraint, and flat or single curved areas of sheet

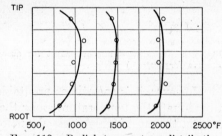

FIG. 118. Radial temperature distribution before turbine nozzle inlet ring for several average temperatures.

metal should not be left unsupported for distances of more than a few inches. Numerous welded or formed ribs and supports are necessary to avoid buckling of flat or single curved sheets. Cooling with secondary air of all metal parts in direct contact with the flame is essential. Since gas velocities in the combustor are generally low, the obstructions presented by generous reinforcing and ribbing of the flame tube or burner basket are not particularly objectionable from an aerodynamic standpoint, and they aid in maintaining turbulence. If laminar flows of cold air can be induced adjacent to the fire-tube or burner-basket walls, very effective cooling is obtained. This construction is shown in Fig. 119 for a can-type-combustor flame tube; the tube is made in several successive sizes of telescoping tubes with flow spaces between the tubes at the joints.

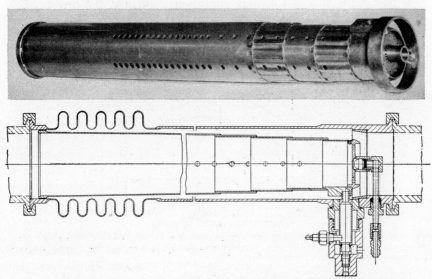

Fig. 119. Can-type burner with laminar-flow cooling of flame tube. (*Westinghouse Electric Corporation.*)

Common materials for use in burners include the stainless steels, Inconel, and special refractory alloys related to turbine disc and blade alloys. For some military applications, jet engines and gas turbines may be required to operate on the same fuel that is provided for reciprocating engines, and it is then important that combustor materials be selected that are not subject to intercrystalline corrosion and embrittlement in the presence of leaded fuels.

23. Spray Nozzles. Fuel is usually sprayed into the combustion space under pressure through small orifices in nozzles. An early type was the British-designed Lubbock nozzle, which contains within the nozzle itself a spring-loaded reducing valve to increase manifold pressures effectively at minimum flow without materially increasing pressures at maximum flow. Because of persistent difficulties with dirt getting through filters and sticking the piston valves, with the attendant serious unbalance of flow distribution to the separate nozzles, a simple vortex-tip nozzle of the Monarch type supplanted the Lubbock nozzle. The penalty of poor performance at low fuel-flow rates with the Monarch nozzle was less serious than the production and operating difficulties incident to the use of the Lubbock nozzle.

Fine sprays are not produced with the Monarch nozzle until about 20 percent of the maximum flow is obtained, with about 300 psi manifold pressure for maximum flow. Since required fuel flows may vary over a range of 40 to 1 from sea level to high altitudes and from idling to acceleration flow rates, this is a serious limitation. Further, the pressure-flow characteristic of the Monarch nozzle is parabolic, whereas for simple control, a straight-line characteristic is desired.

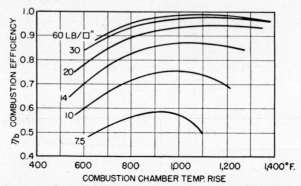

Fig. 120. Combustion efficiency of can-type burner with simple swirl-type spray nozzle. Pressures indicated are absolute combustion-chamber pressures, not nozzle delivery pressures. (*General Electric Company.*)

Starting combustion with coarse fuel sprays requires an excess of fuel, and with direct-driven fuel pumps running at low starting speeds, auxiliary starter pumps or accumulators may be necessary. The combustion efficiency suffers at low rates of fuel delivery through simple vortex nozzles owing to poor fuel atomization, so that a 10 percent drop in combustion efficiency is not uncommon when the fuel flow is 25 percent of the maximum rate. High-altitude operations may be handicapped somewhat, particularly under partial load conditions. The combustion efficiency of a single can-type burner is shown in Fig. 120 for a Monarch nozzle burning kerosene at different rates and different combustion-chamber pressures.

The duplex nozzle system was developed to improve on the low-flow characteristics of the simple vortex nozzle. This nozzle requires two fuel manifolds and contains two separate sets of internal jets in its vortex tip. The smaller set of these jets is connected directly to the fuel supply from the throttle and is used alone under starting and low-fuel-flow operation

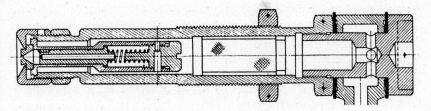

SECTIONAL VIEW OF LUBBOCK NOZZLE

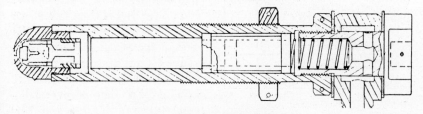

SECTIONAL VIEW OF MONARCH NOZZLE

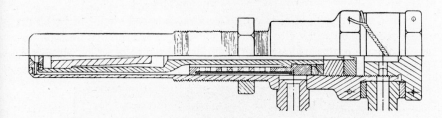

SECTIONAL VIEW OF DUPLEX NOZZLE

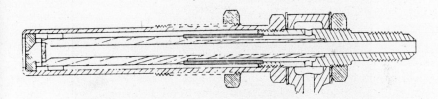

SECTIONAL VIEW OF PEABODY NOZZLE

FIG. 121. Details of different types of fuel spray nozzles. (*General Electric Company.*)

conditions. As fuel requirements increase, the larger set of jets is supplied through a metering valve or splitter valve, which opens as the manifold pressure rises to furnish the additional flow required by the larger slots. Fine sprays are produced at 5 percent of the maximum flow in nozzles designed for maximum flow at 300 psi manifold pressure. Completely interchangeable nozzles with flows matched at low and high rates are difficult to manufacture and require very complete filtering of the fuel supply to the fine jets, but the improvements in performance are generally worth the additional difficulties.

A still further development is the Peabody or recirculating type of

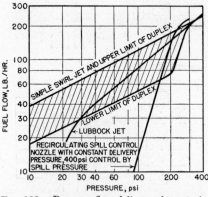

nozzle. The vortex tip is supplied with the full output of the pump so that sufficient pressure drop and swirl velocity are always maintained in the nozzle-tip vortex chamber to ensure a fine spray. The excess fuel is then taken out of the vortex chamber through the back of the nozzle, after which it is subject to the customary governor by-pass control. Figure 121 shows cross sections of several different types of nozzles, and Fig. 122 shows their pressure-flow delivery characteristics.

Fig. 122. Pressure-flow delivery characteristics of nozzles of Fig. 121. (*P. Lloyd, Proc. IME, vol.* 153, *pp.* 409–512, 1945.)

Still another type of nozzle utilizes a compressed-air jet to break up a low-pressure oil spray into a fine mist. Figure 123 shows a flash photograph of such a nozzle along with a simple swirl-type or Monarch nozzle, both under 20 psi fuel pressure. Figure 124 shows the same nozzles under

Fig. 123. Upper spray from air atomizing nozzle, lower from simple swirl-type nozzle. Fuel delivery pressure 20 psi in each case. (*Westinghouse Electric Corporation.*)

5 psi fuel pressure. The complete inadequacy of the simple swirl jet nozzle at very low pressures is evident from these two examples; at higher pressures, the Monarch-nozzle spray is satisfactory and resembles the spray from the air nozzle. While the air nozzle has a very wide range of

flow delivery with satisfactory atomization of even heavy fuel oils, the added complication of a high-pressure air supply has kept it from being applied to aircraft turbines, although it is used with other types of gas turbines.

Preheating the fuel ahead of the spray nozzles as a means of improving atomization and vaporization in the spray is very attractive. But the amount of heat that can be added by this means, even up to the limitation of coking the fuel, is small. Low nozzle pressure at low flow rates is a further limitation on this method, since boiling and vaporization ahead of the nozzle can occur at low pressures.

Fig. 124. Upper spray from air atomizing nozzle, lower from simple swirl-type nozzle. Fuel delivery pressure 5 psi in each case. (*Westinghouse Electric Corporation.*)

Heat is added to the fuel after it leaves the spray nozzle by radiation from the flame body, by injecting part of the spray into and through portions of the flame body, and by spray impingement against hot walls. Partial enclosure of the nozzle in a hot cup appears to aid fuel vaporizing even with coarse sprays. The action is similar to that obtained in a gasoline blowtorch. A successful British burner utilizes a very low pressure spray in a hot cup. Direct impingement of fuel on metal surfaces may result in high rates of cooling, so that keeping the metal hot, rather than cool, is the problem. Heat-transfer rates between the cold liquid and the metal are much higher than between hot gases and the metal. Cup wall temperatures tend to decrease with increased rates of fuel flow. Fuel vapor and fog leave the cup walls by evaporation and bouncing of spray droplets from the heated surfaces; this fog must be dispersed through the air charge to ensure complete combustion, and primary air is introduced around the nozzle for this purpose. Almost all combustion chambers have more or less spray impingement on the parts around the nozzles,

and on the fire-tube or burner shell. Largely as a result of spray impingement on metal surfaces, many burners may have slight amounts of liquid
fuel present in the breech. This condition is probably beneficial where
the wet areas are adjacent to hot wall areas.

Turbulence in the burner and diffusion of fuel are promoted by air
currents induced by the fuel spray, air currents through holes in the burner
structure, by spiral whirls inside the burner tube, and by eddies around
baffles. Frequently a construction that yields excellent results at maximum fuel flow is quite unsuitable for starting and low-power operations.
The fuel spray must be shielded from high-velocity air streams near the
nozzle, particularly in the case of small flames associated with low fuel
flows. A graduated air delivery through the inner burner shell is generally desirable, with low air velocities at the nozzle or breech end of the
burner. Air velocities of about 15 fps around the nozzle are gradually
increased to 200 to 300 fps through holes well downstream from the
spray nozzles; the maximum velocities correspond to pressure differentials
across the perforated burner shell of the order of 1 psi.

24. Combustion Range of Burners. A spark plug is the usual ignition
means in aircraft-gas-turbine engines. Continuous ignition by means of a
spark or pilot flame is not ordinarily necessary in a burner with stable
combustion. When conditions are suitable for rapid flame movement or
propagation, only the initial ignition is necessary, and the combustion
then maintains itself until some abnormal condition results in blowout.
When can-type combustors are used, each section is not ordinarily supplied with a spark plug; only a few burners have spark plugs, and the
remainder are ignited through connecting cross-ignition tubes between
adjacent sections. Nozzle spray angles must place combustible mixtures
at the spark plug under starting conditions without overheating at maximum combustion rates. Ignition in well-designed burners has been
obtained with over-all fuel/air ratios as low as 0.002 at starting; the ratio
in the primary flame zone is, of course, much higher. The type of liquid
fuel used does not appear to be a large factor so far as ignition is concerned,
if atomization is thorough.

The combustion range of a combustion chamber is the heat-release
range in terms of maximum and minimum temperature rises that the
burner will produce, at a reasonable combustion efficiency for the required
range of compressor discharge pressures and temperatures. The maximum capacity of a combustion chamber at a given pressure is reached
when pulsation or roughness of burning occurs, when combustion efficiency drops sharply, or when blowout is encountered. The limitations
on minimum heat release are combustion efficiency and blowout or loss
of the flame. Flame volume diminishes as the fuel/air ratio is decreased,

and finally the small flame will "fray out" at the edges with incomplete combustion occurring and possibly complete blowout. Flames from fuels already well vaporized before introduction into the actual combustion zone burn with a clear blue flame. Yellow "greasy" flames seem to be more stable than white or blue ones in simple forms of burners, although blue flames give freedom from carbon deposits and emit less radiation to flame-tube walls. A larger body or volume of flame improves stability, and higher temperature of the primary air entering the burner aids stable combustion.

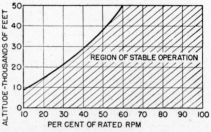

In gas-turbine burners, increasing the rate of fuel flow simply results in a greater volume of flame, the length of the flame increasing until sufficient air is encountered to complete the combustion. With abnormally high fuel flows, the maximum temperature limits of the burner may be exceeded, and flames may even reach through the turbine wheel.

FIG. 125. Zone of satisfactory engine operation and line of marginal burner operation for jet engine with can-type burners and Monarch-type nozzles.

One jet engine with can-type combustion chambers and simple swirl-type spray nozzles runs with stable burner operation at 10 percent of rated rpm at 10,000 ft altitude and at 60 percent of rated rpm at 50,000 ft altitude; or in terms of jet thrust, with 2 percent of its rated thrust at 10,000 ft and 18 percent of rated thrust at 50,000 ft. If the engine is throttled slowly below a line connecting these two points (see Fig. 125), some of the burners will cease to operate, and the engine cannot be accelerated without supplying a considerable excess of fuel during the early stages of the acceleration and reignition period. It is desirable from an operation standpoint to reduce the lower limits of stable burning still further.

An upper limit on temperature rise, or rate of fuel burning, in a given combustion chamber may be imposed by the low velocity of flame propagation in rich fuel-air mixtures. If the rate of fuel injection is sufficiently high, flame propagation rates will fall below the gas stream velocity in the burner, and the flame will then be unable to burn back toward the nozzle. Unstable burning will occur, and the flame may be completely blown out of the burner. This is most likely to occur under high-altitude conditions when rapid engine acceleration requirements call for transient combustion rates and temperatures well in excess of steady-state rates; too sudden opening of the throttle floods the combustion chamber, and the engine has to be restarted.

Compressor surging under acceleration conditions, especially at high altitudes, will impose pressure transients upon the combustion process that may also result in blowout, in addition to difficulties with too-lean and too-rich mixtures. Unstable burning and surging of the above types indicate incipient blowout and are aperiodic in character. Pulsations are most frequently encountered with rich fuel/air ratios and are first evidenced by a dirty exhaust with sooty puffs and sometimes by rumbling noises from the engine.

Sustained or periodic pulsations can also occur, and are believed to be connected with the manner of burning in the primary flame region and the resonance characteristics of the engine. Pulsations between 25 and 60 cps have been observed as well as pulsations between 250 and 600 cps; they are sufficiently vigorous to affect combustion efficiency and could cause mechanical fatigue. Changes in the fuel nozzles and primary combustion zone of the burner eliminate them. Still another type of pressure oscillation has been observed in the 6,000-cps frequency region; it has been observed on tests of a single can-type combustion chamber alone, and also in complete engines.

Carbon deposits can occur in combustion chambers, with increasing deposition rates the heavier the fuel used. Deposits are of two types; one is a very hard "gas" carbon formed in the primary zone, which is capable of building up to the point of blocking flow passages. The other is a soft sooty variety formed in the cooler part of the flame tube; it is easily blown or scrubbed off by gas flows at higher loads and does not build up to a dangerous extent.

Sooty carbon deposits may form on flame-tube surfaces and build up at a fairly high initial rate, perhaps 0.005 percent by weight of the fuel burned, for 30 min or more, and beyond that time may be blown off as fast as formed.

The possibility of pieces of carbon breaking off and damaging turbine blades is also present when hard carbon is formed, or if heavy deposits of soft carbon are present. Solid carbon may also form and be blown through without depositing, causing a dirty exhaust, although the effect on efficiency is negligible.

Usually, carbon formation is most serious with the heavier fuels at rich mixtures and low engine speeds, when turbulence is at a minimum. The aromatic constituents of the fuel, the presence of sulfur, and a large amount of high-boiling fractions are the three principal characteristics of fuels that tend to increase coking.

25. Combustion-space Pressure Losses. The flow of air through a combustion chamber is accompanied by losses that influence the effectiveness and efficiency of the gas-turbine cycle to a marked extent.

Losses can be divided into two types: friction loss and a total pressure-head change associated with momentum changes due to heating.

Friction losses occur as a result of turbulence in the gas flow and viscous friction losses in flow passages.[1] The principal pressure drop occurs across the openings through the fire tube or burner basket in the combustion chamber proper. Friction losses may be measured with cold air flowing through a combustion chamber, and the results can then be translated to the flow conditions during combustion without excessive errors appearing. Friction losses and losses appearing in ducts or passages entering and leaving a combustion chamber are not properly charged to the combustion process, but are commonly included in the pressure-drop figures for combustion chambers. Since a loss in total pressure across the combustion chamber is as serious as an equivalent reduction in compressor efficiency, it is essential that minimum pressure drops be designed for. Low-velocity flow passages with maximum cross-sectional area, no abrupt turns or changes in section, and as few internal obstructions as are compatible with efficient combustion result in minimum losses due to flow friction. A typical velocity survey through a can-type combustor is shown in Fig. 113, and a similar survey through an annular burner appears in Fig. 115.

Momentum pressure drops through a heating passage occur as a result of velocity and volume changes due to heating of the fluid. An exact solution for the theoretical momentum pressure drop is not ordinarily required when Mach numbers in the heating section are less than 0.2 or 0.3. An approximate solution was derived in Chap. 3 for a heating passage of uniform cross section with uniform mass flow and with the mass of the fuel addition neglected in Eq. (72).

$$\frac{\Delta P}{P_3} = \frac{kM_3^2}{2}\left(\frac{T_4}{T_3} - 1\right)$$

The pressure loss calculated by this method is somewhat lower than the correct theoretical loss.

For high Mach numbers in the portion of the combustion space where heat is actually added, a more exact solution taking into full account the compressibility effects in the gas flow is Eq. (85). A graphical solution for $\Delta P/P_3$ is given in Fig. 126.

The preceding heating processes are reversible (neglecting, for the moment, frictional and mixing losses), satisfying the fundamental relation $dq = du + p\,dv$, so that the entire process is reversible. The addition of fuel at the upstream end of the combustor followed by the cooling of the combustion products of the primary flame can then be treated

[1] See *NACA Technical Note* 1,180, February, 1947.

simply in terms of entrance and exit conditions in the idealized burner, rather than from the standpoint of two separate processes, which would take into account the extremely high temperature of the primary flame. The quantity T_3 is therefore total temperature of the entering air, and T_4 is the total temperature of the leaving air, without regard to intermediate heating and cooling processes.

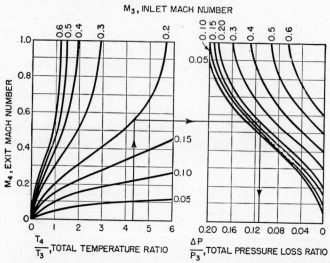

Fig. 126.   Exact graphical solution for total-pressure-loss ratio across heating duct of uniform section in terms of total temperature ratio and inlet Mach number.

Solutions can be derived for burners of variable cross section. A simplified expression for the ratio of total pressure loss to inlet total pressure in a combustion zone with inlet area A_3 and exit area A_4 is

$$\frac{\Delta P}{P_3} = \frac{kM_3^2}{2}\left(\frac{T_4}{T_3}\frac{A_3}{A_4} - 1\right) \tag{155}$$

From the foregoing, it is evident that burners with low pressure drops are burners with low gas velocities. The greatest cross-sectional areas possible at all stages are desirable and lead directly to the lowest pressure drops.

It is sufficiently accurate for estimating purposes to assume that a friction loss section of the burner precedes the heating section, which is assumed to be friction-free. A friction pressure loss ΔP_f can occur without changing the total temperature of the gas from T_3; so that the entrance condition at the heating section in this hypothetical burner must be corrected to a total pressure of $P_3 - \Delta P_f$. With the original assumption of a low entrance Mach number, the total-pressure-drop ratio including friction and momentum losses would approximate

$$\frac{\Delta P}{P_3} = \frac{\Delta P_f}{P_3} + \left(1 - \frac{\Delta P_f}{P_3}\right) \times \frac{kM_3^2}{2}\left(\frac{T_4}{T_3} - 1\right) \qquad (156)$$

Momentum pressure drops in gas-turbine combustion chambers range from about 0.2 percent at full load with 1500°F outlet temperature and 60 fps inlet velocity to 2 percent drop under the same conditions but with 200 fps inlet velocity. The momentum pressure loss is normally of

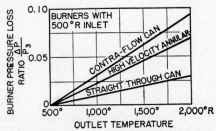

FIG. 127. Fractional total pressure loss vs. burner outlet temperature in various types of gas-turbine combustors.

the order of one-third of the total loss in combustion chambers filled with the usual assortment of perforated flame tubes, swirl nozzles, baffles, etc., the remaining two-thirds being accounted for by friction losses. Total pressure drops in combustion chambers for gas turbines range from 0.5 percent to as much as 7 or 8 percent when high drops have to be accepted in order to achieve a compact burner. Pressure-drop ratios for some typical burners are shown in Fig. 127; the contraflow can type shows the greatest loss in total pressure, most of which is friction loss. The low-velocity, straight-through can-type burner, exemplified by the Lucas-designed Rolls Royce-Derwent combustion chamber, shows the lowest drop; the high-velocity annular burner operates at a high pressure-drop ratio, but this ratio decreases rapidly when the inlet design Mach number is reduced.

CHAPTER 6

TURBINES AND THEIR CHARACTERISTICS

26. General Factors in Turbine Design. Turbines designed for use in aircraft jet engines and turboprop engines are different from those used in other gas-turbine applications, and are greatly different from most steam turbines. In general, steam turbines work through very large pressure or expansion ratios compared to aircraft turbines. In the case of a high-pressure, condensing steam turbine, the pressure ratio between inlet and outlet may be as high as 1,000:1, whereas the aircraft turbine seldom exceeds an 8:1 ratio and is more commonly 2:1 or 3:1. The other principal difference appears in the magnitude of the so-called leaving loss or velocity energy of the turbine exhaust; the steam turbine and gas turbines for land and marine applications are designed for minimum residual energy in the final exhaust. They employ exhaust diffusers and many turbine stages to obtain the maximum possible expansion and energy extraction from the working fluid. The exhaust of the aircraft gas turbine, on the other hand, yields useful jet-propulsive thrust and is an efficient means of obtaining thrust power when the exhaust velocity is selected properly with respect to flight speed. As a matter of fact, a very low exhaust velocity in a turboprop turbine is evidence of poor design, since the engine will be heavier than need be; the excess exhaust energy thus converted to shaft energy in the turbine must be reconverted to propulsive energy through the means of a larger propeller, and the over-all propulsive efficiency of the complete power plant may suffer.

The efficiency of the turbine element of an aircraft gas turbine is not, therefore, defined like the efficiency of other turbines. It is not the ratio of shaft energy to total available energy in the working fluid above the *static* exhaust pressure, but the efficiency is defined as the ratio of shaft energy to available energy in the working fluid above the *total* exhaust pressure. In other words, the available energy is considered to be only the ideal energy in isentropic expansion from the inlet total pressure to the exhaust total pressure, without regard to the remaining velocity energy in the leaving fluid. The exhaust-velocity energy is thus not charged against the turbine because it is utilized for jet thrust as such. The work output of the turbine is then

$$h_t = h_4 - h_5 = c_p T_4 \eta_t \left[1 - \left(\frac{P_5}{P_4} \right)^{\frac{k-1}{k}} \right] \qquad \text{Btu/lb} \qquad (157)$$

156

The temperature of the exhaust is

$$T_5 = T_4 - \frac{h_t}{c_p} = T_4 \left\{ 1 - \eta_t \left[1 - \left(\frac{P_5}{P_4} \right)^{\frac{k-1}{k}} \right] \right\} \tag{158}$$

and the turbine efficiency in terms of pressure ratio and temperature is

$$\eta_t = \frac{1 - (T_5/T_4)}{1 - (P_5/P_4)^{\frac{k-1}{k}}} \tag{159}$$

As in the case of the compressor, it is difficult to measure T_5 with accuracy, and it is even more difficult to measure the higher T_4. Nonuniformity also is a real difficulty in obtaining representative values. Measured T_4 values may tend to be too low. Therefore, turbine efficiency by temperature ratio may be lower than the actual shaft efficiency, the opposite of the effect for compressors. This is not too unfortunate a circumstance, since although the exact performances of turbine and compressor may not be known accurately from temperature measurements, the two errors tend to cancel out, and the product of $\eta_c \eta_t$ for the complete engine is very near the correct value. As used in cycle calculations, the accuracy of the product $\eta_c \eta_t$ is of greater importance than individual minor variations in η_c and η_t, which compensate for each other.

The small pressure ratios ordinarily encountered across aircraft gas turbines result in enthalpy differences across blade paths that are almost invariably smaller than enthalpy differences across blade paths in steam turbines. Therefore, there is much less turning of the fluid flow than in steam turbines (except for topping turbines and high-pressure units of compound steam turbines). The range of blade heights from inlet to outlet is similarly decreased, owing to the much lower expansion ratio; and many aircraft turbine blades bear very close resemblances to conventional airfoil shapes.

The compressible-fluid dynamics that controls the design of axial-flow compressors applies with equal force to the turbine, with the exception that in the turbine the flow is expanding. Higher efficiencies may therefore be achieved in very short expanding-flow passages than are possible in the retarded-flow passages of compressors. A given expansion may be accomplished easily in a single turbine stage with greater efficiency than for the equivalent compression in 5 to 10 or more axial-flow-compressor stages. Flow separation and boundary-layer thickening, as they exist in compressor-blade paths, do not appear in the average turbine-blade-path flow. Mach-number limitations and the prevention of shock formation define the maximum limits on energy conversion per turbine stage. Blade design refinements are not nearly so important in turbines as in compressors, although this does not mean that principles of efficient airflow may be abandoned without serious reductions in efficiency.

27. Blade-path Design. Blade paths may be designed as either predominantly impulse or predominantly reaction, with considerable variation in type from hub to tip. As in the case of the axial-flow compressor, maximum work per stage is obtained from the symmetrical or 50 percent reaction–50 percent impulse type, if gas flow velocity is limited to approximately $M = 1$. Similarly, for a given pressure ratio per stage, the symmetric design is theoretically the most efficient. The actual choice is controlled by the past experience and practices of the designer and the peculiarities and limitations of the compressor and combustion chamber ahead of the turbine.

If the compressor is a centrifugal type with relatively large impeller diameter and low shaft speed for the volume of air inducted, and if it is followed by a group of can-type burners that meet most naturally in a turbine nozzle ring of large diameter, then a nonsymmetric turbine design may be indicated—usually impulse with less than 20 percent reaction. The same factors apply to low-speed nonsymmetric axial-flow compressors with low rates of axial flow velocity and relatively large diameters.

On the other hand, if the compressor is a symmetric axial-flow design with high volumetric flow rate, small diameter, and high shaft speed followed by an annular burner of the same general outside diameter, it may be necessary to use a symmetric turbine-blade-path design in order to get the required amount of work out of the fluid flow without resorting to additional turbine stages. In the final analysis, however, turbine size is generally dictated by the upper limit on exit velocity and the annulus area required to pass the exhaust at that velocity and exit pressure.

British and Continental design practices have leaned toward the impulse-type turbine design, although there are notable exceptions to this generalization. Designers in the United States frequently use 50 percent reaction or symmetric blading for axial-flow-compressor engines.

Impulse blading has one positive advantage in that the absolute velocity of the gas leaving the stationary nozzle ring is higher than for a reaction stage of the same pressure ratio. This high nozzle exit flow velocity or efflux velocity results in a lower static temperature of the gas stream. Partial stagnation of laminar flows near the rotating-blade surfaces restores a part of this temperature drop, but the impulse-bladed turbine usually is working in a cooler environment than would reaction blading. Since a difference in actual blade temperature of only 50 or 100°F may mean the difference between satisfactory and completely unsatisfactory blade life, this is important. It may be desirable to use impulse blading in the first stage of a multistage turbine, followed by the more efficient reaction blading in succeeding stages.

The general subject of turbine design has been thoroughly documented in years past, and the following paragraphs will point out only the over-all factors and the differences from steam-turbine design peculiar to gas turbines. It should be observed that the notation herein follows that used for axial-flow compressors rather than that customary for steam turbines; *e.g.*, flow angles in steam turbines are customarily measured relative to

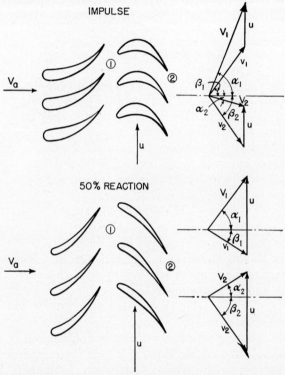

Fig. 128.   Blade shapes and velocity triangles for gas-turbine impulse and reaction blading.

the plane of rotation of moving-blade rows, but here we shall measure flow angles relative to the axis of rotation or a line normal to the plane of rotation. This is contrary to the practice of most turbine designers who have received their training in steam, but the authors believe that a little consistency in the aircraft-gas-turbine field may eventually do more good than harm.

Velocity triangles and typical blade shapes for impulse and reaction blading as used in aircraft turbines are shown in Fig. 128. Absolute velocities are shown as V_a, V_1, and V_2, where V_a is the flow velocity entering the nozzle ring and is usually axial, V_1 is the flow after leaving the nozzle ring or stationary-blade row, and V_2 is the velocity of the gas leaving the rotating-blade row. The peripheral velocity of the moving-blade row is u, and velocities relative to entering and trailing edges of the same blades are v_1 and v_2, respectively. The nozzle efflux angle α_1 and the entrance angle β_1 relative to the moving-blade row are measured from the axis of the rotor; this is contrary to conventional steam practice, which would measure these angles from the plane of rotation of the moving-blade row, as pointed out in the preceding paragraph.

Another factor useful in turbine design work is the actual velocity ratio

$$\frac{u}{V_1} = \sin \alpha_1 - \cos \alpha_1 \tan \beta_1 \tag{160}$$

where the sign of $\tan \beta_1$ must be observed and is negative if the deflection is in the opposite sense to α_1. The ratio u/V_1 is normally in the range of 0.3 to 0.5 for very high impulse blade paths, and may be found between 0.7 and 1.5, say, for symmetric paths.

If the axial velocity of the gas flow does not change in passing through the moving-blade row, the energy extracted from the gas is proportional to the decrease in whirl velocity between entrance and exit.

$$\Delta h = \frac{u}{gJ} (V_1 \sin \alpha_1 - V_2 \sin \alpha_2) \tag{161}$$

A common limitation encountered in aircraft turbines is the velocity of the gas flow leaving the first row of nozzle blades. Because velocities exceeding Mach 1.0 require a convergent-divergent flow passage, and because shock and excessive losses begin to appear soon after $M > 1.0$, the mean flow velocity leaving the nozzle ring is usually sonic or slightly above sonic velocity at maximum flow.

The nozzle spouting or efflux velocity is not necessarily constant at all radial distances in a nozzle blade ring. It varies with design, but is universally greatest at the inner radius, corresponding to the turbine wheel hub.

In order to avoid radial flows of gas in blade passages, blade-row designs may strive for constant angular momentum and constant axial velocity. This means that the swirl, or whirl, component of velocity multiplied by the radius is constant, and centrifugal forces arising from the whirl velocity are just sufficient to balance the radial static pressure gradient. Designs that result in constant mass flow per unit area of cross section result in zero radial flow. When the axial component of velocity is constant and the flow has constant angular momentum, the flow is known as a free-vortex or constant-circulation flow, as employed in many axial-flow compressors. If the axial flow velocity varies with change in radial position, the constant angular momentum is maintained, but the flow is then known as forced-vortex flow. In the following brief discussions, free-vortex or constant-circulation flow is assumed.

The mass flow through the nozzle inlet ring is dependent upon the radial distribution of flow Mach number and the efflux angles along the blade. The product of the radial distance r and the whirl component of velocity V_{1u}, to use the same nomenclature as in the axial-compressor case, is a constant for free vortex flow.

$$\Omega = rV_{1u} = \text{strength of vortex} = \text{constant} \tag{162}$$

V_{1u} is equal to $V_1 \sin \alpha_1$, and since the axial flow velocity V_{1a} is constant and is equal to $V_1 \cos \alpha_1$,

$$\frac{rV_1 \sin \alpha_1}{V_1 \cos \alpha_1} = r \tan \alpha_1 = \text{constant} \tag{163}$$

If the Mach number of the leaving flow relative to the stationary nozzle blades is calculated in terms of a free-vortex flow

$$M_1^2 = \frac{1}{\dfrac{gkRT_4}{V_{1a}^2 + (\Omega^2/r^2)} - \dfrac{k-1}{2}} \tag{164}$$

where Ω is rV_{1u}, the vorticity or strength of the vortex, and is constant

$$V_{1a}^2 + \frac{\Omega^2}{r^2} = V_1^2$$

The mass flow through a unit area at flow Mach number M_1 is expressed in terms of total pressure and total temperature as

$$\frac{W_a}{A} = \frac{P_4}{RT_4} V_{1a} \left(1 + \frac{k-1}{.2} M_1^2\right)^{\frac{1}{1-k}}$$

Substituting the value of M_1^2 from Eq. (164) and rewriting as a differential equation for flow through a ring at radius r and width dr,

$$dW_a = \frac{P_4}{RT_4} V_{1a} \left[1 - \frac{k-1}{2} \frac{V_{1a}^2 + (\Omega^2/r^2)}{gkRT_4}\right]^{\frac{1}{k-1}} 2\pi r\, dr \tag{165}$$

This expression cannot be integrated exactly except in a few special cases, but if the range of M_1 over which the flow is integrated is restricted to 0.5 to 1.2, then the following approximation is correct to within 1 percent for all values of k between 1.3 and 1.4:

$$dW_a = \frac{P_4}{RT_4} V_{1a} \left(0.96 - 0.38 \frac{V_{1a}^2 + (\Omega^2/r^2)}{gkRT_4}\right) 2\pi r\, dr \tag{166}$$

Equation (166) can be integrated, and the total mass flow through the nozzle ring to a very close approximation is then

$$W_a = \frac{P_4}{RT_4} V_{1a}(r_t^2 - r_h^2) \left[0.96 - \frac{0.38}{gkRT_4} \left(V_{1a}^2 + \frac{\Omega^2}{r_t^2 - r_h^2} \log \frac{r_t^2}{r_h^2} \right) \right] \quad (167)$$

where r_t is the radius at the outer diameter of the nozzle ring, r_h is the radius at the hub, and the variation in flow Mach number from hub to blade tip stays within the limits 0.5 to 1.2.

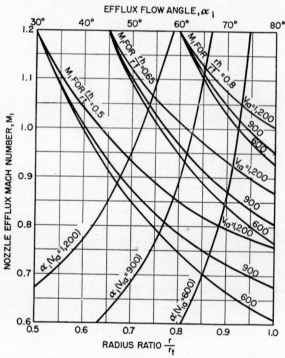

FIG. 129.   Nozzle efflux Mach number and angle vs. blade/tip radius ratio for different axial flow velocities and hub/tip ratios.

Variations in nozzle efflux Mach number from hub to tip are plotted against the radius/tip ratio in Fig. 129 for three different nozzle rings at three axial flow velocities at $T_4 = 2000°R$.   The corresponding curves for efflux angle α_1 are also shown plotted against flow Mach number. The data was calculated from Eq. (164).   The significant point to note is that M_1 is much more dependent upon the value of Ω or strength of the vortex than upon the axial flow velocity V_{1a}.   Also, for a limiting value of M_1, the diameter of the turbine wheel at the hub or blade roots is approximately proportional to the vorticity Ω.   The strength of the vortex flow is therefore connected directly to the physical size of the turbine; the limiting factor is the tangential or peripheral component of flow velocity V_{1u} at the hub.

If the quantity Ω in Eq. (167) is replaced by its equivalent, $r_h V_{1uh}$, then it is possible to plot the mass flow per unit area of nozzle ring, $W_a / \pi (r_t^2 - r_h^2)$ in terms of two parameters V_{1a} and V_{1uh}, where V_{1uh} is the tangential velocity of flow at the hub. Going further, $\tan \alpha_{1h} = V_{1uh}/V_{1a}$, and the unit flow is plotted against the ratio r_h/r_t in Fig. 130 for representative values of V_{1a} and of α_{1h} at the hub or blade roots. It should be

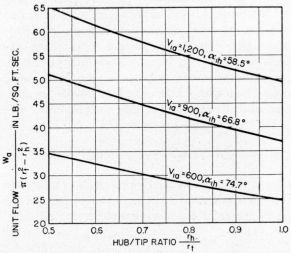

Fig. 130. Mass air flow per unit area of nozzle ring vs. hub/tip ratio at various axial flow velocities.

noted that the ratio r_h/r_t is not the same as the ratio r/r_t in Fig. 129. Values of unit flow extend from reaction-turbine data at lower values of α_1 to impulse turbines at the highest values of α_1. The pressure condition for which the data of Fig. 130 are plotted is $P_4 = 4 \times 14.7 = 58.8$ psi or 8,467 psf, and $T_4 = 2000°R$. The values of α_1 used in the curves of Fig. 130 are selected so that the flow Mach number at the blade roots, M_1, equals 1.2; this is very close to a practical limit for flow velocity in that region. V_{1a} is preserved as an identity in the data because, in general, this velocity is not greatly changed in the flow through a single-stage turbine or some 2-stage turbines, and therefore it is usually close to the leaving velocity of the turbine exhaust. If V_{1a} is multiplied by the correction factor $\sqrt{\theta}$, then the nondimensional correction δ/θ may also be applied to the unit flow.

Equation (167) may be used to calculate flow between any pair of blade rows if the flow is free vortex and V_{1a} and α_{1h} are known. The evidence here points to the desirability, from a mass-flow standpoint, of using turbines with tall blades and a small hub/tip ratio. A greater mass flow is thereby handled through a given annulus area, and a smaller proportion of the flow is at high flow Mach number near the blade roots; also blade tip leakage is less serious. However, tall blades mean high blade and disc stresses, and the blade tips may be too widely pitched for high efficiency at the required flow turning angle.

28. Impulse Turbines. Impulse turbines expand the gas flow fully in the nozzle ring. The gas then issues from the nozzle-blade row at high velocity and at the same static pressure that exists on the downstream side of the rotor. It passes through the rotor in flow passages of substantially constant area, with entering angle relative to the rotor blading approximately equal to the leaving angle on the other side of the rotor. Since in a 100 percent impulse rotor, the gas flow undergoes no further expansion in the rotor flow passages, the forces may be calculated from the velocity triangles. Assuming that flow entry angles match the blade angles at all blade radii and speeds, the conventional expression for rim power of the turbine wheel is similar to Eq. (161) and is

$$E = \frac{W_a u}{g} (V_1 \sin \alpha_1 - V_2 \sin \alpha_2) \qquad \text{ft-lb/sec} \qquad (168)$$

Again, the sign of the angle α_2 relative to angle α_1 must be observed.

If the effects of friction and turbulence losses in the rotor flow passages are expressed as the ratio of entering and leaving relative velocities in the rotor, $v_2/v_1 = K$,

$$V_1 \sin \alpha_1 - V_2 \sin \alpha_2 = v_1 \sin \beta_1 - v_2 \sin \beta_2 = (1 + K)v_1 \sin \beta_1$$

when $\beta_1 = -\beta_2$.

The work relation in Eq. (168) can then be rewritten

$$E = \frac{W_a u}{g} [(1 + K)v_1 \sin \beta_1] = \frac{W_a u}{g} (1 + K)(V_1 \sin \alpha_1 - u) \quad (169)$$

A term common in steam practice is the blade efficiency of a rotor, which is the ratio of useful work extracted by the rotor to the total kinetic energy of the entering flow as it leaves the nozzle. Since we have redefined turbine efficiency for aircraft-engine use, we shall not call this ratio blade efficiency but will add the term η_n for the nozzle flow efficiency and call the ratio the work-extraction or work-recovery coefficient.

$$\text{Work-recovery coefficient} = 2g \frac{E}{W_a V_1^2} \eta_n$$

$$= \eta_n \frac{2u}{V_1^2} (1 + K)(V_1 \sin \alpha_1 - u)$$

$$= 2\eta_n(1 + K) \left(\frac{u}{V_1} \sin \alpha_1 - \frac{u^2}{V_1^2} \right) \quad (170)$$

Equation (170) is shown plotted in Fig. 131; the work-recovery coefficient is the ordinate, and the velocity ratio u/V_1 is the abscissa. The value of η_n is 0.95, and K in Fig. 131 is also assumed to be 0.95.

The maximum amount of work is extracted from the gas flow when $u/V_1 = \frac{1}{2} \sin \alpha_1$, and the work-recovery ratio at that point is

$$\frac{\eta_n}{2} (1 + K) \sin^2 \alpha_1$$

The particular point to be observed here is that the work-recovery coefficient, or in other words, the available shaft energy, of an impulse turbine is quite sensitive to the velocity ratio. This does not mean that the turbine efficiency η_t for aircraft-engine use is of necessity critical with respect to u/V_1, although in actual fact it may be.

Equations (169) and (170) are exact for flow at a particular radial distance from the axis of rotation of the impulse turbine. However, when an attempt is made to integrate the actual work recovery over the entire turbine disc area, a perfectly obvious difficulty appears for free-vortex flows. The definition of a free-vortex flow postulates the existence of a radial static pressure gradient in the flow, balanced by the centrifugal forces due to whirl velocity. Yet by definition, the flow between the nozzle ring and rotating-blade row of the impulse turbine is fully expanded at all points in the flow, and is therefore at a static pressure equal at all points to the exhaust pressure. A 100 percent impulse turbine is incompatible with free-vortex flow.

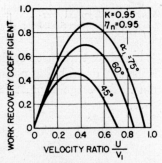

Fig. 131. Work-recovery coefficient plotted against velocity ratio for pure impulse turbine.

Practically all aircraft turbines that are classed as impulse type have from 10 to 20 percent or more of reaction. Flow may be very nearly pure impulse near the hub or roots of the rotor blades, with possibly a slight amount of undesirable recompression there; but at the outer diameter, a very considerable degree of reaction flow must take place if a mixed-velocity exhaust is to be avoided. A rotor with a tip/hub diameter ratio of 1.2, working near the optimum velocity ratio at the hub or blade roots as a pure impulse flow, would find its blade tips working at about 20 percent reaction for an average degree of reaction of the order of 10 percent for the entire blade annulus, and not necessarily at the best velocity ratio.

Aircraft turbine blades are usually designed near the roots by flow-passage methods developed for steam turbines. However, the blade tips are often designed by selecting limiting lift coefficients from cascade tests of airfoil sections. Intermediate blade-setting angles and profiles are then selected by blending the tip and root designs to fit the known flow-angle requirements. Typical turbine-blade sections for 20 percent reaction are shown in Fig. 132. The rotor root is thick to keep down blade-root centrifugal stresses, and tip sections are thin for the same reason. From an aerodynamic standpoint, it would be desirable to keep the root sections thin as well as the tip sections. A view of a complete nozzle ring with connecting sleeves for can-type burners is shown in Fig. 133, and the matching rotor is shown in Fig. 134.

NOZZLE ROTOR

TIP

ROOT

Fig. 132. Typical turbine-blade sections for 20 percent reaction.

When jet-engine compression ratios exceed 4:1, and for turboprop engines of the same or lower compression ratios, it is usually desirable to use two or more rows of rotating blades in the turbine. A 2-stage impulse turbine rotor and nozzle ring are shown in Fig. 135.

Fig. 133. Complete (De Havilland) nozzle ring showing connecting sleeves for can-type combustors.

Blade profiles in nozzle rings usually follow airfoil shapes. The gas flow must be turned through rather large angles with expansion from low velocities to sonic or supersonic flows. Since centrifugal stresses are not

Fig. 134.   De Havilland turbine-rotor matching nozzle ring of Fig. 133.

Fig. 135.   Two-stage impulse turbine elements; Armstrong-Siddeley gas turbine.

present in nozzle blades, somewhat better profiles may be used than in the case of rotor blades. However, blade temperatures in the nozzle are higher than are rotor-blade temperatures, severe vibration problems exist, and nozzle-blade failures are not uncommon. Trailing-edge thickness of blades, both nozzle and rotor, is normally kept under 3 percent of the blade pitch; an increase in average trailing-edge thickness to 6 percent may decrease turbine efficiency by 1 to 2 percent.

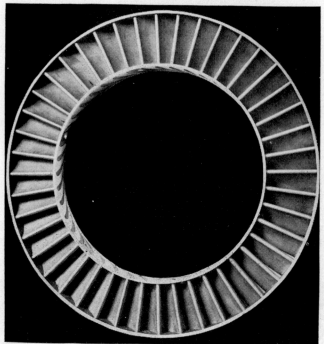

Fig. 136.   Westinghouse gas-turbine nozzle showing inner and outer shroud rings.

Untwisted or straight nozzle blades greatly simplify the manufacturing problem, permitting the use of easily machined blade elements. An untwisted blade does not produce a free vortex flow, however, and nozzle efflux angle is relatively constant, changing principally because of progressive changes in pitch/chord ratio with radial distance. The vorticity Ω is no longer constant but varies with the radius, $\Omega = V_{1u} r^{\cos^2 \alpha}$. Similarly the axial flow velocity varies with the radius and is inversely proportional to $r^{\cos^2 \alpha}$. For short blades and with a large efflux angle $\alpha > 60°$, the flow is a compromise between constant angular momentum and constant efflux angle.

It is general practice to pitch nozzle blades closely, so that flow turning follows the blade camber angle with but small deviations. A representative value of pitch/chord ratio would be 0.75 at the mean diameter. Straight, untwisted blades may be set in a nozzle ring and inclined from the radial position, in the plane of the ring; this is the equivalent of a twisted blade, although the construction is not common.

Nozzle blades may be welded or riveted into shroud rings or shroud segments, or they may simply be set into well-fitted perforations in the shroud that permit limited radial movement. Thermal expansions, especially unequal thermal expansions, can result in harmful distortion of the flow paths and can reduce running clearances to the interference point. Turbine nozzle blades are almost universally fitted with inner and outer shroud rings (see Fig. 136); in the case of the single-stage turbine, tip or shroud leakage is not a problem in the nozzle.

The design of turbine rotating-blade rows is less critical than the design of axial-flow-compressor blade paths. Blade rows will accept flows over a fairly wide range of flow incidence angles, say, 20 deg or more, with but small effect upon efficiency. An example is the closely pitched impulse blade row represented by the curve of Fig. 137. The net result is that turbines will accept off-design flows or changes in velocity ratio with much smaller penalties in decreased efficiency than will axial compressors.

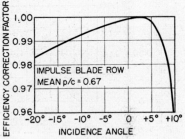

FIG. 137. Turbine-efficiency correction factor vs. incidence angle. Note that efficiency is not greatly impaired at off-design flow conditions.

Flow Mach number relative to the entering edge of the rotor blade is a maximum at the blade root. In order to keep v_1 to an acceptable value, usually $M_{v1} < 0.8$, peripheral velocity u_h at the root is high, and the leaving flow has considerable exit whirl velocity. If the exhaust jet were allowed to leave the engine without straightening the flow, this whirl energy would be lost. Therefore, the whirl angle is kept below 10 to 20 deg; this much swirl can be removed by faired struts downstream from the turbine, normally present for supporting tail-cone structure, etc. A row of straightening vanes behind the turbine rotor to remove large residual whirl is not customary.

Designing the rotating-impulse-blade flow path with a small degree of reaction also reduces the flow Mach number at entry, because of higher blade speeds. For exit swirl angles between 0 and 20 deg, the rim speed at the blade root increases by approximately 12 or 13 percent when the nozzle efflux angle is 70 deg and the flow is changed from pure impulse to 20 percent reaction.[1] The blade entry Mach number may decrease from a value in the neighborhood of $M = 0.75$ for zero exit whirl to $M < 0.55$ when the hub peripheral velocity increases 12 or 13 percent.

Some typical flow relations for a British-designed single-stage impulse wheel with $T_4 = 2000°$R are shown in Fig. 138. The blade row was designed for zero reaction at the hub but with 10-deg exit whirl, and increasing reaction as the blade tip is approached. The exit whirl at the blade tip is small at the designed operating condition. The variations of entry Mach number relative to rotor-blade leading edges, and also the nozzle efflux angles and flow velocities, are shown plotted against the blade radius/tip radius ratio from root to tip. Gas flow turning

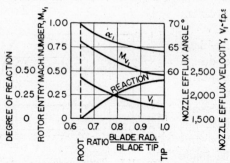

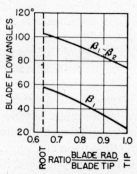

FIG. 138. Flow relations for typical single-stage impulse turbine wheel. (*J. Reeman, Proc. IME, vol. 153, p. 495, 1945.*)

FIG. 139. Gas flow turning and entry angles for turbine wheel of Fig. 138.

angles $\beta_1 - \beta_2$ for the rotor are shown in Fig. 139, plotted against the same blade-radius ratio, along with the blade entry angle β_1.

Assuming that flow at the blade root is pure impulse, and further assuming that the whirl component of velocity in the exhaust flow is small, the axial flow velocity of the gas stream is practically constant across the rotor. This imposes a further restriction upon the nozzle efflux angle in that the axial flow velocity of the turbine exhaust should not be so high as to introduce excessive duct friction losses in the exhaust system, where the jet nozzle may be some distance behind the turbine. The axial flow Mach number should be no larger than 0.7 in the exhaust; the actual velocity permitted, in fps, depends upon the temperature of the exhaust. For a jet engine with 4:1 compression ratio, the exhaust temperature is usually about 80 percent of the turbine inlet temperature, and therefore sonic velocity in the exhaust is of the order of 90 percent of sonic velocity on the upstream side of the turbine rotor. The maximum local nozzle efflux Mach number near the blade roots is also usually

[1] REEMAN, J., *Proc. IME*, vol. 153, pp. 495–504, 1945.

limited to a flow of $M = 1.25$, so that the cosine of the critical nozzle efflux angle is approximately $0.8 \times 0.90/1.25 = 0.6$. Under these circumstances, nozzle efflux angle at the blade roots is limited to about 55 deg if the turbine leaving velocity is to be held to a reasonable limit. Unfortunately, a high nozzle efflux angle requires a high turbine rim speed, so that blade and disc centrifugal stresses must be weighed against high exhaust velocity in deciding upon the nozzle design. A 2-stage turbine immediately relieves this difficulty, unless total pressure ratios across the turbine of the order of 3:1 or 4:1 are reached, when the problem again arises.

Turbine rpm is fixed by compressor design in open-cycle gas-turbine engines. The double-sided centrifugal compressor runs about 30 percent faster than the larger diameter single-sided centrifugal compressor for the same mass air delivery. An equivalent symmetric, or 50 percent reaction, axial-flow compressor may run at the same speed as the dual-entry centrifugal impeller, the nonsymmetric axial compressor at somewhat lower speeds, and the vortex-entry axial-flow unit may run at half of this speed. The smallest and lightest weight compressors and turbines are usually the high-speed small-diameter designs. A single-stage turbine can be designed to handle the shaft power requirements of any of the above directly coupled compressors in a jet engine with compression ratios below 4:1. If the turbine must also supply shaft power for a propeller, or if the compression ratio is appreciably higher, single-stage-turbine efficiency falls off rapidly, and a 2-stage turbine is desirable. When a symmetric axial-flow compressor is used in jet engines of 3,000 lb thrust and higher, a 2-stage turbine may be desirable from an efficiency standpoint.

29. Reaction Turbines. Many of the limitations and design factors that apply to impulse turbines also apply to reaction turbines. For example, the energy equations for impulse-turbine flow paths may be applied to reaction turbines if account is taken of the expansion, which results in an increased velocity occurring in the rotating-blade row. A few of the simpler flow-path relations will be shown, and then design problems will be discussed from the standpoint of airfoil theory.

The tangential force on the moving-blade row is proportional to the total component of velocity change of the fluid relative to the moving row in the plane of rotation. The work done per pound of gas flowing per second is then this force multiplied by the blade velocity u. From the velocity triangles of Fig. 128,

$$E = \frac{W_a u}{g} (V_1 \sin \alpha_1 - V_2 \sin \alpha_2)$$

which is the same as Eq. (168) for the impulse turbine. This relation may also be written

$$E = \frac{W_a u}{g} (V_1 \sin \alpha_1 - u - v_2 \sin \beta_2) \tag{171}$$

and again the direction of the flow angle β_2 must be observed with respect to the assumed positive direction of angle α_1. We shall now introduce the velocity ratio u/V_1 and also a new velocity ratio u/v_2, where u/v_2 is the ratio of blade velocity to relative leaving flow velocity in the rotor. Equation (171) is rewritten to include these terms and η_p, the flow efficiency of the nozzle- and rotor-blade paths, and is divided by $E_n + E_r$, the fixed nozzle spouting energy plus the flow-expansion energy in the rotor; the resultant is the work-recovery factor for the reaction turbine

$$\eta_p \frac{V_1^2[(u/V_1) \sin \alpha_1 - (u_2/V_1^2)] - (u/v_2)v_2^2 \sin \beta_2}{g(E_n + E_r)} \tag{172}$$

With the velocity triangles known, the work-recovery factor is calculated

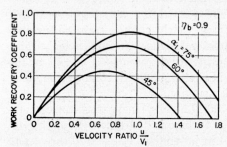

FIG. 140. Work-recovery coefficient vs. velocity ratio for 50 percent reaction or symmetric turbine. Compare with Fig. 131.

for a turbine of any degree of reaction from Eq. (172). The reaction is by definition

$$\text{Degree of reaction} = \frac{E_r}{E_n + E_r} \tag{173}$$

To take a specific case of the 50 percent reaction turbine with $E_n = E_r$, the velocity triangles must let $V_1 = v_2$ and $\alpha_1 = -\beta_2$. The work-recovery coefficient of the symmetric or 50 percent reaction turbine is then

$$\eta_p \frac{V_1^2[2(u/V_1) \sin \alpha_1 - (u^2/V_1^2)]}{2gE_n}$$

or

$$\eta_p \left[2\frac{u}{V_1} \sin \alpha_1 - \frac{u^2}{V_1^2} \right] \tag{174}$$

The work-recovery coefficient is at a maximum when $\sin \alpha_1 = u/V_1$, and is then equal to $\eta_p u^2/V_1^2$. A typical plot of Eq. (174) is shown in Fig. 140 for $\alpha_1 = 45$, 60, and 75 deg and for $\eta_p = 0.9$; this should be compared with Fig. 131 for the pure impulse turbine. The reaction turbine has about the same general energy-flow characteristic as the impulse turbine except that u/V_1 ratios are consistently higher, and the peaks of the curves in Fig. 140 are slightly flatter relatively than are the peaks in Fig. 131.

30. Symmetric Stage Reaction Turbines. There are a number of very well known relations that have been derived many times for the case of the 50 percent reaction or symmetric turbine with free-vortex flow or constant-circulation stages. The velocity ratio of Eq. (160), of course, applies; it is the ratio of the blade velocity divided by the actual absolute gas-stream-flow velocity.

There is another useful ratio known as the isentropic velocity ratio. The isentropic velocity ratio is the ratio of blade velocity to the ideal nozzle spouting velocity if all the energy conversion in the nozzle flow had been perfect and without loss; for the symmetric turbine, it is

$$\frac{u}{\sqrt{gJ\,\Delta h_s}} \tag{175}$$

where Δh_s is the total stage (two blade rows) enthalpy drop. European practice commonly presents turbine characteristics plotted against the isentropic velocity ratio instead of the actual velocity ratio.

Still another useful relation is the ratio of the actual velocity ratio to the isentropic velocity ratio; it is

$$\frac{\text{Actual velocity ratio}}{\text{Isentropic velocity ratio}} = \sqrt{\frac{2(u/V_1)\sin\alpha_1 - (u^2/V_1^2)}{\eta_s}} \tag{176}$$

where η_s is the turbine stage efficiency. It follows that

$$\frac{u}{V_1} = \frac{2\sin\alpha_1}{1 + \dfrac{\eta_s}{(\text{isentropic ratio})^2}} \tag{177}$$

The foregoing relations, used with the free-vortex conditions and the velocity triangles of Fig. 128, permit basic turbine requirements to be established for 50 percent reaction turbines.

An example of the initial calculations for a symmetric turbine for a turbojet engine illustrates the method. The engine's compressor inducts 90 lb of air per second under standard conditions. A small amount of this air is bled from the compressor for cooling and miscellaneous purposes, so that the addition of the fuel in the combustion chamber just offsets this loss and the net flow through the turbine nozzle ring remains at 90 lb/sec. The turbine shaft speed is fixed by the compressor, which is a symmetric axial-flow unit rated 8,400 rpm or 140 rps at the design point. The shaft power requirement of the compressor plus fuel pump and auxiliaries is 10,200 hp at a compression ratio of 4.6. The total pressure loss in the combustion chamber is 5 percent, so that the turbine receives gas at $4.6 \times 0.95 \times 14.7 = 64.3$ psi.

The turbine efficiency is assumed to be 90 percent, and the temperature $T_4 = 2000°R$, $c_p = 0.28$, and $k = 1.31$. The amount of energy the turbine must extract from each pound of gas is

$$10,200 \times \frac{550}{778 \times 90} = 80 \text{ Btu/lb}$$

The temperature decrease in the expansion would then be $80/0.28 = 280$ deg; the exhaust total temperature $T_5 = 2000 - 286 = 1714°\text{R}$, and the temperature ratio $T_5/T_4 = 0.856$. Inserting this value of T_5/T_4 into Eq. (159) for $\eta_t = 0.9$, P_5/P_4 is solved for and is equal to 0.432. The total pressure in the turbine exhaust is $0.432 \times 64.3 = 27.8$ psi, or 1.89 times atmospheric pressure.

Since this jet engine may be equipped with a duct between the tur-

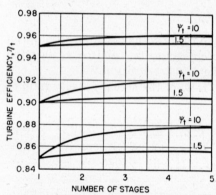

FIG. 141. Effect of compounding on turbine efficiency for different stage efficiencies and total turbine pressure ratios.

bine exit and the jet nozzle, an arbitrary limit of 900 fps is placed on the axial leaving velocity of the exhaust. At a total exhaust temperature of 1714°R, this means that the exit flow Mach number will not exceed $M_5 = 0.5$.

The first-stage turbine-blade tip speed is to be kept under 1,100 fps in order to hold blade and disc stresses within low limits, so that at 8,400 rpm, the turbine-rotor diameter is 2.5 ft maximum over the first-stage blade tips. This matches generally with the outside diameter of the compressor of about 3.0 ft.

Assuming that the blade velocity at the mean diameter is 950 fps and inserting this value into Eq. (175) for the isentropic velocity ratio, it is found that if the entire 80-Btu/lb enthalpy drop is taken in a single stage, the isentropic velocity ratio is 0.66. This is too low for high efficiency in this type of turbine, and the ratio is recalculated for a 2-stage turbine. Δh_s is then $\frac{8.0}{2} = 40$ Btu, neglecting the effects of turbine reheat. The turbine reheat factor is quite small for high stage efficiency in a 2-stage turbine, and is assumed to offset mechanical losses in this example, so that stage efficiency is practically the same as over-all turbine efficiency. Turbine reheat factors are obtainable from Fig. 141; if reheat were used in Eq. (175), the stage enthalpy would be multiplied by the reheat factor. The isentropic velocity ratio for the 2-stage turbine is

$$\frac{950}{\sqrt{\frac{8.0}{2} \, gJ}} = 0.95$$

This is within reasonable limits for a symmetric turbine.

Assuming an axial flow velocity of approximately 600 fps, the flow efflux angle α_{1m} at the mean diameter should be about 55 deg. Using this value for α_{1m} in Eq. (177),

$$\frac{u}{V_{1m}} = \frac{2 \sin 55°}{1 + (\eta_s/0.95)} = 0.84$$

The flow efflux velocity at the mean radius is therefore $950/0.84 = 1,113$ fps. This is a nozzle efflux flow Mach number of 0.535 at the mean radius and is considerably lower than the values frequently encountered in gas-turbine designs, particularly impulse designs. However, it is not unreasonably low and is the result of the fact that this particular turbine cannot quite do the required job with a single stage and does not work 2 stages as hard as they could be worked.

With $u_m = 950$ fps and $N = 8,400$ rpm, the mean radius $r_m = 1.08$ ft. The tangential flow velocity at mean radius $V_{1u} = V_{1m} \sin \alpha_{1m} = 927$ fps, and the vorticity $\Omega = 927 \times 1.08 = 1,000$ ft^2/sec. The actual axial flow velocity is $V_{1a} = V_{1m} \cos \alpha_{1m} = 1,113 \cos 55° = 648$ fps instead of the assumed 600 fps.

In order to calculate the root and tip radii of the nozzle-blade ring, Eq. (167) may be used. However, it is obvious from Fig. 129 that the nozzle efflux root Mach number will be much lower than 1.2 for any reasonable design, and an approximation of the required nozzle area is arrived at by assuming the gas density at the mean radius to be a representative average value for the entire flow. The approximate area is therefore

$$A_{\text{approx}} = \frac{W_a}{\dfrac{P_4}{RT_4} V_{1a} \left(1 + \dfrac{k-1}{2} M_1^2\right)^{\frac{1}{1-k}}}$$

$$= \frac{90}{\dfrac{64.3 \times 144}{53.3 \times 2,000} 648(1 + 0.155 \times 0.535^2)^{-3.22}} = 1.85 \text{ sq ft}$$

The tentative value of r_h is therefore 0.933 ft, and the tentative value of the tip radius $r_t = 1.208$ ft. These values are then checked by insertion into Eq. (167) and yield a flow of 89.7 lb/sec. Apparently, using the density at the mean diameter does not introduce a significant error in calculating the mass flow when flow Mach numbers are small, and the tentative values of root and tip radii above will be corrected to 0.93 ft and 1.21 ft, respectively, for preliminary design use.

The tangential velocity at the hub is then $V_{1uh} = \Omega/r_h = 1,076$, and at the tip $V_{1ut} = \Omega/r_t = 826$. The nozzle spouting velocity at the hub is $\sqrt{648^2 + 1,076^2} = 1,255$ fps, and at the tip is $\sqrt{648^2 + 826^2} = 1,048$

fps. The flow Mach numbers are obtained from the relation between velocity and total temperature

$$M = \frac{1}{\sqrt{(gkRT/V^2) - [(k-1)/2]}} \tag{178}$$

so that $M_{1h} = 0.608$ and $M_{1t} = 0.503$. The nozzle efflux angles are $\alpha_{1h} = \tan^{-1}\left(\frac{1076}{648}\right) = 58.9°$ and $\alpha_{1t} = \tan^{-1}\left(\frac{826}{648}\right) = 51°$. Nozzle blading is then selected on the basis of cascade-test data to yield efficient flow turning from the axial approach flow to 58.9 deg at the root, 55 deg at the mean diameter, and 51 deg at the tip. As indicated earlier, a closely pitched ring of nozzle blades is to be preferred. The axial inlet velocity ahead of the nozzle ring is fixed by the total temperature and pressure conditions and the area of 1.88 sq ft. From Fig. 32, M is 0.272, and therefore the nozzle inlet axial flow velocity is 573 fps.

Entrance angles relative to the first moving-blade row are determined from the velocity triangle, and

$$\beta_1 = \tan^{-1}\left(\frac{V_{1u} - u}{V_{1a}}\right) \tag{179}$$

so that β_1 is 21.9 deg at the root radius of 0.93 ft, -1.9 deg at the mean radius of 1.08 ft, and -21.6 deg at the tip radius of 1.21 ft. Since in a symmetric turbine, v_2 is at the negative angle of V_1 in direction and is equal to V_1 in magnitude, then the first-stage rotor-blade exit angles are $\beta_2 = -\alpha_1$ at the same radii. The flow turning angle in the rotor is $\theta = \beta_2 - \beta_1$, and at the root radius is -80.8 deg, at the mean radius -53.1 deg, and at the tip -30.4 deg.

Blade sections and setting angles in the second stage, for both stationary and rotating rows, would duplicate the forms and angles of the first row for the same radii. However, an increase in blade annulus area is required at the exit, owing to the lower density of the exit flow. Pressure and temperature at the exit are $P_5 = 27.8$ psi and $T_5 = 1714°$R. Since the exit velocity is equal to $V_{1a} = 648$ fps, the exit Mach number from Eq. (178) is 0.333. The mass flow per unit area is

$$\frac{27.8 \times 144}{53.3 \times 1714} \, 648 \left(1 + \frac{k-1}{2} \, 0.333^2\right)^{\frac{1}{1-k}} = 27 \text{ lb/sq ft/sec}$$

The turbine exit area $A_5 = \frac{90}{27} = 3.43$ sq ft.

If the second-stage blade tips were held at the 1.21-ft radius, the root radius would then be 0.61 ft; and the hub/tip ratio would be 0.504, an undesirably low ratio. The tip diameter of the last-stage rotating row is therefore increased to 2.7 ft for $r_t = 1.35$ ft and $r_h = 0.856$ ft and a hub/tip ratio of 0.632. The last-stage flow angles are calculated for the extended hub and tip distances by applying the free-vortex flow conditions to the already known flow angles obtained from the first stage at 0.93-, 1.08-, and 1.21-ft radii. The turbine inlet and outlet annuli are connected by smooth curves to take the flow passage area from 1.88 sq ft at the inlet to 3.43 sq ft at the exit.

The blade pitch of the rotating rows is fixed by the results of cascade tests and the limiting lift coefficient that can be expected at the blade tips. Flow velocities relative to the moving blade, v_1 and v_2, vary from entry to exit positions, and the effective stream velocity that has been

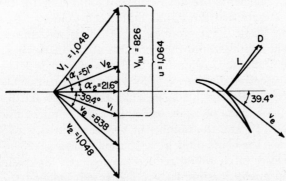

Fɪɢ. 142. Velocity diagram for example discussed in text showing median flow vector for symmetric-turbine stage rotor.

found to be accurate is the median vector v_e lying between v_1 and v_2 in Fig. 142 at the mid-point of $v_1 \sin \beta_1 - v_2 \sin \beta_2$. For the first-stage tip condition

$$v_e = \sqrt{V_{1a}^2 + \left(\frac{u^2}{2}\right)} = 838 \text{ fps}$$

at an angle of -39.4 deg.

The resolution of lift and drag forces on a unit blade area in the plane of rotation of the blade row is made in terms of the effective stream velocity, 823 fps, and the effective angle, -39.4 deg. The resultant force is then equal to the tangential change in flow momentum at the same radius for blade chord c and blade pitch s.

$$-L \cos 39.4° + D \sin 39.4° = \Delta r \, s V_{1a}\rho(v_2 \sin \beta_2 - v_1 \sin \beta_1)$$

Then, since

$$L = C_L \rho \frac{v_e^2}{2} c \, \Delta r$$

$$D = C_D \rho \frac{v_e^2}{2} c \, \Delta r$$

the force equation may be rewritten

$$C_L - \frac{C_D}{C_L} \tan 39.4° = 2\frac{s}{c} \frac{764 \times 648}{823^2 \cos 39.4°}$$

Now since C_D/C_L is normally less than 0.02 for a good airfoil profile, the term $(C_D/C_L) \tan 39.4°$ may be neglected without introducing a serious error, and as an approximation

$$C_L = 2\frac{s}{c} 0.96$$

High lift coefficients are not ordinarily obtainable for cambered airfoil sections in retarded flows, but quite high values of C_L are possible in accelerated flows. Therefore, a C_L of 1.0 is not unreasonable and would result in a pitch/chord ratio of 0.521 at the blade tip at a radius of 1.21 ft in the first stage. Since the blade-stagger angle is approximately equal to the effective flow angle of 39.4 deg, the ratio of blade pitch to axial distance across the blade is 0.525/cos 39.4° = 0.676. Assuming an axial width of blade of $1\frac{5}{8}$ in. or 0.135 ft, the required pitch at radius 1.21 ft is 0.0913 ft, and the number of blades required is 83.2 minimum. Using 84 blades, the blade pitch at the hub in inches is 0.833. Additional blades at a closer pitch would reduce the required lift coefficient at the blade tips and might possibly lead to higher efficiency.

The exact blade-tip shape and the correct angle of attack can be determined correctly only from the results of cascade tests. The blade shape at the root is determined by the requirements of the flow-passage areas and the centrifugal- and bending-stress limitations at that point. The root and tip shapes are then blended along the blade length, and minor adjustments are made in the last row to reduce whirl velocity in the exhaust. Blade profiles at root and tip for the example worked out here are shown in Fig. 143 along with the velocity triangles.

The nozzle flow velocities in this example are far from critical and are due to two factors. The turbine design is 50 percent reaction, and two stages are used. Further, the compressor is somewhat lower in speed than would be designed for if minimum engine diameter were the major consideration, and a generous nozzle annulus area is assumed in order to reduce the effects of tip leakage losses in the rotor and second-stage nozzle ring. The same nozzle ring could be redesigned to be followed by a 2-stage impulse turbine, and the efflux Mach number at the inner radius of the nozzle ring would then be approximately 0.89. This is a low flow Mach number and the velocity ratio would be higher than desirable, about 0.66 at the mean diameter, so that a reduction in turbine diameter would be in order. Ordinarily impulse turbines are designed for average critical flow in the nozzle, and reaction turbines for somewhat lower flow velocities.

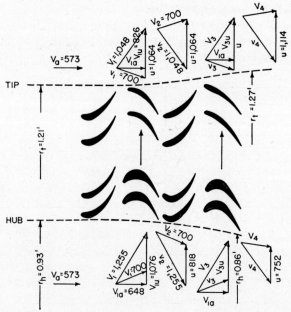

Fig. 143.   Root and tip blade profiles and velocity triangles for 2-stage symmetric turbine.

31. Turbine Flow Characteristics. In spite of the general practice of pitching turbine blades closely, turbines are not very stiff devices from a volumetric flow standpoint, at least for single-stage and 2-stage units. Their characteristics are close to those of axial-flow compressors, but because the slope of the flow-regulation curve plotted against pressure ratio for a given shaft speed is opposite to that of the compressor, a single line may very nearly express the turbine flow characteristic over the useful working ranges. Flows of a typical turbine corrected to standard conditions are shown plotted in Fig. 144 for various corrected shaft speeds and pressure ratios. The curves for the different speeds almost connect

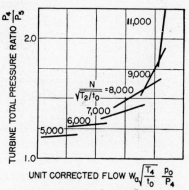

Fig. 144.   Corrected turbine flow vs. turbine pressure ratio for various corrected turbine rotational speeds.

in a single line. This turbine will accept the same flow at a given pressure ratio over a rather wide range of shaft speeds, and without serious loss of efficiency, as was indicated in Fig. 137. This is a most desirable characteristic when a turbine must be matched to a stiff compressor.

A somewhat more useful relation in gas-turbine work is obtained when the shaft power delivered by the turbine per unit mass flow of gas is plotted against corrected mass flow. Since the work available is dependent upon temperature also, it is desirable to indicate a temperature ratio

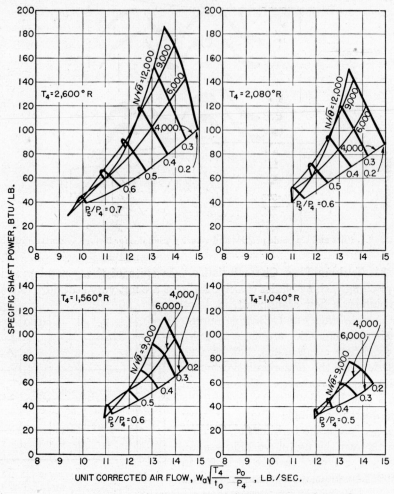

Fig. 145. Specific shaft power of gas turbine vs. corrected mass flow.

on the plot, and this is usually the ratio of the turbine total inlet temperature to the ambient atmospheric temperature (normally taken at standard atmospheric conditions for corrected flow plots). Lines of constant pressure ratio, P_5/P_4, are crossed by lines of constant corrected shaft speed, $N/\sqrt{\theta}$, as in Fig. 145.

The flow of a turbine is greatly influenced by the back pressure at the turbine exhaust, so that in a jet engine particularly, the characteristics of the exhaust nozzle are important. If the nozzle has a fixed exit area, then a single family of curves as in Fig. 145 may be used to represent the flow characteristic of a given turbine; but if the nozzle exit area is adjustable or otherwise variable, a different set of flow curves is required for each nozzle area. Some turbojet engines and practically all present designs of turboprop engines use fixed-area exhaust nozzles, although this degree of simplicity is not likely to persist for long when significant improvements in over-all performance may be gained with variable-area jet nozzles.

32. Blade Temperatures. The actual temperature of the metal in a turbine blade is a quantity that is determined accurately with great difficulty, if at all. The blade temperature will depend upon the total temperature of the gas flow, the flow Mach number relative to the blade surface, the effects of laminar flow-stagnation layers next to the blade, radiation to and from nearby hot bodies and the gas stream, and heat conduction in the blade itself and to the turbine disc. Thus, we may expect large temperature variations radially and also from leading edge to trailing edge of any given blade. Some estimates have been made, however, of typical uncooled-rotor-

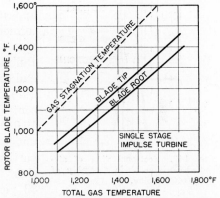

FIG. 146.   Uncooled-rotor-blade temperatures plotted against total (or stagnation) gas temperature for a single-stage impulse turbine.

blade temperatures for single-stage impulse turbines, and these are plotted against total gas temperature in Fig. 146. A 2-stage impulse turbine would show a smaller difference between first-stage blade temperatures and gas-stream total temperature. A reaction turbine would have a smaller difference also, usually of the order of 100°F at 1500°F gas temperature.

Cooling of turbine blades, both rotating and stationary, is attractive because of the high cycle efficiencies possible with high turbine inlet temperatures.[1] This also may make it possible to utilize less expensive blade materials; many elements now commonly used in uncooled gas-turbine blades would be in critical supply under wartime restrictions. It was the shortage of tungsten, nickel, and other metals that forced the

[1] ELLERBROCK, H., *J. IAS*, Vol. 15, pp. 721–730, 1948.

German turbojet designers to the use of low-alloy steels, which had to be cooled for use as turbine blades.

Blades may be cooled by air bled from the compressor. Frequently, small centrifugal blower vanes are placed on the front face of the turbine disc to assist further in moving cooling air across the disc and around the roots of solid blades. Hollow blades may also be used, and shroud plates are placed on the sides of the rotor disc to direct air through openings in the root of the hollow blade. The cooling air is then allowed to escape at the tip between the tip and turbine casing. With a single-stage turbine (20 percent reaction) operating at 1400°F inlet temperature, approximately 2 percent of the compressor air is used for cooling both stator nozzle blades and rotor blades of a turbine sufficiently to keep blade temperatures below 1000°F. A sectional view of an air-cooled turbine blade assembly appears in Fig. 147; the blades were formed from rolled sheet of tapered thickness and welded on their trailing edges. Bulb-type roots were inserted in the disc, and cooling air entered through the hollow bulb in the rotating row. Blade-root centrifugal stresses were of the order of 19,000 psi, and gas bending stresses were under 4,000 psi in the blade. Life of this particular turbine before failure was very short, 60 to 80 hr, and efficiency was under 80 percent, owing to poor blade form, high tip-clearance leakage, and operation at a low velocity ratio.

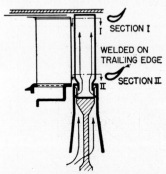

Fig. 147. Sectional view of air-cooled turbine blade assembly of BMW003 turbine.

Methods of cooling turbine blades with auxiliary air, better than those of Fig. 147, should result in substantial allowable increases in top turbine temperatures when high-alloy blade materials are used instead of the low nickel, chromium, etc., alloys used in the German designs. However, much more refined blade shapes and manufacturing methods will be required if high turbine efficiency is to be obtained. Improvements in cycle efficiency through higher temperature limits must, however, be balanced against the cost of cooling air bled from the compressor; this cooling air may be taken by interstage bleed in order to keep pumping losses at a minimum.

A limited number of experiments have been performed on water-cooled turbine blades. The use of a closed-end drilled blade with a supply tube down the center will result in very rapid circulation of fluid in the blade due to accelerated thermosiphon action under the centrifugal forces existing in the rotating blade. Heat can then be removed from the blade and conveyed to a heat exchanger or rejected in waste water at a very fast rate. The rate of heat transfer between the water and the turbine-blade contact surface is approximately 2000 Btu/(sq ft)(hr)(°F) under these conditions. The rate of heat transfer between the gas stream and the blade surface is about one-tenth of the rate for liquid heat transfer, or 200 Btu/(sq ft)(hr)(°F). With a gas temperature of 2000°F and a blade temperature of 900°F, the heat-transfer rate is of the order of 200,000 Btu/(sq, ft)(hr) and temperature gradients in the metal walls

Fɪɢ. 148.   Rotor for single-stage jet-engine turbine with symmetric blading.

of the hollow blades may approach 200°F from outer surface to inner surface with stainless-steel blades.

Liquid-cooled blades for aircraft engines would normally require a heat exchanger for recirculation of the cooling water, since a 3,000-lb-thrust jet engine operating under the above conditions might be required to reject as much as 15,000 lb of water per hour or more. This presents a large problem in that the temperature of the cooling water is high after leaving the turbine blade; centrifugal force pressures will prevent vaporization of the water while it is actually in the blade, but very high steam pressures due to the high temperature will carry over to the heat exchanger. The large mass flows of liquid required for really effective cooling appear to rule out cooling by means of the gas-turbine fuel flow itself, since the fuel flow is very small compared with the required coolant flow. The latent heat of vaporization of the liquid fuel is not available for cooling inside the blade, since centrifugal heads are high, to say nothing of cracking difficulties and carbon deposits.

33. Blade Materials. Uncooled turbine blades are required to operate at metal temperatures only slightly below the inlet gas temperature (see Fig. 146). Combined centrifugal and bending stresses may result in tensile loadings between 12,000 and 25,000 psi, depending upon the design. In addition, the material must be oxidation-resistant under operating conditions and must be fatigue-resistant and stable in mechanical properties. When we add the requirement that it be possible to fabricate the material into complicated shapes and thin sections held to very precise tolerances, the number of suitable alloys is narrowed quite rapidly. Presently available turbine-blade alloys cannot withstand temperatures beyond approximately 1700 to 1800°F for more than a few seconds. These same alloys are unsuitable for continuous service ratings at gas temperatures beyond 1400 to 1500°F.

There are two general classes of metal alloys used for turbine blades. One group consists of wrought or forgeable alloys that can be machined readily for final shaping into blades. The other group consists of the casting alloys, cast to almost the final size and shape by the so-called precision or lost-wax process. Final shaping is done by grinding, since these alloys as cast are almost universally too hard for ordinary machining operations. British designs have used wrought alloys almost exclusively, while American practice favors cast blades. Some American turbines also use wrought alloys, but the large store of experience gained in this country in the manufacture of engine turbosuperchargers with cast blades has overshadowed the excellent progress in research here on wrought materials.

Forgeable or wrought alloys are normally either ferritic or austenitic. The ferritic alloys are iron-base alloys and are inherently less strong at high temperatures than the austenitic alloys with a large proportion of nickel in the composition. In alloys of high nickel content, small quantities of iron and nickel appear to be interchangeable without affecting properties seriously. The British-developed Nimonic 90 is reported to have a composition very close to that of K42B, developed at the Westinghouse Research Laboratories, except that only traces of iron and cobalt are present and the nickel content is higher. Properties of these two materials are quite similar.

The chromium content of wrought alloys is almost universally high, from 13 to 30 percent, and provides oxidation resistance for the exposed surfaces of blades. This chromium content does not appear to influence mechanical properties greatly. Cobalt is often substituted for nickel to improve ductility and forgeability; it has other effects upon final properties after heat-treatment.

TABLE 4. SOME TYPICAL ANALYSES OF WROUGHT ALLOYS (PERCENT)

Alloy	C	Mn	Si	Ni	Co	Cr	Mo	W	Cb	Ti	Al	Fe
K42B	0.03	0.78	0.34	41.3	21.7	17.7	....	....	....	2.55	0.55	15.3
Refractaloy 26	0.04	0.8	0.93	37	20	18	3.2	....	....	2.52	0.24	17
Refractaloy 70	0.11	1.97	0.25	20.1	30.1	20.2	8.3	3.8	....	....	....	15.2
Discaloy 26	0.05	0.7	0.4	25.2	.....	8.3	....	....	....	2.33	0.42	Remainder
S-816	0.40	0.58	0.54	20.23	47.7	19.5	3.93	3.45	4.06	....	....	2.95
N-156	0.33	1.48	0.57	33.23	23.69	15.66	3.02	2.10	1.03	....	....	Remainder
Nimonic 80*	0.04	0.56	0.48	74.23	.....	21.18	....	....	....	2.44	0.63	0.38
Inconel W	0.03	0.53	0.52	74.82	.....	14.4	....	....	....	2.77	0.63	6.17
Rolled vitallium	0.22	0.73	0.57	2.92	61.4	27.56	5.9	....	....	....	....	0.50
17-W	0.46	0.58	0.43	19.16	.....	13.19	0.52	2.48	....	....	....	Remainder
Timken 16-25-6	0.08	1.34	0.31	23.15	.....	17.95	6.79	....	....	....	....	51
Hastelloy B	0.05	0.59	0.19	65.10	.....	.....	28.63	....	....	....	....	4.7
Rex 78*	0.08	....	....	18	.....	14	4	....	....	0.6	....	Remainder (Cu 4.0)
Tinidur†	0.15	0.6	0.7	30	.....	15	....	....	....	1.7	....	Remainder

* British alloy.
† German alloy.

The austenitic blade alloys are hardened both by hot-cold-working (below the recrystallization temperature) and through the use of precipitation hardening agents such as beryllium, titanium, and molybdenum. Carbon is also used in some alloys that are almost entirely work-hardened.

Approximate chemical compositions of a few alloys are given in Table 4. These materials do not have remarkable properties at room temperatures, but retain their strength at temperatures well above 1000°F, so that they can be forged only at temperatures well above those for mild steel and the lower alloys. When properly heat-treated, they machine without great difficulty (with the exception of carbon-hardened alloys) and are then given final heat-treatment.

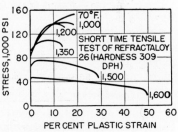

FIG. 149. Short-time stress-strain curves for Refractaloy 26.

Short-time tensile and elongation tests carried out on high-temperature alloys are useful primarily in evaluating heat-treatment, work-hardening, and basic composition variables. Short-time tensile tests are usually made by subjecting the test specimen to a constant strain rate (800 percent/hr) at the test temperature. Typical stress-strain curves for test samples of Refractaloy 26 (after solution treatment at 2100°F for 1 hr, aging at 1500°F for 20 hr, and second aging at 1350°F for 20 hr) are shown in Fig. 149.

Turbine blades are required to withstand static stress loads due to centrifugal force, and in addition are subjected to vibratory stresses.

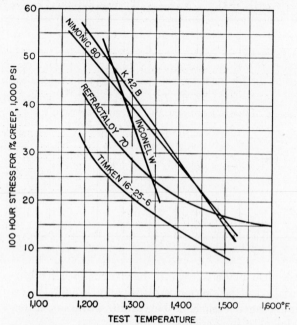

Fɪɢ. 150.   Results of 100-hr creep tests for wrought alloys of Table 4.

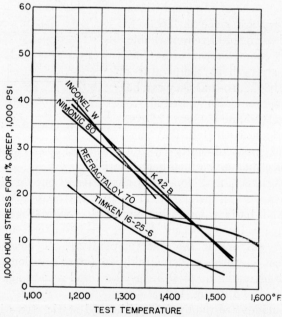

Fɪɢ. 151.   Results of 1,000-hr creep tests for wrought alloys of Table 4.

Blades suffer a slow, plastic yielding or deformation on the static loads, whether the cyclic loads are superimposed or not, and creep tests are made to determine stress required to produce a given creep in a given time. Short-time creep strength is based upon the load necessary to produce 1 percent permanent elongation in 100 hr; a longer test is made for 1,000-hr creep strength also. Since most gas-turbine blades are short, 1 percent elongation can be tolerated without producing rubs or interference. Results of 100-hr creep tests are given in Fig. 150 for some of the alloys of Table 4, and 1,000-hr results are shown in Fig. 151.

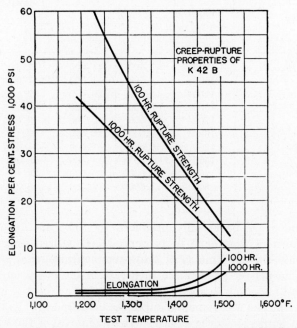

Fig. 152.   Rupture strength and elongation tests for K42B.

Actual rupture under static load may occur in some materials before 1 percent elongation is achieved, and in any case rupture tests are of much concern, as is also ductility or elongation before failure. Curves of stress for rupture in 100 and 1,000 hr are plotted against temperature in Fig. 152 along with elongation for K42B. Data for other alloys are presented in Table 5.

The data presented in Figs. 150, 151, and 152 are subject to rather wide variations, depending upon the previous history of the test piece, cold-working schedule, heat-treatment, etc. Usually blade designs are worked somewhat too close to average test results for safety. The normal statistical spread of creep-rupture strengths for a given alloy of specified work- and heat-treatment leads one to wonder just how some turbines with 50 to 200 blades get through type testing without losing at least one blade. More uniform results would be expected of the wrought alloys, with controlled schedules for reduction of the ingot and subsequent working and heat-treatment, than for cast blades. However, this is not necessarily true in the present state of the art.

TABLE 5

Alloy	Temper- ature, °F	Creep-to-rupture stress, psi		Elongation, percent	
		100 hr	1,000 hr	100 hr	1,000 hr
K42B................	1200	67,000	41,000	1.2	0.5
	1500	15,000	11,000	7.0	4.0
Nimonic 80...........	1200	49,000	39,000	2	1
	1500	17,500	10,000	7	2
Inconel W............	1200	60,000	40,000	3	0.5
	1500	32,000	16,500	2	1
Refractaloy 70.........	1200	55,000	41,000	34	31
	1500	18,500	14,500	22	14
Timken 16-25-6........	1200	52,000	35,000	29	18
	1500	13,000	3,500	8	3.5

Cast blades are universally produced by the lost-wax process. A master pattern of the shape to be reproduced is used as a pattern in forming semipermanent molds of a low-temperature-metal alloy. Wax replicas of the master pattern are then cast in the metal molds. After trimming and fastening to a gate, the wax models are coated with a silica investment, and the wax is melted out of the investment. Molten casting alloy is then poured into the cavities left by removal of the wax to form the cast blade shapes. Blades so cast receive no work-hardening after casting, which is their principal difference from wrought blades, and the grain structure of the metal and other physical properties depend upon composition of the alloy, conditions under which the cast is made, and heat-treatment subsequent to casting.

A number of the wrought-blade alloys have been used in making blades by the casting technique. However, the principal advantage of the casting process, apart from a possible lower production cost, is in being able to fabricate into blades materials whose mechanical working characteristics are so difficult as to make machining impractical. The typical compositions of a number of casting alloys are listed in Table 6.

Creep-stress curves for 1 percent elongation are shown for 100 hr in

Fig. 153 and for 1,000 hr in Fig. 154 for a number of selected alloys. A tabulation of creep-rupture data is shown in Table 7.

TABLE 6. SOME TYPICAL ANALYSES OF CASTING ALLOYS (PERCENT)

Alloy	C	Mn	Si	Ni	Co	Cr	Mo	W	Cb	Fe
S-816............	0.40	0.58	0.54	20.23	43.7	19.5	3.93	3.45	4.05	2.95
Vitallium............	0.22	1.0	0.6	1.5	62	28.6	5.74			
422-19............	0.4	....	0.51	15.92	Remainder	24.75	6.08	....	....	0.65
S-495............	0.4	....	....	20	....	14	4	4	4	Remainder
19-9 W Mo............	0.29	0.65	0.79	9.4	....	18.85	1.33	1.15	0.4	Remainder (0.16 Ti)
S-590............	0.47	0.94	0.71	20.55	20	20.28	4.08	4.22	4.72	Remainder
Stellite 23............	0.56	....	....	....	65.12	26.57	0.39	5.08		
Stellite 27............	0.50	....	....	30.91	33.85	26.4	6.14			
X-40............	0.48	0.64	0.72	9.69	55.23	25.12	....	7.23	....	0.55
Ticonium............	0.18	0.7	0.37	31.42	32.46	27.46	5.29	....	....	1.56
Co-Cr (9 Mo)............	0.42	0.68	0.68	2.88	Remainder	22.73	9.24	....	....	0.85
60 Cr-25 Fe-15 Mo............	0.022	....	0.70	....	....	60.44	14.63	....	....	Remainder
AN-95............	0.36	....	....	22.15	27.45	29.14	17.64	....	....	0.63

TABLE 7

Alloy	Temper- ature, °F	Creep-to-rupture stress, psi		Elongation, percent	
		100 hr	1,000 hr	100 hr	1,000 hr
Vitallium..............	1200	56,000	33,000	7.5	5
	1500	18,000	10,000	9	5.5
Stellite 23..............	1200	51,500	42,000	4	2.7
	1500	27,000	21,000	8	5
S-816..............	1200	56,000	49,000	6	20
	1500	24,000	17,000	9	7
S-495..............	1200	40,000	33,000	8.4	10.4
	1500	17,500	14,000	10	7

In addition to the alloys already discussed, some of the pure metals and high-percentage alloys of these metals have sufficiently elevated melting points that strength is maintained in the temperature ranges of interest to turbine designers. These metals are molybdenum, titanium, tungsten, and tantalum. Tungsten and tantalum are sufficiently scarce in nature that their general use as blade materials is prohibited. Molybdenum and titanium are relatively abundant, and molybdenum is now being produced as a pure wrought metal in substantial quantities. Titanium is in the early development stages of such production. The creep strength of molybdenum at temperatures beyond those allowable for any of the previous alloys appears to hold much promise for the future;

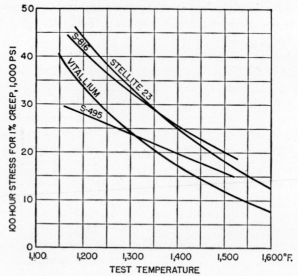

Fig. 153.   Results of 100-hr creep tests for casting alloys of Table 6.

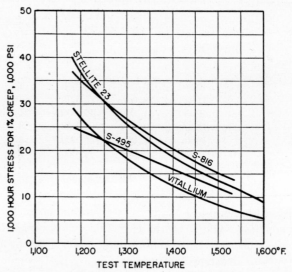

Fig. 154.   Results of 1,000-hr creep tests for casting alloys of Table 6.

however, molybdenum must be protected against oxidizing atmospheres beyond about 750°F and this problem has not been solved as yet.   Titanium has the further advantage of low specific gravity, but the oxidation protection problem is also present.

Ceramic materials have also been investigated for use as turbine blades.   The alumina-type ceramics have fairly high melting points and maintain strength close to their melting points. Beryllia ceramics extend the temperature range still farther. However, ceramic materials have low resistance to heat shock and are very prone to stress-concentration brittleness; in other words, elongation before failure is exceedingly small. There is no short-time plastic flow of ceramics in the way that metals yield; while there is a definite long-time plastic flow, a sudden shock may result in fracture. A fundamental change in turbine design to permit compression loading of blades instead of tensile loading might make ceramic blades practical. Of course, such a design change would greatly extend temperature limits for metals also. Ceramics were used as coating materials for blades in Germany for nozzle vanes. Low-alloy steels were given porcelain-enamel coats to provide oxidation protection; results were of questionable value.

34. Turbine-disc Materials. Operating conditions for turbine discs are as critical as for turbine blades. Disc temperatures are lower than blade temperatures, but stresses are generally higher by a large margin. Some of the alloys used for wrought blades are suitable for use as disc materials and have been so used. Timken 16-25-6 and Rex 78 are examples. K42B, Refractaloy 26, and Discaloy 26 also have a dual usefulness as blade and disc materials. G18B has been widely used in England and has a nominal composition of 0.4 C, 13.5 Ni, 13.5 Cr, 2.5 W, 2 Mo, 10 Co, and niobium and tantalum 2.8 percent, with the remainder iron. The alloy 19-9 DL of nominal composition 0.3 C, 0.6 Si, 1.0 Mn, 1.9 Cr, 9 Ni, 1.25 Mo, 1.0 W, 0.4 Cb, 0.3 Ti, and the balance iron has been widely used in this country along with Timken 16-25-6.

Discaloy 25, similar to Discaloy 26, except that chromium is 13 percent instead of 8 percent, appears to have good properties for turbine discs, as does N-155, similar to N-156 except for higher chromium and lower nickel content. The 1,000-hr rupture and creep characteristics of a number of these alloys are given in Table 8 for 1200°F disc temperature.

TABLE 8

Alloy	1,000-hr rupture		1,000-hr stress for 1 percent creep, psi
	Strength, psi	Elongation, percent	
K42B	48,000	0.5	48,000
N-155	42,000	10	35,000
19-9 DL	38,900	2	36,700
Timken 16-25-6	35,500	11.5	35,000
Discaloy 25	36,000	5	37,000
G18B	37,000	2.5	33,500

Discs require a certain amount of ductility at the rim under present practice for blade fastenings. Early turbine designs used bulb-type roots with loose fits in the discs; stretching of the necks between blades in disc rims was excessive, however. The tendency now is to use tree-type roots driven in for rather snug fits, or to weld the blades to the disc rim. Some composite discs have been made with rims of high-temperature austenitic steel welded to centers of ferritic steel; this makes easier the problem of forging a stub shaft onto the center of the turbine wheel. Other turbine discs have had very short stub shafts forged on the blank, and low-alloy-steel shafts then flash-welded to the stub. Still other discs are drilled for through bolts at the center with the holes reamed and polished to reduce stress concentration.

It may prove practical to precision-cast complete wheels, disc with blades in one piece, for small turbines. This has not been done for larger turbine wheels. Large discs of N-155 have been cast experimentally both in sand and centrifugally.

CHAPTER 7

THE JET NOZZLE

35. Gas Flows in Nozzles. Aircraft-turbine exhaust systems have one point in common, whether connected to a jet engine or a turboprop engine; the gas flow leaves at a relatively high velocity and provides a substantial forward thrust. In the case of the jet engine, all the useful thrust derived from the engine comes from the exhaust velocity. In the case of a turboprop engine or one of the hybrid types known generally as thrust augmenters, from 15 to 50 percent of the useful thrust in flight

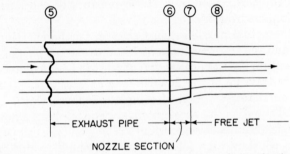

FIG. 155. Exhaust duct and nozzle, illustrating abrupt nozzle termination in region of converging flow.

may be attributed to the velocity of the nozzle exhaust flow. Therefore, substantial pressure differentials must exist between nozzle inlet and nozzle outlet. The sections of Chap. 3 relating to flows in ducts and passages are particularly useful in nozzle design, and Figs. 31, 32, and 33 may be used to assist in the solution of many nozzle problems. Section 9 is devoted to nozzle flow problems, and the basic theory will not be repeated here.

There are a number of design factors in aircraft-gas-turbine exhaust nozzles that may result in departures from the theoretical flows of Sec. 9. Perhaps the most common cause for divergence between practice and theory appears in the theoretical assumption of streamline flow and the neglect of transverse velocity effects in flow passages of changing area. Gas-turbine exhaust nozzles often terminate abruptly before flow streamlines are parallel and while large transverse components of flow velocity are present.

An exhaust duct and nozzle of this type are shown in Fig. 155. The section of the exhaust duct at station 5 represents the point at which the turbine efflux is received. The section from 5 to 6 is a relatively low velocity exhaust duct of uniform section. Between 6 and 7 is the nozzle section within which the flow is accelerated. However, the flow streamlines close to the nozzle walls are not parallel as the gas leaves the nozzle at station 7, and the transverse flow velocities of these streamlines produce a vena contracta in the flow at station 8. The energy of transverse flow velocity is in large part translated to parallel flow velocity at the vena contracta. The flow process between stations 7 and 8 is quite efficient. Here, the flow takes place much as though the nozzle walls followed the streamlines down to the vena contracta with the transverse flow velocities of the outer flow sheaths providing effective ram or velocity pressure heads to balance the positive differential between static pressure at station 7 and the atmospheric pressure. At station 8, the vena contracta, the flow is fully expanded, and static pressure of the flow is equal to atmospheric pressure (for subsonic flows).

While the actual nozzle exhaust area is A_7, the effective nozzle exit area is A_8, and the static pressure at 7 is above atmospheric. The velocity or momentum thrust of the actual nozzle can be calculated if a velocity and pressure traverse of the flow is made at station 7. It may also be calculated on the assumption of complete expansion at 7 by using the conventional equations for accelerated flow and applying a flow coefficient.

If the nozzle section between 6 and 7 is long and the exit end terminates in a pipe of constant area (of a length over one diameter or more), the flow-contraction coefficient, or more briefly the flow coefficient, may be as high as 0.98 to 0.99. Weight, space, and efficiency limitations frequently dictate short, abrupt nozzles with high transverse velocities at the exit. Effective exit areas of such exhaust nozzles may be as low as 70 percent of the actual areas. A common figure is 85 percent contraction or flow coefficient. Effective flow velocity is calculated on the basis of experimentally determined efficiency and flow coefficients for different nozzles.

While a long nozzle with a slow taper may have an actual flow within 2 or 3 percent of the theoretical flow, a large part of this flow would take place at very high Mach numbers in the average jet-engine exhaust system. Friction flow losses would be high, and efficiency would suffer. Therefore, even when there is ample physical space for a long nozzle with a small taper to the walls, it is customary to make the flow-accelerating portion of the nozzle short and to hold the flow velocity in the connecting duct to $M < 0.5$. Common efficiency values for short expansion nozzles lie between 0.9 and 0.95. If the exhaust nozzle suffers from an overabundance of struts and other structures that interfere with the flow, or if the nozzle walls are irregular or rough by design, or buckled by unequal thermal expansions, the efficiency may be considerably lower.

Losses in ducts connecting the exhaust nozzle to the turbine exit area are measured experimentally and are also estimated by the methods used in Section 11, which deals with gas flows with friction. Results are normally obtained as a loss in total pressure from duct entrance to duct exit. The new value of total pressure is then used as the entrance condition for the nozzle proper. Figure 40 applies with only slight errors for total pressure ratios up to 1.03. Since the usual jet engine operates with an exhaust velocity in the region of $M = 0.6$ to 1.0, a loss of 1 percent total pressure due to friction in the connecting exhaust duct will result in approximately 1 percent loss of thrust. About the best that can be

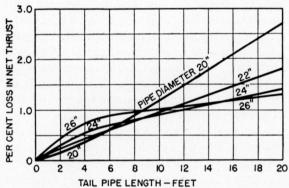

FIG. 156. Dependence of net thrust loss on tail-pipe length and diameter. (*Based on General Electric Company data.*)

expected is 0.6 percent loss in thrust for each 10 ft of connecting exhaust pipe (for jet engines of 3,000- to 4,000-lb thrust rating), and losses may be as large as 2 percent or more for small-diameter pipes of the same length or tail pipes continuously tapered to the desired nozzle exit area.

A very large exhaust pipe or tail pipe on the gas turbine may require retardation or diffusion of the exhaust flow leaving the turbine. The flow velocity in the pipe section will be low, and friction losses may be quite low, but the flow must be accelerated in the nozzle section from this low velocity to the final exhaust velocity. The total loss is the sum of friction losses in the tail pipe and entrance diffusion and nozzle losses due to low pipe-flow velocity. For any specified flow and length of exhaust system, there is a best diameter for the tail pipe from the over-all efficiency standpoint. Figure 156 shows the decrease in net thrust for different exhaust-pipe diameters plotted against length of tail pipe for a jet engine with a flow of 80 lb of gas per second at a total temperature of approximately 1200°F at sea-level exit condition. The lower envelope of the family of curves indicates a different tail-pipe diameter for each length for minimum thrust loss. The shapes of the curves for the larger pipe sizes show the effects of excessive diffusion and acceleration losses when large tail pipes are used for short lengths of exhaust system. Flow Mach number in the small 20-in.-diameter pipe is about 0.65, increasing to approximately $M = 0.95$ at the vena contracta after the nozzle. The flow velocity in the 26-in.-diameter pipe is at the other extreme, approximately $M = 0.26$.

36. Variable-area Nozzles. Turbojet engines may have exhaust nozzles with either fixed or adjustable exit areas. If performance is calculated on the basis of a fixed effective nozzle exit area, such a jet engine suffers by comparison with the performance of a similar jet engine with a jet nozzle whose exit area may be controlled. The only control available to the pilot or operator of the open-cycle aircraft jet-turbine engine is the fuel/air ratio, when a fixed-area nozzle is used. There will be occasions when upper limits on turbine shaft speed or upon turbine inlet temperature, or both, will force the use of a restrictively low fuel/air ratio. The available net thrust may then be as much as 30 percent lower than the thrust that would be available if a controllable nozzle were applied, thus permitting better matching of the compressor-burner–turbine characteristic to the ideal jet condition.

A large nozzle exit area at A_7 reduces the turbine back pressure and leads to easier starting at a lower rpm and lower turbine inlet temperature. This is of a great deal of importance in large engines where the mechanical power required for starting the engine is a serious problem in aircraft installations. The engine will also accelerate to its rated speed more quickly with an open tail position than it will when the jet nozzle has a small area and the turbine is working against a high back pressure. In general, starting conditions and low-velocity flight with low thrust requirements are best met with an open jet nozzle. Maximum thrusts at take-off and in flight may require a smaller nozzle exit area, and the fixed-area nozzle always imposes a performance penalty under some conditions. Too small a nozzle area may even result in choking flows in the jet, with a serious limitation on mass air intake at higher flight velocities.

However, the actual performance of a jet engine with a nozzle such as the one shown in Fig. 155 is somewhat better than would be expected on the basis of a fixed effective exhaust area. The flow coefficient of the nozzle is not rigidly fixed, and is somewhat larger for the lower mass flows. The vena contracta moves downstream and is smaller in diameter for the higher flow Mach numbers. Therefore, under starting conditions, the effect is equivalent to opening the nozzle exit area slightly. However, engine control is still by fuel/air ratio or turbine inlet temperature, and the shaft speed of the engine for a given altitude and flight speed is definitely tied to the thrust requirement. If the particular requirement at the moment results in an engine speed that is unfavorable from an efficiency standpoint, nothing can be done about it without changing the exit area.

A variable nozzle exit area permits operation of a jet engine over a wide range of inlet conditions at shaft speeds preselected for the most

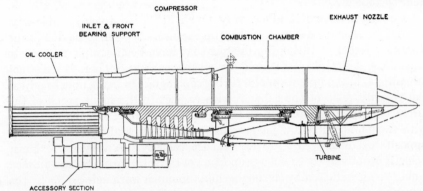

Fig. 157. Sectional view of Westinghouse 19XB jet engine with manually adjustable tail cone for varying exhaust nozzle area.

efficient over-all operation. A further advantage is that jet thrust may be changed as quickly as the tail-adjustment mechanism can be moved, without waiting for the rotating parts of the jet engine to go through a large speed change. The position of the nozzle-area control may be maintained manually or by means of an automatic engine flight control.

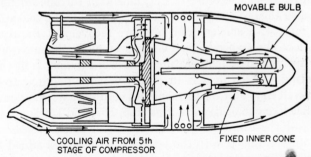

Fig. 158. Exhaust end of Jumo 004 jet engine, movable bulb for adjusting exhaust nozzle area.

A sectional view of an axial-flow jet engine with manually adjustable exhaust nozzle area is shown in Fig. 157; the tail cone is moved to the right to reduce the nozzle area and to the left to increase the flow area. A bulb-type valve for controlling exhaust nozzle area of the Jumo 004 jet engine is shown in Fig. 158. Functionally, the Jumo bulb valve is no different from the tail cone of Fig. 157, but the flow of cooling air through struts and around the nozzle structure is of particular interest. Cooling-air requirements are severe when high-temperature alloys are not used in the tail pipe and nozzle cone construction. Exhaust-gas total temperatures of 1100 to 1200°F are usual for jet engines with a turbine inlet temperature of 1500°F. Transient temperatures at starting may exceed 1200°F by a considerable margin, even when the turbine inlet is held to 1500°F.

Designers have not given very much attention to adjustable-area exhaust nozzles for use with turboprop engines. This may be due to the limited number of turboprop designs that have been completed to date and to the desirability of simplicity in early engines. There is a distinct advantage, in the operation of a turboprop engine, in being able to adjust the velocity ratio of the exhaust with respect to the flight speed of the aircraft. It is possible then to avoid excessively high exhaust velocities with their inherently low jet-propulsive efficiency, and also to avoid the opposite extreme of too low an exhaust velocity. A very low exhaust velocity results in too small a proportion of the total thrust being obtained from the air inducted by the engine and too much work being done by the propeller. A proper balance results in a smaller propeller and reduction gear, which should mean a lighter weight engine and quite probably a more efficient one. This will be discussed more fully in Chap. 9 under the subject of controls.

37. Supersonic Jet Flows. The preceding pages of this discussion of jet nozzles have carried the assumption of a subsonic jet velocity at the nozzle exit. This is generally the case for jet engines at low flight speeds, compression ratios of the order of 4:1, and with turbine inlet temperatures limited to 1500 to 1600°F. However, at high flight velocities above 500 to 600 mph with efficient ram pressure recovery at the compressor inlet, or at low flight speeds with engines of higher compression ratios and higher turbine inlet temperatures, the work available in the nozzle for accelerating the jet flow is in excess of that required to produce critical flow velocity, and a supersonic jet results. When a simple convergent nozzle like one of those in Figs. 155, 157, and 158 is used, critical flows occurs at the exit or slightly downstream at the vena contracta. The momentum thrust due to the jet velocity then has added to it the static pressure differential existing across the exhaust area above the atmospheric static pressure at the exhaust. If the exhaust nozzle exit area A_7 is taken as the effective flow area, the gross thrust at the nozzle is

$$F_g = W_a \frac{V_7}{g} + A_7(p_7 - p_0) \tag{180}$$

where p_0 is the atmospheric pressure and is equal to p_8.

The net thrust is the gross thrust less the ram drag, where V_0 is the flight speed,

$$F_n = W_a \frac{V_7 - V_0}{g} + A_7(p_7 - p_0) \tag{181}$$

If the jet nozzle were a convergent-divergent nozzle of the correct form, an ideal thrust would result from the fully expanded supersonic jet flow

$$F_{ideal} = W_a \frac{V_{ideal} - V_0}{g} \tag{182}$$

The ratio of the actual net thrust from a simple convergent nozzle with critical flow at the exit to the ideal thrust of a convergent-divergent supersonic nozzle is then Eq. (181) divided by Eq. (182)

$$\frac{F_n}{F_{ideal}} = \frac{V_7 - V_0}{V_{ideal} - V_0} + \frac{A_7 g}{W_a} \frac{p_7 - p_0}{V_{ideal} - V_0}$$
$$= \frac{M_7 a_7 - M_0 a_0}{M_i a_i - M_0 a_0} + \frac{g R T_7}{M_7 a_7} \frac{1 - (p_0/p_7)}{M_i a_i - M_0 a_0} \tag{183}$$

M_i in Eq. (183) is the flow Mach number of the ideal supersonic flow. By making $M_7 = 1.0$, and by introducing θ as the ratio of the total temperature T_7 in the jet to the free-stream atmospheric temperature t_0, and by introducing the ratio of the static pressure p_0 to the static pressure p_7, which is

$$\frac{p_0}{p_7} = \left\{ \frac{1 + [(k-1)/2]M_7^2}{1 + [(k-1)/2]M_i^2} \right\}^{\frac{k}{k-1}}$$

Eq. (183) may be reduced to a dimensionless equation in terms of M_0, M_i, and θ_n

$$\frac{F_n}{F_{ideal}} =$$

$$\frac{\dfrac{1}{\sqrt{1 + \dfrac{k-1}{2}}} - \dfrac{M_0}{\sqrt{\theta_n}} + \dfrac{1}{k\sqrt{1 + \dfrac{k-1}{2}}}\left[1 - \left(\dfrac{1 + \dfrac{k-1}{2}}{1 + \dfrac{k-1}{2}M_i^2}\right)^{\frac{k}{k-1}}\right]}{\dfrac{M_i}{\sqrt{1 + \dfrac{k-1}{2}M_i^2}} - \dfrac{M_0}{\sqrt{\theta_n}}} \tag{184}$$

The thrust ratio of Eq. (184) is plotted in Fig. 159 against $M_0/\sqrt{\theta_n}$ for different values of M_i. Scales for M_0 are also shown with $\theta_n = T_7/t_0 = 3$ and 4, corresponding to exhaust total temperatures of 1040°F and 1560°F

with an ambient atmospheric temperature of 520°R.   The derivation of
Eq. (184) was based upon a loss-free expansion process.   A solution for
a nozzle with less than 100 percent efficiency requires a step-by-step
solution, and for nozzle efficiencies of the order of 85 to 90 percent, the
results are not substantially different from those of Eq. (184) at low flight
speeds.   For small values of M_0 in the conventional flight-speed ranges
below $M_0 = 1.0$, the thrust lost as a consequence of using a simple convergent nozzle with critical exit flow instead of a supersonic nozzle is
small.   The same is true of higher flight velocities when the temperature
ratio is larger.   A high flight
Mach number requires a high
value of θ.

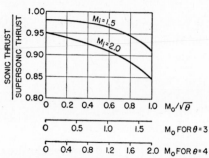

FIG. 159.   Thrust ratio of Eq. (184) plotted
against flight Mach number for two values of
ideal jet velocity.

The mechanical difficulties in
a convergent-divergent exhaust
nozzle with adjustable throat area
are formidable.   Adding an adjustable final exit area in order to
obtain a matched supersonic jet
exhaust has not yet appeared
worth the small gain in thrust
that might be realized.   Added
to these practical difficulties of
increased mechanical complications, space, and engine weight, is the
difficulty of designing the supersonic portion of the nozzle to be free of
shock.

Design criteria have been established for shock-free supersonic nozzles
in which the rate of change of area with length is carefully controlled.[1]
However, it would prove very difficult to adhere to these limitations in an
adjustable jet-engine exhaust nozzle.   It is general practice to use a
simple convergent nozzle, with critical flow at the exit if sufficient energy
is available in the jet flow to produce acoustic velocity.   The unexpanded
flow at the exit then explodes out of the nozzle, following the limitations
established in Chap. 3 for supersonic flows around corners.   That part
of the flow divergence angle after the nozzle which is due to supersonic
expansion, rather than to diffusion and entrainment of the surrounding
atmosphere, can be estimated from Fig. 65 if the ideal supersonic Mach
number of the flow is known.   For a pressure ratio corresponding to a
flow $M_{\text{ideal}} = 1.4$, the divergence angle after leaving the nozzle at $M = 1.0$
is approximately 8 deg on a side.   Figure 65 is for two-dimensional flow,
but at low divergence angles, the two-dimensional flow turning angle is

[1] SHAPIRO, Nozzles for Supersonic Flow without Shock Fronts, *J. Applied
Mechanics*, vol. 11, p. A93, 1944.

very nearly the same as the three-dimensional flow turning angle for cylindrical coordinates. Therefore, the total included angle of the cone of exhaust gas leaving the nozzle exit would be about 16 deg. Since the ideal supersonic flow for the conventional jet engine would seldom if ever approach $M_{ideal} \geq 1.4$, the expansion of the exhaust-jet cone due to supersonic explosion of the gas out of the nozzle is small.

Velocity- and temperature-distribution maps of the jet efflux of a typical nozzle are shown in Fig. 160 for approximately 1100°F total temperature and sonic flow at the exit, and at a mass flow rate of 50 lb of air per second at sea level. Supersonic flows after the nozzle exit would increase the flow divergence angles only slightly beyond those of Fig. 160.

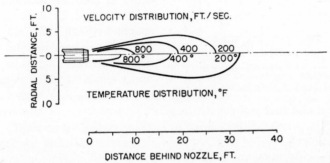

FIG. 160. Temperature and velocity distributions in the jet wake of a typical nozzle.

38. Exhaust-system Construction and Materials. The same types of materials are used in jet-engine and turboprop exhaust systems as are used in combustion chambers. Columbium-stabilized stainless steel is an example of a current material. Total temperature of the exhaust gas after leaving the turbine is of the order of 1200°F for jet engines with turbine inlet temperatures in the range of 1500 to 1600°F. The total temperature in a turboprop-engine exhaust may be more than 200°F lower. At the nozzle exit of this jet engine, the static or free-stream temperature will be about 1000°F; but in the remainder of the exhaust system, it is very close to the total temperature if flow Mach number is kept to a low value. Gas turbines operated at higher turbine inlet temperatures will have correspondingly higher exhaust-system temperatures.

Exhaust temperatures of a typical jet engine under actual flight conditions are shown in Fig. 161. Corresponding jet thrusts are shown on the same figure. The need for materials capable of resisting high temperatures is evident. Because of the high velocity of flow of the hot exhaust over the inner surfaces of tail pipes and nozzles, it is difficult to provide effective cooling by cold air flow over the external surfaces.

High cooling rates would require excessively large flows of cooling air; so that ordinarily cooling is achieved by means of heat baffles or radiation shields inside the pressure-carrying shell, or the shell is wrapped in insulating material and allowed to rise almost to the exhaust temperature.

A shell with one heat baffle and a very small amount of cooling air moving between the baffle and shell at approximately the turbine inlet

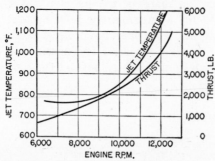

Fig. 161. Exhaust temperatures and corresponding thrusts of a typical jet engine in flight. Static test of Rolls Royce Nene.

pressure would be expected to have a hot-spot temperature of 900 to 950°F for a 1500°F jet-turbine admission temperature. A nozzle and exhaust pipe wrapped with insulating material such as asbestos blanket, metallic screen, thin metal foils with dead air spaces between foils, etc., would have a temperature under the insulation very close to 1200°F under similar turbine inlet conditions. Insulating materials that soak up oil and fuel and constitute a fire hazard are to be avoided. The sketch of the Jumo 004 jet engine in Fig. 158 shows a half-length cooling shroud inside the nozzle shell. Cooling air extracted after the fifth compressor stage (8 stages total) flows around bearings, turbine disc, through hollow turbine blades, struts, etc., and finally between nozzle shroud and shell. A sheath of cold air continues to flow along the inner surface of the nozzle after the shroud is terminated and provides effective cooling.

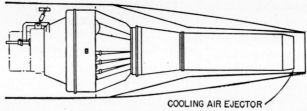

COOLING AIR EJECTOR

Fig. 162. Schematic of General Electric I-40 jet-engine installation illustrating ejector cooling action.

It is usual practice to place the end of the jet nozzle with respect to other aircraft structure so as to induce a flow of cooling air over the nozzle shell by ejector action (see Fig. 162).

Highest exhaust-system temperatures are encountered under starting conditions. Turbine inlet temperatures are at the upper limit, and sometimes a little beyond limits, in order to permit starting at the lowest possible engine-cranking speed and power. However, both compression ratio and turbine expansion ratio are very low under starting conditions, and gas from the burners flows through the turbine without giving up much heat. As a consequence, exhaust temperatures are only a few degrees below the maximum permissible turbine nozzle inlet temperatures under transient starting conditions. The thermal capacity of thin sheet metals used in exhaust pipe and nozzle construction is low, so that tail pipe and nozzle reach their maximum temperatures in a few seconds.

Exhaust systems are subjected to the static pressure loads of gas flows inside the ducting, and also to the pressure forces of cooling air and ram air in flight on external surfaces. These forces are considerable, and must be taken into account for each particular gas-turbine application. In addition to the relatively steady air flow forces, large transient pressure forces may appear in the event of unsteady engine operation described earlier in the discussion of combustion stability.

CHAPTER 8

GAS-TURBINE CYCLES

39. The Joule Cycle. An open-cycle gas turbine without heat exchangers or reheaters operates on the Joule or Brayton cycle. This consists of two isentropic and two isobaric processes, in the ideal case. The pressure-volume changes throughout the cycle are shown in Fig. 163. The enthalpy-entropy diagram is also shown in the same figure. Air is taken in at normal atmospheric conditions at A, is compressed to state B; heat is added at constant pressure between B and C; expansion takes

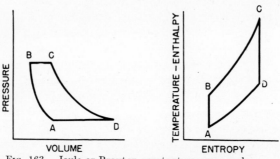

Fig. 163.   Joule or Brayton constant-pressure cycle.

place from C to D. Cooling then occurs between D and A to return the working gas to the initial conditions. In the open-cycle gas turbine, fresh air is continuously inducted at A, and the exhaust is continuously discharged to the atmosphere at D.

The mechanical work expended in compressing the air is proportional to $T_B - T_A$ on the temperature-entropy (or enthalpy-entropy) diagram. The heat added is proportional to $T_C - T_B$, and the work of expansion to $T_C - T_D$. The excess of available energy of expansion over the required work of compression is available as shaft energy from the turbine or may be used to accelerate the exhaust to high velocity in a jet nozzle. The work output for the idealized gas turbine per pound of air is therefore

$$\frac{P}{J} = c_p[(T_C - T_D) - (T_B - T_A)]$$

Since the fuel energy input is $c_p(T_C - T_B)$, the ideal cycle efficiency is

$$\eta = \frac{c_p(T_C - T_D) - c_p(T_B - T_A)}{c_p(T_C - T_B)}$$

204

Expansion and compression are both between the same pressure limits in the ideal case, so that $T_B/T_A = T_C/T_D$. The cycle efficiency therefore reduces to

$$\eta = 1 - \frac{T_A}{T_B} \tag{185}$$

It is interesting to observe that the ideal cycle efficiency as defined by Eq. (185) is dependent only upon the ratio of T_B/T_A, a function of the compression ratio. It is independent of the top temperature of the cycle, T_C, and changes only when the compression ratio changes. If losses are associated with the various changes of state, as always occurs in practice, Eq. (185) does not apply, and the ratio of top temperature to inlet temperature, T_C/T_A, is of equal importance with compression ratio in determining the efficiency of gas-turbine cycles with current component efficiencies and temperature limits.

Figure 164 is a temperature-entropy chart for air with lines of constant pressure shown. The temperature-entropy diagram for an actual gas-turbine cycle is plotted over this chart. This plot is for a turbojet engine with the various stage numbers corresponding to the numbers shown on the schematic diagram of the axial-flow jet engine in Fig. 165. These stage numbers correspond to similar illustrations previously used. The ideal temperature-enthalpy plot would follow 0-3'-4'-7''-0. The actual stages are as described below.

The jet engine shown is in an aircraft at a pressure-altitude of 10 psi and $t_0 = 0°F$ at flight Mach number $M_0 = 0.5$ or $V_0 = 525$ fps. The total ram temperature is

$$T_2 = t_0 \left(1 + \frac{k-1}{2} M_0^2 \right) = 483°R$$

The total ram pressure would have been $P_2 = 1.185 P_0 = 11.85$ psi if the entire ram diffusion process had been loss-free. However, the diffusion is assumed to be 90 percent effective, and the total pressure at state point 2 is $P_2 = (1 + 0.185 \times 0.90)10 = 11.66$ psi. The compressor receives air at a reduced total pressure of 11.66 psi and at an unaltered $T_2 = 483°R$, and compresses it through a ratio of 4:1 at an efficiency of $\eta_c = 0.85$ to a final pressure of $P_3 = 46.64$ psi and $T_3 = 758°R$.

Heat is then added in the burner between states 3 and 4. Ideally, this is an isobaric process. Actually there is a loss in total pressure assumed to be 5 percent in this case. The final temperature is limited to $T_4 = 2000°R$, and the pressure is $P_4 = 44.31$ psi.

This hot gas is expanded through the turbine, and the assumption is made here that about 2 percent of cooling air bled from the compressor is sufficient to offset the increase in mass of gas due to fuel addition, so that the mass flow through the turbine is the same as through the compressor. If the mass flow were not the same, the change in flow would have to be used as a multiplier in calculating turbine and nozzle energy processes.

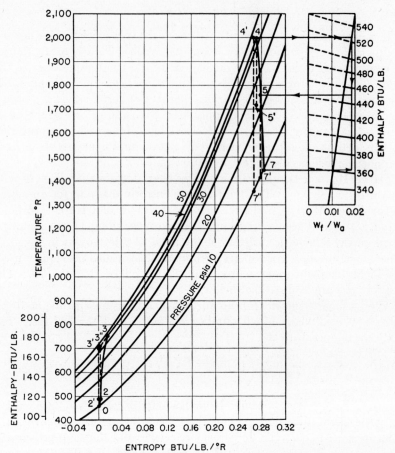

Fig. 164.   Complete cycle diagram of turbojet engine at flight speed $M_0 = 0.5$.

The turbine must provide a shaft output just sufficient to drive the compressor plus fuel pump, lubricating oil pump, electrical accessories, etc.

The compressor shaft input is the difference between the enthalpy at T_3 and the enthalpy at T_2 or $h_3 - h_2 = 66.4$ Btu/lb.   The enthalpy scale on the left side of Fig. 164 is based upon the properties of dry air. The auxiliary load is small, 0.2 Btu/lb of air per second, and is added to the above for a total turbine shaft output requirement of 66.6 Btu/lb of gas flowing.

The specific heat of the hot gas entering the turbine changes with fuel/air ratio, so that a separate enthalpy chart is shown on the right of Fig. 164. Enthalpy lines are plotted against fuel/air ratio, and an upper envelope is shown on this example for the fuel/air ratios required to raise the burner temperature from a T_3 of 758°R to T_4, with 95 percent efficient combustion and 18,600 Btu/lb fuel. A horizontal line is drawn from stage point 4 on the temperature-entropy diagram, intercepting the envelope curve at $W_f/W_a = 0.0193$ on the enthalpy line $h_4 = 525$ Btu. Enthalpy h_5 is therefore $h_4 - 66.6 = 458.4$ Btu/lb. A vertical line is dropped from the envelope intercept at 2000°R and crosses the $h_5 = 458.4$ line. This second intercept then establishes the total temperature of the turbine exhaust at $T_5 = 1760°R$.

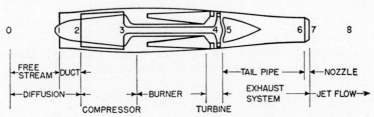

FIG. 165. Schematic of gas turbine showing stage numbers.

The total exhaust pressure of the turbine, P_5, is established on the temperature-enthalpy diagram by dividing $T_4 - T_5$ by $\eta_t = 0.87$ and subtracting from T_4 to find $T_{5'} = 1717°R$. The turbine efficiency is $(T_4 - T_5)/(T_4 - T_{5'})$, by definition. $T_{5'}$ is on an isentropic expansion line below T_4 and establishes the turbine exhaust pressure of $P_{5'} = 23.8$ psi; the constant-pressure line from $P_{5'}$ is followed back up to the temperature T_5 for location of state point 5.

The useful work output of the jet engine is now developed through further expansion of the turbine exhaust in the exhaust system, consisting of the tail pipe and jet nozzle. This expansion is carried to a static atmospheric pressure of 10 psi. If the expansion were perfect, the final static temperature would be $t_{7'} = 1414°R$; however, there are losses in the tail pipe and nozzle, and η_n is observed to be 0.9 in this case. Therefore, $t_7 = T_5 - \eta_n(T_5 - t_{7'}) = 1449°R$, and is located on $P = 10$ psi; h_7 is found by extending t_7 across to the $W_f/W_a = 0.0193$ vertical and finding the h_7 intercept at 365.6 Btu/lb. The velocity of the exhaust relative to the engine is therefore $V_7 = \sqrt{2gJ(h_5 - h_7)} = 2,150$ fps. This is a nozzle efflux Mach number of $M_7 = 1.15$ and would require a convergent-divergent nozzle; actually a simple convergent nozzle would be used with a very small loss in thrust.

However, for the supersonic nozzle, the net thrust of the engine depends only upon the velocity change through the engine

$$F_{net} = \frac{V_7 - V_0}{g} = 50.6 \text{ lb}/(\text{lb})(\text{sec})$$

The thrust power is equal to (net thrust $\times$ flight velocity)/550 = 48.4 hp or 34.2 Btu/lb of air per second. The over-all efficiency is found by dividing the thrust power, in Btu, by the fuel input

$$\frac{h_4 - h_3}{0.95} = \frac{342}{0.95} = 360 \text{ Btu fuel input}$$

and

$$\eta_0 = \frac{34.2}{360} = 0.095$$

Propulsive efficiency is the ratio of thrust power, in Btu, to the difference of the velocity energy at the nozzle and the flight ram energy. The over-all efficiency is the product of the propulsive efficiency, the thermal efficiency, and the burner or combustion efficiency. Therefore, the cycle or thermal efficiency may be calculated as

$$\eta_{th} = \frac{0.095}{0.95 \times 0.392} = 0.255$$

Thermal efficiency is the ratio of energy added to the gas flow (the difference between nozzle energy and ram energy) and the heat energy furnished.

If Fig. 164 were redrawn for static test conditions, state point 2 would correspond to state point 0 except for duct losses, and the absolute pressure at 3 would be lowered accordingly. Available energy between 5 and 7 for acceleration of the exhaust jet would be lower also, and all the jet velocity would be applicable to static thrust.

A turboprop engine would extract a larger amount of expansion energy in the turbine between states 4 and 5, with excess energy over that required to drive the compressor and accessories available for use by the propeller. The available exhaust-jet energy would be reduced by approximately the amount delivered to the propeller. Figure 166 shows enthalpy-entropy diagrams for jet and turboprop engines under static and flight conditions.

While the use of an actual enthalpy-entropy diagram for the solution of thermodynamic problems of gas turbines may be satisfactory for rough work and illustrative purposes, it can lead to unacceptably large errors in actual applications. The difficulty is that the composition of the working fluid changes between states 3 and 4, owing to the addition of fuel and the partial combustion of this fuel. Both the specific heat and the adiabatic coefficient change with the amount of water vapor in the air and also with the fuel/air ratio, as well as with the type of fuel used (usually defined by the H/C ratio for petroleum derivatives). An accurate enthalpy-entropy plot (Mollier diagram) may be drawn for dry air over the ranges of temperatures and pressures encountered in gas turbines. However, air is the working fluid only through the compressor, and even then it normally contains varying amounts of water vapor. The compressor may also ingest water in the form of fog droplets, rain, or snow.

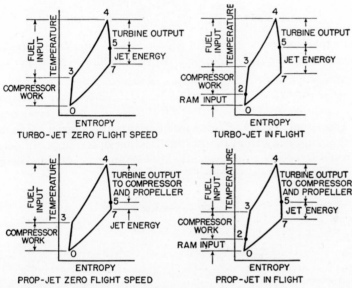

FIG. 166. Temperature-entropy-cycle diagrams of turbojet and propjet power plants, at rest and in flight.

A number of graphical methods of computation of gas-turbine cycles have been worked out with most of the variables encountered adjusted for in the form of correction factors.[1] The graphical data shown in the previous Fig. 164 are incomplete, however, in that no corrections are shown for humidity, and the turbine fluid is correct only for gasoline as the fuel, in a limited range of temperatures.

The gas-turbine cycle involves two basic types of thermodynamic processes. The simplest is a change of enthalpy at substantially constant pressure. The other is a change of enthalpy or temperature with pressure; the pressure-change process is usually without appreciable heat conduction or transfer.

[1] Two good examples of this method are to be found in *NACA Wartime Report* E-23, Thermodynamic Data for the Computation of the Performance of Exhaust-Gas Turbines, by Pinkel and Turner, and in *Trans. SAE*, 1946, Graphical Solution for the Performance of Continuous-Flow Jet Engines, by R. E. Boltz.

Both of these transformations are expressed by the relation

Energy change per unit mass = specific heat $\times$ temperature change

The isobaric addition of heat to a gas involves a constant-pressure mean specific heat, which occurs in almost all changes as a multiplying factor or coefficient. This coefficient has been called the arithmetical mean specific heat of the gas.[1]

$$c_{p,\text{am}} = \frac{h_b - h_a}{T_b - T_a} = \frac{\int_{T_a}^{T_b} c_p \, dT}{T_b - T_a} \tag{186}$$

Ideal expansion or compression processes also require the use of the specific-heat term for their solution. In the familiar expression

$$\frac{P_b}{P_a} = \left(\frac{T_b}{T_a}\right)^{\frac{k}{k-1}} \tag{187}$$

$k/(k-1)$ is equal to c_p/R. This specific heat is also a mean value, which will differ significantly from the arithmetical mean for large temperature differences. It occurs in almost all cases as an exponent and is called the logarithmic mean specific heat. From Eq. (187)

$$\frac{c_{p,\text{lm}}}{R} \log \frac{T_b}{T_a} = \log \frac{P_b}{P_a}$$

since

$$\frac{c_p}{R} \frac{\Delta T}{T} = \frac{\Delta P}{P}$$

$$\log \frac{P_b}{P_a} = \int_{T_a}^{T_b} \frac{c_p}{R} \frac{dT}{T} = \frac{1}{R} (\phi_b - \phi_a)$$

where

$$\phi = \int_{400}^{T} c_p \frac{dT}{T}$$

Therefore

$$c_{p,\text{lm}} = \frac{\int_{T_a}^{T_b} c_p \frac{dT}{T}}{\log \frac{T_b}{T_a}} = \frac{\phi_b - \phi_a}{\log \frac{T_b}{T_a}} \tag{188}$$

The source of the thermodynamic data for air in Table 1 was used by Hall to calculate both the arithmetical and the logarithmic mean specific heats for air. Results are plotted in Fig. 167 to show the nature of the deviations between $c_{p,\text{am}}$ and $c_{p,\text{lm}}$ in terms of the two temperature limits

[1] HALL, N. A., Mean Specific Heats for the Working Media of Gas Turbine Power-plants, *SAE Preprint*, 1947.

T_b and T_a. The mean-specific-heat curves are symmetric about the diagonal, so that temperature scales may be used interchangeably, and lines of constant pressure ratio are drawn on the upper half while lines of constant enthalpy are drawn on the lower half. By example, air is compressed to a pressure ratio of 6:1 from 520°R. Enter at $T_a = 520°R$

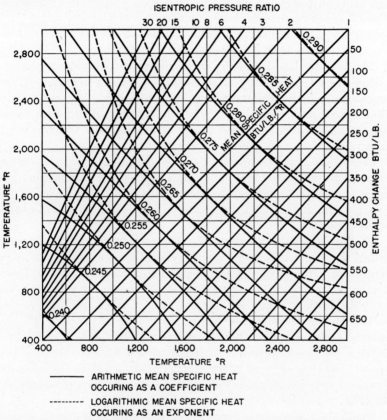

Fig. 167. Mean specific heats of dry air. (*N. A. Hall, SAE Preprint,* 1947.)

on the abscissa, and find T_b at 863°R on the 6:1 insentropic-pressure-ratio line. The logarithmic mean specific heat is 0.243 at the same point on the chart. For a check of this point, from Eq. (187),

$$T_b = 520 \times 6^{\frac{0.06854}{0.243}} = 863°R$$

Also at the same point, the arithmetic mean specific heat is 0.243, and since enthalpy is connected directly with total temperature, the work of an ideal compression is

$$h_b - h_a = 0.243(863 - 520) = 83.3 \text{ Btu/lb}$$

This same value is found on the lower half of Fig. 167 by entering on the ordinate as $T_a = 520°R$ and going to $T_b = 863°R$ on the abscissa; this point falls on the enthalpy change scale at 83.3 Btu. However, the isentropic-pressure-ratio lines and the enthalpy-change lines on this figure should be used only for first-approximation purposes, since the scale is much too rough for gas-turbine-cycle work. The exponent $c_{p,lm}$ should be used for pressure-ratio–temperature-ratio calculations, and the coefficient $c_{p,am}$ should be used with the calculated temperature differences to obtain work or heat energy change.

The ideal work is divided by the efficiency of a compression process or multiplied by the efficiency of an expansion process to obtain the actual work done. Figure 167 may then be reentered at the known value of initial temperature and the actual enthalpy change to find a corrected value of $c_{p,am}$, which is applied to the actual enthalpy to find the actual temperature change in degrees Rankine.

Corrections may be applied to data so obtained to compensate for the effects of water vapor, fuel vapor, and products of combustion. However, the process is relatively tedious, and it is normally easier to use the basic air data from which the above was derived and apply corrections for other factors.

40. Precise Cycle Calculations. The computation methods generally used in this text will follow those developed by the United States Navy Department, Bureau of Ships, Research and Standards Branch, Research Memorandum 6-44. The thermodynamic data reproduced in the charts of the Appendix and in Figs. 109 and 110 are taken from this report.

The properties of dry air are charted in the Appendix in Chart 1; absolute temperature, enthalpy, and relative pressure are shown with 400°R as the base temperature. These are the same data that appear in Table 1, and they are used in the manner explained there for computation of expansion and compression changes of state (the only difference is that 520°R is used as the temperature base in Table 1).

The values given in Chart 1 are long-time equilibrium values of temperature and enthalpy. The most sudden changes of state of large magnitude in a gas turbine occur across a row of turbine blading, where the time interval is of the order of 10^{-4} sec. *NACA Report* L-21 quotes 5.9×10^{-3} as the relaxation time of nitrogen in dry (0.05 percent water vapor) air at 1000°R. Therefore, equilibrium would not necessarily be sufficiently complete to permit the use of normal gas constants for air in calculating the change of state. The vibrational part of the internal energy of a gas requires a finite time, the relaxation time, to adjust to a change in temperature. Nitrogen is the only major constituent of the gas-turbine working fluid that has a relatively long relaxation time.

The presence of water vapor in the nitrogen greatly shortens the relaxation time; 3 percent water vapor decreases the relaxation time to 1.4×10^{-4} sec at 1000°R. Steam alone has approximately 3×10^{-8} sec relaxation time at 1000°R. The values quoted here are for 14.7 psi pressure; higher pressures coupled with higher temperatures result in more frequent bimolecular collisions and therefore a faster approach to equilibrium.

The effect of a relaxation time that is long compared with the time required for the working fluid to flow through a nozzle or blade part is a reduction in the energy conversion that takes place. A loss of 2 percent for a high-temperature flow through an impulse-turbine nozzle inlet ring may be realized as a result of departures from thermodynamic equilibrium between vibrational and translational energies. This is not an efficiency decrease; the energy simply is not released in the time available and can be recovered farther downstream.

Molecular dissociation of the constituents of air does not occur to an appreciable extent below 2500°R. The air charts of Chart 1 may be used with but negligible errors up to 2500°R. However, the error increases with increase in temperature and becomes very large at temperatures of 4500 to 5000°R. At 4500°R, the energy change per unit temperature change due to dissociation of nitrogen and oxygen amounts to 5 percent of the instantaneous value of c_p. This condition is even worse for carbon dioxide and water vapor, so that correction charts for the presence of carbon dioxide and water vapor show dashed lines for temperatures above 2500°R. Revision of correction curves to take into account dissociation of the products of combustion is complicated, since dissociation of water vapor and carbon dioxide is dependent on pressure as well as temperature.

The limit of 2500°R for accurate use of the thermodynamic data in the Appendix is adequate for most gas-turbine cycles. It is somewhat low for athodyd or ramjet-engine calculations, but can be used with reduced accuracy to the limits of the data. The presence of relatively large amounts of water vapor and carbon dioxide from the combustion of stoichiometric mixtures of hydrocarbons and air introduces larger errors in the correction data than are normally found in the air charts owing to dissociation.

The correction factors required for the presence of water vapor in the inducted air ahead of the compressor, as well as those for products of combustion in the gas in expansion, were calculated using the Gibbs-Dalton equations:

$$W_g h_g = W_a h_a + W_b h_b + W_c h_c + \cdots$$
$$W_g c_{pg} = W_a c_{pa} + W_b c_{pb} + W_c c_{pc} + \cdots$$

where W_g = mass of gas mixture

W_a = mass of air

$W_b, W_c, \ldots$ = masses of other constituents of gas

The water-vapor correction factors for compression are shown in Chart 2, for both temperature-rise and enthalpy-rise correction. The temperature rise of the wet air is found by first finding the temperature rise for dry air from Chart 1 and then applying the correction A_{tm} from Chart 2 for m, the proportion of moisture vapor present in the gas.

$$\Delta T_g = \Delta T_a (1 - A_{tm}) \tag{189}$$

where ΔT_g is the temperature change of the gas and ΔT_a is that for dry air from Chart 1. The same procedure is carried out for enthalpy change, except that the correction factor A_{hm} adds instead of subtracts.

$$\Delta h_g = \Delta h_a (1 + A_{hm}) \tag{190}$$

Correction factors are calculated on the basis of ideal or 100 percent efficient processes. Therefore, in order to apply corrections to compressions of less than 100 percent efficiency, the corrected ideal temperature and enthalpy changes are calculated, and are then divided by the efficiency to obtain the actual quantities. The order in which efficiency and water-vapor corrections are applied does not affect the final result.

An example is a compressor with a compression ratio of $\psi = 6$, inlet air temperature $T_2 = 540°R$, 2 percent water vapor in the air by weight or $m = 0.02$, and an actual shaft efficiency of 84 percent with an inlet mass flow of 100 lb/sec at $P_2 = 14$ psi. From Chart 1, for $T_2 = 540°R$ the relative pressure $p_{r2} = 2.862$ and $h_2 = 33.62$. The relative pressure after compression to $\psi = 6$ or 84 psi is $p_{r3} = 2.862 \times 6 = 17.172$. This corresponds to an h of 120.08 Btu/lb on Chart 1 and Δh for the ideal or isentropic compression is $120.08 - 33.62 = 86.46$ Btu/lb. The actual Δh from 2 to 3 is then $\Delta h_{ideal}/\eta_c = 86.46/0.84 = 102.87$ Btu/lb for dry air.

The temperature at T_3 for dry air corresponds to the enthalpy at 3 for dry air where h_3 is $102.87 + 33.62 = 136.49$, or $963.2°R$ from Chart 1. The ΔT between 2 and 3 for dry air is then $963.2 - 540 = 423.2°R$.

The correction factors for 2 percent moisture in the air are read from Chart 2 for $\psi = 6$, $A_{hm} = 0.0107$ and $A_{tm} = 0.006$. The corrected value of compressor enthalpy change is then $\Delta h = 102.87(1 + 0.0107) = 103.76$ Btu/lb. The corrected value of temperature change is

$$\Delta T = 423.2(1 - 0.006) = 420.7 \text{ deg}$$

and the final temperature at the compressor outlet is

$$T_3 = 540 + 420.7 = 960.7°R$$

The shaft power requirement of the compressor when inducting 100 lb of moist air per second is therefore

$$\text{hp} = \frac{100 \times 103.76 \times J}{550} = 14,700$$

Secondary effects of fluid density changes, due to the presence of water vapor in the compressor air, appear as changes in compressor efficiency. These have been neglected in the example.

The calculation of combustion processes was explained in Chap. 5. The air flow from the compressor in the above example is carried through a combustion calculation to illustrate the method. Air containing 0.02 part of water vapor leaves the compressor at a total temperature $T_3 = 960.7°R$. A fuel of H/C ratio = 0.18 and lower heat value $H = 18,800$ Btu/lb is burned with $\eta_b = 96$ percent efficiency, to raise the temperature to $T_4 = 1960°R$.

On a "dry" air basis, $h_{3a} = 135.87$ Btu/lb at $T_3 = 960.7°R$, and $h_{4a} = 398.44$ Btu/lb at $T_4 = 1960°R$. The enthalpy change per pound of dry air through the burner is therefore

$$h_{ba} = h_{4a} - h_{3a} = 398.44 - 135.87 = 262.57 \text{ Btu/lb}$$

A correction factor is now needed for the presence of water vapor in the air, and this is found in the Appendix (see Chart 8), for different values of average temperature and moisture content. The average temperature here is $(960.7 + 1960)/2 = 1410°R$, and heat-exchange enthalpy correction factor for 2 percent water vapor from Chart 8 is $C_{hm} = 0.0185$.

A correction for the enthalpy of the "additional" products due to fuel burned in the gas leaving the burner is also essential for accurate computations. These data are given in Figs. 109 and 110, which give temperature and unit enthalpy for λ, where λ is defined as the carbon dioxide and water vapor formed minus the oxygen consumed from air on the complete combustion of 1 lb of fuel. The reference datum for the enthalpy of the constituents of λ, and hence of λ itself, is zero at 0°R with all constituents in a gaseous state. Figure 109 is for H/C = 0.15, and Fig. 110 is for H/C = 0.18. The assumption that the fuel is either H/C = 0.15 or H/C = 0.18 can lead to an error if H/C is different from these values. However, the magnitude of the error can be readily evaluated by comparing the corrections for H/C = 0.15 and 0.18. Since the temperature of the fuel supply is 520°R, Δh_λ is required for H/C = 0.18 between the temperature limits of 520 and 1960°R. From Fig. 110, $\Delta h_\lambda = 1125.2 - 187.7 = 937.5$ Btu/lb of fuel.

The lower heat value of the fuel was determined from the liquid state, so that the correction for latent heat of the liquid in Eq. (151) is neglected.

Rewriting Eq. (151) to include the water-vapor correction, and neglecting h_{latent} and h_{loss} through the walls,

$$\frac{W_f}{W_a} = \frac{h_{ba}(1 + C_{hm})}{\eta_b H - \Delta h_\lambda} = \frac{262.59(1 + 0.0185)}{0.96 \times 18,800 - 937.5} = 0.0156 \text{ lb/lb} \quad (191)$$

The fuel-flow rate for 100 lb of moist air per second is 1.56 lb of fuel per second or 5,616 lb/hr. The total gas flow is 101.56 lb/sec, or 365,616 lb/hr.

The preceding combustion-chamber calculations were made on the assumption that heat is added at constant pressure. Actually, there is almost always some loss in total pressure through the combustion chamber. While this does not affect the total temperature or the amount of fuel required, it does decrease the availability of energy in the gas that can be recovered through subsequent expansion. In this particular case, the burner has a combined momentum plus friction loss of 3 percent of the total pressure, so that the pressure ratio is $\psi_4 = 5.82$ instead of 6 and $P_4 = 81.48$ psi.

Expansion of gas from the combustion chamber through a turbine requires the use of a number of corrections not applied to the expansion of dry air. The effects of any moisture inducted at the inlet to the compressor must be added to the effects of the products of combustion upon both turbine exhaust temperature and turbine shaft energy. The same corrections apply to other expansion processes, such as in a nozzle where the energy conversion appears in the velocity of the accelerated flow.

The calculation is on the basis of dry air, for both temperature and enthalpy changes; corrections are then made for the other quantities in the flow. The air charts of Chart 1 are used to determine Δh and ΔT in the expansion, including the efficiency of the expansion process in this part of the calculation.

The corrections for original water vapor in the air are found in Chart 3 for temperature and Chart 4 for enthalpy. To determine B_{tm}, the temperature-correction factor for initial water content of the air, the chart is entered at the expansion ratio ψ, vertically to the initial peak temperature, then horizontally to the initial moisture-content line m; then drop vertically to find B_{tm} on the abscissa. The corrected temperature change is then equal to the change for dry air reduced by the factor $1 - B_{tm}$, or

$$\Delta T_g = \Delta T_a(1 - B_{tm}) \quad (192)$$

Correction for initial water vapor in the expansion enthalpy is obtained from Chart 4. Here the temperature is not a factor, as long as the maximum or inlet temperature is not high enough to result in appreciable dissociation. The correction factor B_{hm} is found on the ordinate for the correct values of m and expansion ratio ψ. The corrected value of Δh for the gas is

$$\Delta h_g = \Delta h_a(1 + B_{hm}) \tag{193}$$

This correction factor is additive.

Similar corrections are found in Chart 5 for the effects of products of combustion of the fuel upon temperature. Chart 5 covers the range of hydrocarbon fuels from $H/C = 0.15$ to $H/C = 0.18$ using but one set of data; the maximum error as a result of this assumption is less than 4 percent in the B_{tf} correction factor in the inlet temperature range of 800 to 2500°R. The corrected gas ΔT is

$$\Delta T_g = \Delta T_a(1 - B_{tf}) \tag{194}$$

Enthalpy expansion corrections for fuel require different data for different H/C ratios, and Chart 6 yields the enthalpy correction B_{hf} for expansion for $H/C = 0.15$, and Chart 7 that for $H/C = 0.18$. Again, these data are quite accurate for all temperatures at which dissociation may be neglected. The corrected enthalpy change is

$$\Delta h_g = \Delta h_a(1 + B_{hf}) \tag{195}$$

Let us apply this expansion calculation method to the above gas-turbine-cycle example. Assume that the turbine speed is such that the ratio of total inlet pressure to total exhaust pressure is 4.65 and that the shaft efficiency of the turbine is $\eta_t = 0.88$ according to the turbine-efficiency definition in Chap. 6. From the air charts, for $T_4 = 1960°R$ find $p_{r4} = 332.27$ and $h_4 = 398.88$. Then

$$p_{r5} = \frac{p_{r4}}{\psi} = \frac{332.27}{4.65} = 71.6$$

From the air charts with $p_{r5} = 71.6$, find $h_5 = 227.54$ (this value is for an ideal or isentropic expansion process) and

$$\Delta h_{ideal} = 398.88 - 227.54 = 171.34 \text{ Btu/lb of dry air}$$

The dry-air enthalpy change corrected for turbine efficiency is

$$\Delta h_a = \eta_t \, \Delta h = 0.88 \times 171.34 = 150.8 \text{ Btu/lb}$$

The exhaust enthalpy for dry air is then

$$h_4 - \Delta h_a = 398.88 - 150.8 = 248.08 \text{ Btu}$$

and from the air charts, this corresponds to a temperature of 1401.8°R. The ΔT_a for dry air through the 88 percent efficient turbine is

$$1960 - 1401.8 = 558.2°F$$

Now from Chart 3 for $m = 0.02$, $\psi = 4.65$, and $T_4 = 1960°R$, the expansion temperature correction for water vapor is $B_{tm} = 0.0054$. From Chart 4 for the same conditions, the expansion enthalpy correction for water vapor is $B_{hm} = 0.0131$. Similarly, from Chart 5, the expansion temperature correction for fuel at $W_f/W_a = 0.0156$, and at $T_4 = 1960°R$ is $B_{tf} = 0.0177$; and from Chart 7 for $H/C = 0.18$, the expansion enthalpy fuel correction is $B_{hf} = 0.0059$.

The corrected value of Δh_t is then

$$\Delta h_t = \Delta h_a(1 + B_{hm} + B_{hf}) = 150.8(1 + 0.0131 + 0.0059)$$
$$= 153.7 \text{ Btu/lb}$$

The corrected value of ΔT is then

$$\Delta T_t = \Delta T_a(1 - B_{tm} - B_{tf}) = 558.2(1 - 0.0054 - 0.0177) = 545.4° \text{ deg}$$

The exhaust temperature of the turbine is $1960 - 545.4 = 1414.6°R$ at a total pressure of $81.48/4.65 = 17.5$ psi. The turbine shaft output is

$$\text{hp} = 100 \times \frac{153.7J}{550} = 21,700$$

The excess of turbine shaft power over the power required to drive the compressor is $21,700 - 14,700 = 7,000$ hp. This is available to turn a propeller and to drive the various auxiliaries, such as fuel pump, generator, etc. Since the engine is burning 1.56 lb of fuel per second, the shaft energy efficiency of the engine is

$$\eta = \frac{7,000 \times 550}{1.56 \times 18,800 \times 778} = 0.169$$

In addition to the shaft output of the gas turbine, the turbine exhaust is at a total pressure of 17.5 psi and total temperature of 1414.6°R. The flow is then expanded through a jet nozzle to obtain the maximum velocity jet possible after the turbine. The jet velocity energy is calculated by the same process as employed for the turbine expansion, and with a tail-pipe-plus-nozzle efficiency of 90 percent, is equal to 19.5 Btu/lb of moist air. Since the actual gas flow is 1.0156 lb/lb of moist air, the jet velocity is

$$V_7 = \sqrt{2gJ\frac{19.5}{1.0156}} = 980 \text{ fps}$$

The jet thrust of the exhaust when the engine is at zero flight speed is then the total mass flow of gas multiplied by the jet velocity and divided by g.

$$F_j = 101.56\frac{980}{g} = 3,100 \text{ lb}$$

The total velocity energy of the jet is, of course,

$$100 \times 19.5 \times 778 = 1{,}516{,}000 \text{ ft-lb/sec}$$

equivalent to 2,760 hp. If this energy is added to the shaft output of the engine, the total output is $7{,}000 + 2{,}760 = 9{,}760$ hp. The cycle efficiency, including combustion efficiency, is

$$\eta_{\text{cycle}} = \frac{9{,}760 \times 550}{1.56 \times 18{,}800 \times 778} = 0.22$$

If a heat exchanger had been used in this gas turbine between the turbine exhaust gas and the air flow to the burner, there would have been a reduction in the fuel/air ratio and a somewhat smaller percent reduction in total power output, shaft plus jet. The cycle efficiency could have been improved at the expense of increased weight and bulk as well as lowered output. (Heat exchangers have not yet been found generally desirable on aircraft gas turbines, the disadvantages outweighing advantages.) Enthalpy corrections for the presence of inducted water vapor and of products of combustion are needed for heat-exchanger calculations. Chart 8 for the heat-exchange enthalpy water-vapor correction has already been used in the preceding example for the combustion calculation. Chart 9 in the Appendix gives the heat-exchange enthalpy fuel correction for a fuel of H/C = 0.15. Chart 10 gives the same information for H/C = 0.18. The correction coefficient C_{hf} is plotted against the fuel/air ratio W_f/W_a for different values of T_{avg}, where T_{avg} is the average of the entering and leaving temperatures of the gas in the heat-exchange process.

There is one further group of corrections that are needed in gas-turbine calculations as a result of the presence of water vapor and combustion products in the flow of working fluid. Chart 11 gives the corrections for both gas density and mass flow through an orifice against water-vapor content and fuel/air ratio. Returning to the previous example, the static temperature at the jet exit is 1342.8°R and the static pressure is 14 psi or 2,016 psf. The density of dry air would be

$$\rho_a = \frac{p_7}{Rt_7} = \frac{2{,}016}{53.3 \times 1{,}342.8} = 0.0281 \text{ lb/cu ft}$$

From Chart 11, the density correction for 2 parts per hundred of water vapor is $X_{\rho m} = -0.0116$ and for $W_f/W_a = 0.0156$ is $X_{\rho f} = -0.0015$ with fuel of H/C = 0.18.

The corrected density is

$$\rho_g = \rho_a(1 + X_{\rho m} + X_{\rho f}) = 0.0281(1 - 0.0116 - 0.0015)$$
$$= 0.0277 \text{ lb/cu ft}$$

The mass flow rate for dry air per square foot of "effective" nozzle area is the density multiplied by the flow velocity

$$\frac{W_a}{A} = 0.0281 \times 980 = 27.44 \text{ lb/(sq ft)(sec)}$$

The corrected mass flow from Chart 11 for $W_f/W_a = 0.0156$ and $m = 0.02$ is

$$\frac{W_g}{A} = \frac{W_a}{A}(1 + D_m + D_f) = 27.44(1 - 0.0058 - 0.008)$$

$$= 27.06 \text{ lb/(sq ft)(sec)}$$

This is, of course, the same result as ρ_g multiplied by the flow velocity.

The above corrections can also be obtained if the change of the gas constant R is known for different contents of water vapor and combustion products. It is found that R increases with water vapor approximately 0.57 part for each part of water vapor present; 1 percent water vapor results in an increase in R of 0.57 percent or $R_g = R_a(1 + 0.0057)$. The variation of R with products of combustion of fuel is somewhat more complicated, and is plotted against W_f/W_a for various values of H/C in Chart 12. It should be noted that the changes due to both water vapor and the presence of combustion products are almost exactly additive in the narrow range of corrections found in gas-turbine working fluids, so that R for $m = 0.02$ and $W_f/W_a = 0.0156$ with H/C = 0.18 is 1.0114×53.4 (from Chart 12) and is $R = 54$. Using this value of R in calculating the above jet density yields

$$\rho_g = \frac{2,016}{54 \times 1,342.8} = 0.0277 \text{ lb/cu ft}$$

the same value obtained by using the corrections of Chart 11.

Use of the corrections described in the last few pages will ensure accurate calculation of gas-turbine cycles. The order of accuracy obtainable is considerably better than the accuracy now possible in making laboratory and field measurements of the characteristics of most gas-turbine components. For conventional gas-turbine power plants, the combined error is probably less than 0.2 percent of the state-function change.

41. Characteristics of Joule-cycle Gas Turbines. There are seven major factors that influence the static performance of a gas turbine; these are inlet air temperature, turbine inlet temperature, compression ratio, compressor efficiency, combustion efficiency, turbine efficiency, and in the case of the jet engine, nozzle efficiency. In addition, there are other factors that exert varying degrees of influence upon performance, such as inlet duct losses, momentum pressure loss and friction losses in the burner, tail-pipe friction, turbine swirl leaving loss, heat conduction through the walls of flow passages, power requirements to drive auxiliaries, etc. When the engine is in flight, the effects of flight ram must also be taken into account. To see clearly what happens when several variables change simultaneously in such a maze of factors is quite difficult. The use of dimensional analysis helps in many instances but has its limitations.

Therefore, at the expense of a great many charts, we propose to show here what happens to the basic gas-turbine cycle when these many variables are manipulated, one at a time. In order to do this, a brief recapitulation of the elements of the simple-cycle gas turbine is given. Some old expressions will reappear with new equation numbers, for the sake of continuity at this point.

Flight Mach number is the familiar ratio

$$M_0 = \frac{V_0}{\sqrt{gkRt_0}} \tag{196}$$

The total temperature through the inlet diffuser depends only on flight Mach number and static ambient temperature and is a constant regardless of diffuser losses. We may write then

$$T_0 = T_1 = T_2 = t_0 \left(1 + \frac{k-1}{2} M_0^2\right) \tag{197}$$

where the stage numbers correspond to those of Fig. 165.

Total pressure at the compressor inlet is P_2 and depends upon the flight Mach number, the static atmospheric pressure p_0, free-stream diffusion losses, duct friction loss, and duct diffusion losses. These last three effects may be grouped under the term ram effectiveness or pressure recovery effectiveness. This quantity is the ratio of $P_{2,\text{actual}}/P_{2,\text{ideal}}$. It is not an efficiency ratio, as was pointed out several times in Chap. 3, although for flight Mach numbers up to but not greatly in excess of 0.5, it is numerically quite close to the efficiency of the flow process between stages 0 and 2. A symbol has not been assigned to this ratio, and since it is seldom used in equations, the ratio will be written out in the following expression for total pressure at the compressor inlet:

$$P_2 = p_0 \left(1 + \frac{k-1}{2} M_0^2\right)^{\frac{k}{k-1}} \frac{P_{2,\text{actual}}}{P_{2,\text{ideal}}} \tag{198}$$

The same equation may be used in ramjet calculations.

Flow relations through the compressor are usually expressed in terms of total temperatures and total pressures.

$$\Delta h_c = h_3 - h_2 = c_p T_2 \left(\frac{T_3}{T_2} - 1\right) \tag{199}$$

$$\Delta h_c = \frac{c_p T_2}{\eta_c}\left[\left(\frac{P_3}{P_2}\right)^{\frac{k-1}{k}} - 1\right] \tag{200}$$

The cycle pressure ratio is the product of the effective-ram-pressure ratio and the compressor's pressure ratio

$$\psi_{\text{cycle}} = \frac{P_2}{p_0}\frac{P_3}{P_2} \tag{201}$$

Conditions through the combustion process involve a total pressure drop in the burner due to momentum and friction losses. For low values of the entering Mach number M_3 and a combustion chamber of uniform cross section

$$\frac{\Delta P}{P_3} = \frac{P_3 - P_4}{P_3} = \frac{\Delta P_f}{P_3} + \left(1 - \frac{\Delta P_f}{P_3}\right)\frac{kM_3^2}{2}\left(\frac{T_4}{T_2} - 1\right) \tag{202}$$

where ΔP_f is the pressure loss due to friction. If the entrance flow has a Mach number greater than 0.2, it may be advisable to use a different expression for $\frac{1}{2}kM_3^2[(T_4/T_2) - 1]$ in Eq. (202), substituting the exact relation for the momentum pressure loss

$$\frac{\Delta P_{\text{momentum}}}{P_3} = 1 - \left(\frac{1 + \dfrac{k-1}{2}M_4^2}{1 + \dfrac{k-1}{2}M_3^2}\right)^{\frac{k}{k-1}}\frac{1 + kM_3^2}{1 + kM_4^2} \tag{203}$$

and

$$\frac{T_4}{T_3} = \frac{1 + \dfrac{k-1}{2}M_4^2}{1 + \dfrac{k-1}{2}M_3^2}\left[\frac{M_4(1 + kM_3^2)}{M_3(1 + kM_4^2)}\right]^2 \tag{204}$$

A useful chart for determining the ratio of burner exit total pressure to inlet total pressure, in terms of entrance Mach number M_3 and the temperature ratio T_4/T_3, is shown in Fig. 126 in Chap. 5. Friction pressure losses must be added to this decrease.

The enthalpy change through the burner, neglecting several terms for simplicity, is

$$\Delta h_b = h_4 - h_3 = c_p(T_4 - T_3) = \eta_b H \frac{W_f}{W_a} \tag{205}$$

Expansion of the hot gases from the burner through the turbine results in useful work imparted to the turbine shaft. The enthalpy change is adiabatic, so that the shaft energy is measured by the enthalpy change

$$\Delta h_t = h_4 - h_5 = c_p(T_4 - T_5) \tag{206}$$

Since the expansion is adiabatic but not isentropic, the turbine efficiency must be introduced when the work is expressed in terms of expansion ratio.

$$\Delta h_t = c_p \eta_t T_4 \left[1 - \left(\frac{P_5}{P_4} \right)^{\frac{k-1}{k}} \right] \tag{207}$$

In order for the gas-turbine engine to run continuously, Δh_t must be equal to or larger than Δh_c plus bearing friction, extraneous shaft windage losses, auxiliary power requirements, and propeller load, if it is a turbo-prop engine. If Δh_t exceeds these power requirements, either the turbine inlet temperature must be reduced, or propeller load increased, or turbine-exhaust back pressure increased, or else the excess turbine power will accelerate the engine until an equilibrium condition is reached, or the engine fails.

When matching turbine output to compressor power requirements, etc., the exact gas flow through the turbine with respect to the air flow through the compressor must be taken into account. Compressor air bled off for cooling or other purposes must be subtracted from the total mass flow ahead of the turbine, and the increase in mass due to fuel added in the burner must be accounted for, either directly or by the correction factors in the Appendix.

The simplified expression for jet velocity from the exhaust nozzle is

$$V_7 = \sqrt{2gJc_p(T_5 - t_7)} \tag{208}$$

or

$$V_7 = \sqrt{2gJ\eta_n c_p T_5 \left[1 - \left(\frac{p_0}{P_5} \right)^{\frac{k-1}{k}} \right]} \tag{209}$$

This neglects the problems of exhaust swirl, nonparallel flow streamlines at the jet exit, and possible limitations of supersonic jet flow. The net jet thrust is

$$F_n = \frac{V_7 - v_0}{g} \qquad \text{lb/lb of air per second} \tag{210}$$

Thrust power of the jet is

$$\text{hp}_{\text{jet}} = \frac{F_n v_0}{550} = v_0 \frac{V_7 - v_0}{550g} \qquad \text{hp/lb of air per second} \tag{211}$$

Thermal efficiency of the jet engine is the ratio of added exhaust-jet energy to fuel heat input, exclusive of combustion or burner efficiency.

$$\eta_{\text{th}} = \frac{V_7^2 - v_0^2}{2gJ \, \Delta h_b} = \frac{V_7^2 - v_0^2}{2gJ\eta_b H \dfrac{W_f}{W_a}} \tag{212}$$

Propulsive efficiency of the jet is determined entirely by the velocity ratio between jet and flight speeds

$$\eta_p = \frac{2v_0}{V_7 + v_0} \tag{213}$$

Over-all efficiency of the jet engine is the product of thermal efficiency, propulsive efficiency, and burner efficiency

$$\eta = \eta_{th}\eta_p\eta_b = \frac{(V_7 - v_0)v_0}{gJH \dfrac{W_f}{W_a}} \tag{214}$$

When the gas turbine is connected to a propeller, the thrust and power of the propeller must be included in Eqs. (210) to (214), and these are modified accordingly

$$F_n = \eta_F \frac{550\text{hp}_s}{v_0} + \frac{V_7 - v_0}{g} \tag{215}$$

where the shaft horsepower hp_s is equal to $J(\Delta h_t - \Delta h_c)/550$ if minor variables are neglected, and η_F is the propulsive efficiency of the propeller.

$$\text{Total thrust power} = \eta_F\text{hp}_s + v_0\frac{V_7 - v_0}{550g} \tag{216}$$

$$\eta_{th} = \frac{550\text{hp}_s + (V_7^2 - v_0^2)/2g}{J\eta_b H(W_f/W_a)} \tag{217}$$

$$\eta_p = \frac{550\eta_F\text{hp}_s + v_0[(V_7 - v_0)/g]}{550\text{hp}_s + (V_7^2 - v_0^2)/2g} \tag{218}$$

$$\eta = \frac{550\eta_F\text{hp}_s + v_0[(V_7 - v_0)/g]}{JH(W_f/W_a)} \tag{219}$$

Using the relations expressed in Eqs. (196) through (219), the characteristics of gas-turbine engines may be calculated. In the illustrations that follow, the inlet duct is assumed to be a part of the compressor, so that compressor efficiency includes the inlet losses. Friction and momentum pressure losses in the burner are similarly included in the turbine-loss figure, and the exhaust nozzle is assumed to have the same efficiency as the turbine.

Cycle efficiencies of gas-turbine engines under static or zero-flight-speed condition are plotted in Fig. 168. The dependence of cycle efficiency upon compression ratio, turbine inlet temperature, and efficiency of components is evident. The ideal efficiency curve of an engine with perfect components is also shown; clearly, there is a point of diminishing return in seeking perfection in components, although we are at present far from it. The shifts of peak cycle efficiency with changes of compression ratio become more abrupt as turbine inlet temperature decreases and component efficiencies are lowered. For the very low efficiency compressor and turbine, large decreases in cycle efficiency appear for

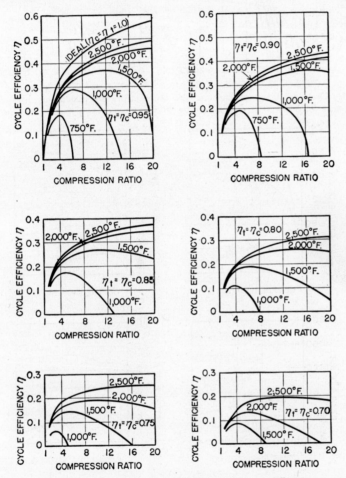

Fig. 168. Cycle efficiency of open-cycle gas-turbine engines at different compressor and turbine efficiencies and for different turbine inlet temperatures as a function of compression ratio ($t_0 = 60°F$).

relatively small shifts in compression ratio in the neighborhood of design point. This is important, because the compression ratio varies almost as the square of the engine shaft speed, and under starting, idling, and some cruising conditions, it is necessary or desirable to operate at considerably lower than rated speed. With higher efficiency components,

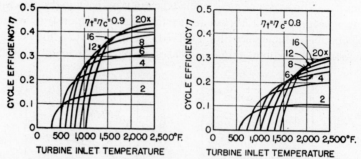

Fɪɢ. 169. Cycle efficiency vs. turbine inlet temperature for various compression ratios for $\eta_t = \eta_c = 0.90$ and $\eta_t = \eta_c = 0.80$. ($t_0 = 60°F.$)

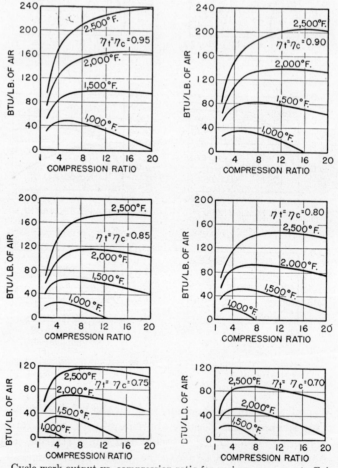

Fɪɢ. 170. Cycle work output vs. compression ratio for various component efficiencies and turbine inlet temperatures ($t_0 = 60°F$).

the cycle-efficiency changes are relatively smaller, and the necessity for maintaining the optimum design compression ratio largely disappears.

Cycle-efficiency data from Fig. 168 are replotted in Fig. 169 against turbine inlet temperature instead of against compression ratio. Envelopes of best efficiency for optimum temperature and compression-ratio combinations are easily visualized.

Figure 168 also shows that as it becomes possible to design very efficient compressors and turbines with low duct losses and small pressure

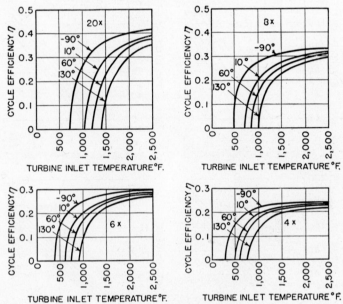

Fig. 171. Cycle efficiency vs. turbine inlet temperature for various compression ratios and ambient temperatures, $\eta_c = \eta_t = 0.85$.

drops in burners, design compression ratios will increase, and high cycle efficiency will be possible at moderate turbine inlet temperatures. However, the work output available per pound of air expanded through turbine and nozzle still depends in large measure upon peak cycle temperature. High-output gas turbines will operate at high temperatures, although jet engines for subsonic flight speeds may be limited in temperature by other consideration. Work output in Btu per pound of air is plotted against compression ratio in Fig. 170 for different peak temperatures and component efficiencies. This quantity is also called "heat to work." The general shape of these curves resembles the efficiency curves of Fig. 168.

So far, the cycle performance curves have all been shown for 60°F ambient temperature condition. The great importance of intake air temperature on cycle efficiency and work output of a turbine appears in Figs. 171 and 172, as well as in the basic equations.   If the turbine inlet temperature is held constant at some upper value by metallurgical limitations, decreasing the ambient temperature serves to increase the temperature ratio for the engine and invariably results in higher efficiency and higher work output per pound of air through the engine.

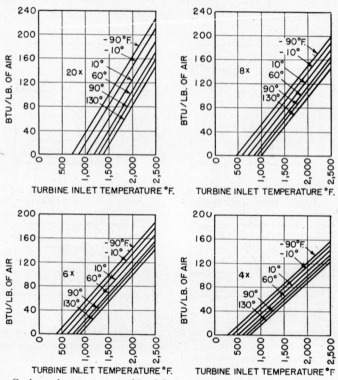

FIG. 172.   Cycle work output vs. turbine inlet temperature for various compression ratios and ambient temperatures, $\eta_c = \eta_t = 0.85$.

If the entire engine work output plotted in Fig. 170 is used to accelerate the jet exhaust, the specific static thrust of the jet engine in pounds per pound of air per second may be calculated.   Specific thrust is plotted in Fig. 173 against turbine inlet temperature for different engine compression ratios and component efficiencies.   While it should be observed that specific thrust always increases when the turbine inlet temperature is raised, the highest thrusts at high turbine temperature are obtained in high-compression engines.   Supersonic jet nozzle flows are assumed in Fig. 173 where nozzle energies exceed the critical value.

The effects of changes in ambient or intake air temperature upon static specific thrust are shown in Fig. 174.   Very large increases in thrust per pound of air per second are obtained when the intake air temperature is decreased.   It should be pointed out also that the curves of Fig. 174 and the preceding figures are for specific thrust and are drawn per pound of air per second.   If the static thrust of a given engine were plotted, not only would the thrust per pound of air per second increase with a drop in

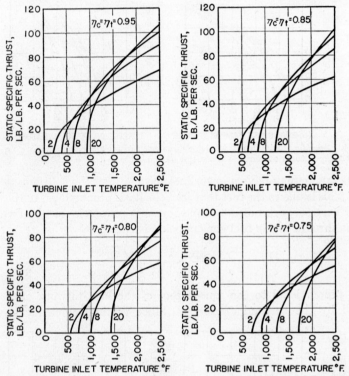

Fig. 173.   Specific static thrust of jet engines vs. turbine inlet temperature for various compression ratios and component efficiencies ($t_0 = 60°F$).

ambient temperature, but the number of pounds of air inducted per second would increase, owing to its greater density at the lower temperature. This might be offset to some extent in practice if Mach-number limitations at the lower temperatures resulted in the necessity for reduced compressor speed.

Using the cycle-efficiency data, the thrust specific fuel consumption may be calculated for the jet engine, and this has been done in Fig. 175 for compression ratios of 4 and 12 and for various ambient temperatures and turbine inlet temperatures.   It is interesting to observe that a low ambient temperature is desirable for a low fuel specific rate at low turbine inlet temperatures, where cycle efficiency is of utmost importance; but at the higher turbine inlet temperatures, where low ambient temperature has a larger effect upon cycle work output than upon cycle efficiency,

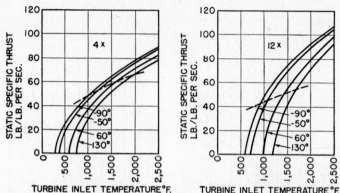

Fig. 174. Specific static thrust for jet engine vs. turbine inlet temperature for various ambient temperatures at compression ratios of 4 and 12, $\eta_c = \eta_t = 0.85$.

the hot intake may have a lower fuel specific than the cold intake condition. This is due to the fact that jet velocity is proportional to the square root of heat-to-work output, while thrust is proportional to jet velocity. The jet thrust specific fuel consumption is therefore

$$\frac{W_f}{F_g} \propto \frac{\text{hp}}{\eta_{\text{th}}} \frac{1}{\sqrt{\text{hp}}} \propto \frac{\sqrt{\text{hp}}}{\eta_{\text{th}}}$$

and is proportional to the square root of the heat-to-work output rate divided by the thermal efficiency. Since thermal efficiency levels off

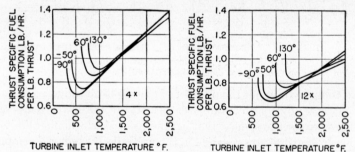

Fig. 175. Static thrust specific fuel consumption vs. turbine inlet temperature for various ambient temperatures at compression ratios of 4 and 12, $\eta_c = \eta_t = 0.85$.

faster than does the work output at high temperatures, the specific fuel consumption increases after a rather low optimum value of turbine inlet temperature is exceeded. The fuel for the examples cited has an H of 18,600 Btu/lb and was burned at 95 percent combustion efficiency.

42. Turbojet Flight Performance Characteristics. Behavior of both the jet engine and the turboprop engine in flight may be deduced from the preceding illustrations. The gas-turbine jet engine in flight operates through the same thermodynamic cycle as on the static test stand. However, the compression of the air now includes the ram pressure rise at the inlet to the compressor proper, so that the cycle compression ratio is higher by a factor equal to the ram pressure ratio. Similarly, the expansion process is through the new, larger ratio. Some of the increase in work output of expansion through turbine and jet nozzle from the higher pressures in the combustion space must be used to compress the air at the ram inlet. Under favorable conditions, there is a net increase in the amount of work available, and the cycle efficiency is improved. Under less favorable conditions, the cycle efficiency may decrease, as when the turbine inlet temperature is a limiting condition and ram temperature rise is sufficiently high to result in a serious reduction in the fuel/air ratio.

To take a practical example, suppose that the gas turbine with 85 percent efficient turbine and compressor and with a compression ratio of 6:1 at zero flight speed is equipped with an 85 percent efficient ram inlet, and with suitable means of utilizing the additional expansion energy in flight. Detailed calculations of performance are required for reasonably accurate results, but Fig. 168 may be used for purposes of approximation.

At 1500°F turbine inlet temperature and 60°F ambient air temperature, the cycle efficiency is approximately 0.24. At a flight speed of 300 mph, which is $M_0 = 0.38$, the ram pressure rise at 85 percent efficiency is $1/0.90 = 1.11$ from Fig. 33. The new cycle compression ratio is therefore $6 \times 1.11 = 6.66$, and returning to Fig. 168, the cycle efficiency is found to be 0.25 for 1500°F turbine inlet temperature. Similarly, at 600 mph, the new cycle pressure ratio is $6 \times 1.36 = 8.16$, and the cycle efficiency is 0.26.

However, if the same engine is operated at 1000°F turbine inlet temperature, cycle efficiency at 0 mph is 0.17; at 300 mph, η_{th} is 0.165, approximately, and at 600 mph, η_{th} is about 0.135. The net work in Btu per pound of air is obtained in a similar manner from Fig. 170; net work decreases with increasing flight speed in this example because cycle efficiency does not increase fast enough with increasing cycle compression ratio to offset the decrease in fuel/air ratio.

· Specific thrust is calculated from the net work available per pound of air and V_0, the flight velocity. The jet nozzle flow velocity is obtained from $V_7 = \sqrt{V_0^2 + (223.7)^2 \, \Delta h}$ where Δh is the net work available in Btu per pound. Specific thrust is then found from Eq. (210). The curves for specific thrust in Figs. 173 and 174 cannot be used directly for obtaining thrust in flight by applying simple compression-ratio corrections.

Figure 176 shows the performance characteristics of the above jet engine at various flight speeds as estimated by this method. Since the engine is in flight, the net over-all efficiency is also calculated and shown,

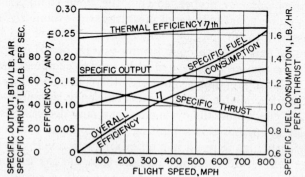

FIG. 176. Specific performance of turbojet engine vs. flight speed for $\eta_c = \eta_t = 0.85$, compression ratio 6:1, $t_0 = 60°F$, and 1500°F turbine inlet.

as well as thrust specific fuel consumption in pounds of fuel per hour per pound of thrust for 18,600 Btu/lb of fuel at $\eta_b = 0.95$.

The specific performance data of a given cycle, such as that described

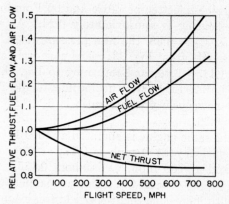

FIG. 177. Relative performance of jet engine of Fig. 176 at various flight speeds.

in Fig. 176, may be translated to the results to be expected from an actual engine in flight if the air flow is known. From Chap. 3, the air flow for 85 percent compression efficiency may be estimated and plotted as in Fig. 177. With air flow known, the net thrust and fuel-flow rate are both obtained by multiplying air flow by specific thrust and the product of specific thrust and specific fuel consumption, respectively. Thrust and fuel-flow data for an actual turbojet engine are plotted in Fig. 178. While the actual engine shown has a static compression ratio of 4:1 instead of 6:1, the maximum per-missible turbine inlet temperature is approximately the same, and the curves of Figs. 177 and 178 closely resemble each other. The performance of the hypothetical engine of Fig. 177 can be reesti-mated for other ambient tempera-tures and operating conditions by using the approximation methods just described with the data of Figs. 171 and 172.

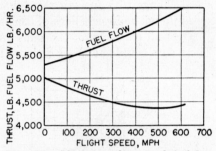

FIG. 178. Maximum thrust and fuel-flow rate of Rolls Royce Nene I turbojet under sea-level standard conditions.

The complete thrust and fuel-consumption curves for another turbo-jet engine have been experimentally determined in flight and are plotted on Figs. 179 and 180 for different altitudes. Ambient temperatures

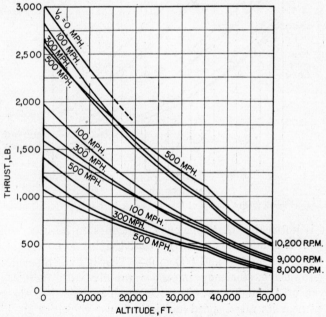

FIG. 179. Thrust performance of De Havilland Goblin II turbojet engine. Rated sea-level static thrust, 3,000 lb at 10,200 rpm.

correspond approximately to the temperature-altitude standard adopted in Chap. 1, but with the tropopause altitude at 36,000 ft instead of 45,000 ft; this accounts for the breaks in the curves at 36,000 ft. This engine has a fixed-area jet nozzle, and the only way in which thrust may be controlled for a given altitude and flight speed is to let the engine speed change with fuel/air ratio changes.   The lines of constant engine speed do not represent lines of constant turbine inlet temperature.

Over-all efficiency of the same engine in flight is shown in Fig. 181. These data could have been deduced from Figs. 179 and 180 by interpola-

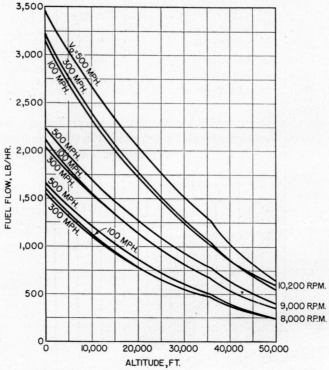

FIG. 180.   Fuel flows for jet engine of Fig. 179 using kerosene for fuel (18,600 Btu/lb).

tion.   It is noticeable that efficiency continues to improve with flight speed for all engine speeds shown, except that at 7,000 rpm, the curve flattens out between 500 and 600 mph.   This is due to several causes. The jet-propulsive efficiency improves rapidly with increasing flight speed, even up through the 500- to 600-mph region when the engine is running at near its rated speed and jet exhaust velocities are high.   At the same time, the cycle efficiency changes but little with flight speed, as indicated generally in Fig. 176.

At lower engine rpm, the opposite condition holds.   Jet flow velocities are comparatively low.   From Fig. 179, the thrust at 8,000 rpm is about 50 percent of the thrust at 10,200 rpm.   Assuming a compressor with flow proportional to rpm, the flow would have been reduced to about 77 percent. From momentum relations, the jet velocity is about 0.50/0.77 = 0.65 of the velocity at full rpm or approximately 1,100 fps. With exhaust-jet flow velocities of this order, the jet-propulsive efficiency would be up to 70 percent at 400 mph and to about 85 percent at 600 mph.

However, the over-all efficiency for low engine rpm continues to increase with flight speed at a faster rate than does the jet-propulsive efficiency, because the cycle efficiency is also increasing significantly.

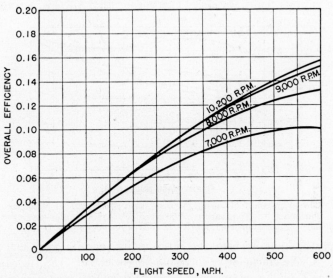

Fig. 181. Over-all efficiency in flight of Goblin II turbojet under sea-level standard conditions. Efficiency at 30,000 ft altitude is approximately one-tenth better at the higher speeds, owing to the lower ambient temperature.

This is because the effective cycle compression ratio increases with flight speed, and at low engine rpm the compression ratio is definitely low enough to result in greatly depressed cycle efficiency. A drop from 10,200 to 7,000 rpm would result in a decrease in compression ratio from 4:1 to approximately 1.9:1 at zero flight speed. When flight speed is increased to 600 mph at 7,000 rpm, the effective compression ratio is increased to about 2.6:1. The beneficial effect of this increase upon cycle efficiency is evident in Fig. 168.

Effective cycle compression ratios at full-rated engine speed also increase in a similar manner with increasing flight speed, but in this instance the compression ratio is already near the optimum value, and a further increase may even be harmful to cycle efficiency. This is a limiting factor for turbojet engines at supersonic flight speeds when the top turbine inlet temperature is critical. The importance of the proper selection of static cycle pressure ratio when the engine is intended for use at very high flight speeds is apparent from Fig. 182.

The over-all efficiency of a jet engine equipped with a variable-area jet nozzle differs significantly from the example (Fig. 181) of an engine with fixed-area nozzle. This is because the nozzle flow characteristic can be changed at will. The turbine inlet temperature may be held at any specified value within operating limits, and the turbine back pressure is controlled by nozzle area and is continuously adjustable to hold a fixed rpm for various flight speeds. This means that the cycle compression

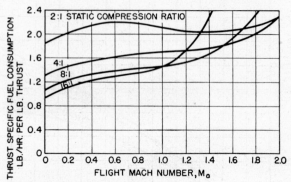

Fig. 182. Thrust specific fuel consumption vs. flight Mach number for high-temperature turbojet. Turbine inlet temperature, 2000°F; all compression and expansion processes 85 percent efficient; constant rpm, and variable-area jet nozzle.

ratio may be kept up near the rated value even for very low required thrusts. Cycle efficiency is correspondingly higher. At the same time, a large mass air flow is maintained because engine rpm is constant, and the jet velocity for low thrusts is correspondingly lower than for the fixed-nozzle engine, so that propulsive efficiency is better at low flight speeds.

The over-all efficiency of a jet engine with adjustable-area exhaust nozzle is plotted in Fig. 183 against flight speed for different turbine inlet temperatures; the engine rpm is kept constant at all flight and thrust conditions. A very significant improvement in over-all efficiency at low flight speeds is obtained, especially for the lower thrust conditions at low turbine inlet temperature. It is particularly noticeable that at low flight speeds, maximum over-all efficiency is not obtained with maximum turbine inlet temperature, but at lower temperatures. Cycle efficiency is decreased, but the lower jet velocity that results from the decreased gas horsepower or work available per pound of air flow through the engine at these lower temperatures results in very much higher jet-propulsive efficiency. Since the over-all efficiency is the product of cycle and propulsive efficiencies, it may reach a peak well below the maximum allowable

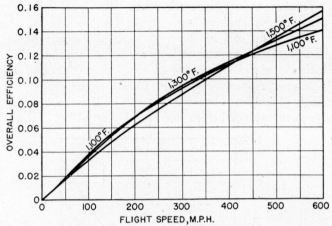

FIG. 183. Over-all efficiency vs. flight speed for contemporary turbojet with adjustable area jet nozzle and running at rated rpm. Temperatures indicated are at turbine inlet.

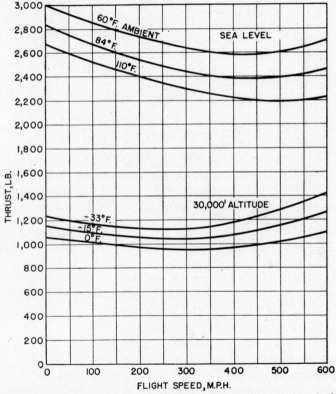

FIG. 184. Thrust of Goblin II engine at sea level and 30,000 ft altitude. Ambient temperatures are for standard, temperate-summer, and tropical-summer conditions.

engine temperature at low flight velocities.   This is seldom the case with fixed-nozzle turbojet engines, and argues for the use of larger than ordinary turbojet engines of the variable-nozzle-area type in aircraft that may be required to cruise at low speeds for maximum flight endurance.   Static thrusts of the engine of Fig. 183 at 1300 and 1100°F are 88 and 75 percent, respectively, of the 1500°F thrust.

The effects of ambient temperature upon jet thrust and fuel consumption have been mentioned before (see Figs. 174 and 175).   The variations

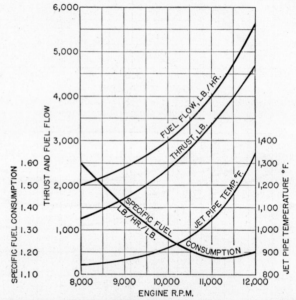

Fig. 185.   Performance of General Electric I-40 turbojet under standard static sea-level conditions.   Rated rpm, 11,500; compression ratio, 4.126; compressor discharge temperature, 413°F; combustion-chamber pressure drop, 5.24 percent or 3.18 psi; turbine inlet temperature, 1492°F; and mass air flow, 79 lb/sec.

in thrust for different flight speeds and ambient temperatures are shown in Fig. 184 for the De Havilland Goblin II engine.   Variations in thrust specific fuel consumption are not shown, since its ambient-temperature dependence is very close to zero at sea-level static conditions, and the thrust specific fuel consumption at 600 mph increases only about 3 parts in 100 between the minimum and maximum ambient-temperature limits shown.

The variations of static thrust and specific fuel consumption with engine rpm at standard sea-level conditions for the General Electric I-40 turbojet engine are shown in Fig. 185.   The I-40 engine has a fixed-area jet nozzle.   These curves are a composite of published data on a number of engines.   Also shown is the actual fuel-flow rate in pounds per hour, and the total temperature of the gas in the jet pipe after it leaves the turbine. The total exhaust- or jet-pipe temperature is connected to the turbine work and the turbine inlet temperature, as well as the jet-nozzle available energy, so that it is a useful quantity.

A further variable that has a large effect upon the performance of a turbojet engine in flight is the efficiency of the ram inlet system. The subject was partially covered in Chap. 3, and again earlier in this chapter. The influence of ram efficiency upon a specific engine rated at 5,000 lb ssl thrust when operating at 35,000-ft standard altitude conditions and 500 mph is shown on the two charts of Fig. 186. The maximum possible

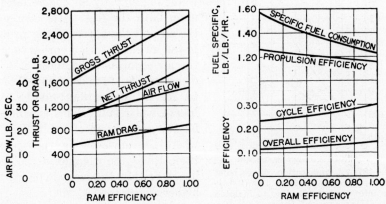

FIG. 186. Effect of varying ram efficiency on the performance of a turbojet engine running at maximum output at 35,000 ft and 500 mph.

thrusts are shown; increase in ram drag with improved ram efficiency is due principally to increased mass air flow.

High atmospheric humidity results in a loss of maximum output from reciprocating engines; the oxygen displaced by the water vapor is no longer available for the combustion process, and both temperature and total available heat energy are reduced. Water vapor to the extent of 2 parts per 100 by weight in the air will reduce the maximum output of a reciprocating engine by about 6 percent; 0.01 part water vapor by weight corresponds approximately to 100 percent relative humidity at 58°F. In any continuous-flow thermal engine burning fuel in air at the stoichiometric ratio, as might be the case with a high-temperature ramjet engine, the jet power output is similarly reduced. However, practically all turbojet and turboprop engines operate with very lean fuel/air ratios, and the presence of water vapor in the atmosphere results in very little effect upon either jet thrust or shaft power.

This is not the case when unevaporated water is ingested at the air intake, as in the presence of rain. The general effect is that of interstage cooling of the compressor plus the advantages of increased gas flow through the turbine. The latent heat of vaporization of the water droplets, as they evaporate in air warmed by passage through the compressor, decreases the compressor temperature and therefore its power requirement. Ingested rain in a ramjet intake may be harmful at stoichiometric fuel/air ratios. Ingested rain in turbojet and turboprop engines operating at 1500°F turbine inlet temperature results in increased heat-to-work output, so that the turbojet engine has increased thrust, and the turboprop engine has an even larger shaft power increase (see Fig. 187). The actual weight of liquid water ingested by an engine depends upon both the free water content of the air and the nature of the air inlet. If the air must turn a corner to enter the air scoop or inlet, heavier water drops may fail to make the turn, owing to inertia separation, and a drier intake will result. This is indicated for the scoop ratio of 3.0 in Fig. 187, where the air entering the scoop is three times the volume of the space intercepted by the scoop in flight. At higher flight speeds, the scoop ratio could be less than unity, and more water would be ingested than normally existed in the free atmosphere. A further discussion of ingested water will be found in the next chapter under the subject of coolant injection.

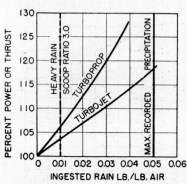

Fig. 187. Augmentation of turbojet and turboprop outputs at 1500°F turbine inlet temperature due to ingested rain. (*Dolinsky and Disch, SAE Preprint*, 1947.)

43. Turboprop Engine Performance Characteristics. While propeller-drive gas-turbine performance characteristics may be calculated, or readily estimated from the Joule-cycle performance illustrations, there has been only a limited amount of data published for actual engines. Several turbojets have been converted to turboprop engines for experimental purposes, but very few gas turbines designed to power airplane propellers have been brought through the model shop, and even fewer have been flight-tested at this time. A number of British engines have been flown, and the General Electric Company's TG-100 has had several hundreds of hours of flight testing.

The Armstrong Siddeley Python turboprop engine is shown in Fig. 188. This design is a conversion of the ASX jet engine in which air enters the axial-flow compressor at a plenum chamber in the rear of the engine, flows forward through the 14-stage compressor, turns 180 deg, and flows toward the rear through 11 can-type burners clustered around the compressor casing, thence through a 2-stage turbine to the jet pipe and nozzle.

FIG. 188. Armstrong Siddeley Python turboprop engine. Compression ratio 5:1.

Redesign for conversion from jet engine to turboprop engine entailed the provision of a suitable reduction gear and redesign of the turbine to give the heat drop required to provide the necessary shaft power. The ASX jet engine is rated at 2,500 lb static thrust, and the Python turboprop engine is rated 3,670 shp plus 1,150 lb ssl jet thrust.

Sea-level static characteristics of the Python are shown in Fig. 189 plotted against engine rpm. The relatively high engine idling speed (50 percent of rated rpm) requires that the propeller be in "flat" or zero pitch at this engine

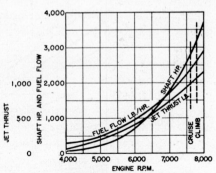

FIG. 189. Sea-level static characteristics of Python turboprop engine.

speed; otherwise the propeller load would stall the engine. Flight characteristics at sea level are shown in Fig. 190 for the same engine. The

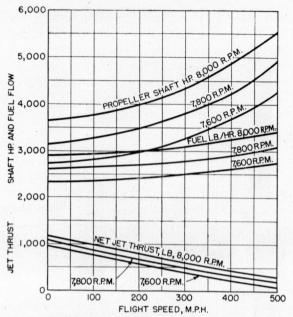

FIG. 190.   Sea-level flight characteristics of Armstrong Siddeley Python.

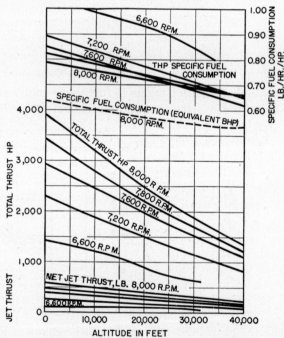

FIG. 191.   Flight performance at 300 mph of Armstrong Siddeley Python turboprop.

rather large increases in shaft horsepower with flight speed are due equally to increases in the mass of air inducted and to reductions in the jet energy, which then appears on the propeller shaft. The net jet thrusts shown are gross thrusts less ram drag.

The variations in available power with altitude for a flight speed of 300 mph are shown in Fig. 191, as are also specific fuel consumption in pounds of fuel per hour per total *thrust* horsepower. The power availability is shown as total thrust horsepower assuming an 80 percent efficient propeller; total thrust horsepower is the sum of propeller thrust power and jet thrust power. The actual jet thrust in pounds is also shown, as well as the specific fuel consumption for the engine at its military rating of 8,000 rpm.

In the previous illustrations, the effects of ram inlet losses have been small, since ram efficiency was assumed to be very close to 100 percent. Ram efficiency losses have about the same effects upon the turboprop-engine air flow and specific fuel consumption as they have upon turbojet engines shown in Fig. 186.

44. Gas Turbines with Heat Exchangers. If the temperature-entropy diagram of Fig. 164 for an open-cycle gas turbine is referred to, it is at once noticeable that the final exhaust gas is discharged to atmospheric pressure at a temperature well above the temperature of the air entering the combustion chamber. This is the temperature or enthalpy difference between states 7 and 3 on the diagram. Therefore, any means for transferring a part of the heat of the exhaust gas to the compressed air before it enters the burner would reduce the amount of fuel required to bring the combustion gas to the specified turbine inlet temperature. The cycle efficiency of the engine is thereby improved through reduced fuel requirements.

Since the mass of air entering the combustion space is almost exactly the same as the mass of exhaust gas leaving the turbine exhaust system, a complete transfer of heat between the two fluids is ideally possible in a counterflow heat exchanger. The effectiveness of the heat exchanger, or regenerator, as it is frequently called, would then be 1.0. Actually, the size and weight of regenerators increase about in proportion to their effectiveness up to an effectiveness of 0.5, and beyond that point, size and weight increase much more rapidly than effectiveness. A heat exchanger of effectiveness 0.75 may be as much as four times as large as one of 0.5 effectiveness. Heat-exchanger limitations will be discussed in some detail in Chap. 10 on engine accessories; it will be sufficient to point out here that very practical limits exist in the physical use of heat exchangers in aircraft practice.

The effects of regenerator effectiveness, or efficiency η_r, upon the cycle efficiency of a turbine with $\eta_t = 0.90$ and $\eta_c = 0.85$ are shown in Fig. 192. Combustion pressure loss is assumed to be 3 percent, and total regenerator friction flow losses are assumed to be 3 percent of total cycle pressure for $\eta_r = 0.50$, 6 percent for $\eta_r = 0.75$, and 12 percent for $\eta_r = 0.90$.

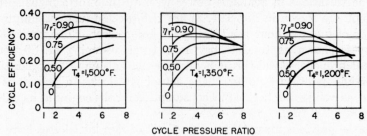

FIG. 192. Effect of heat regeneration upon open-cycle gas-turbine efficiency for $\eta_t = 0.90$ and $\eta_c = 0.85$.

Heat to work is plotted against cycle pressure ratio for the same variables in Fig. 193; the reductions in heat to work per pound of gas are largest in the case of greatest regeneration, owing to increased flow friction losses.

A comparison of Fig. 192 with Fig. 168 shows one of the most inter-

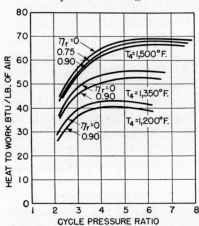

FIG. 193. Work output of gas turbine with exhaust heat regenerator, $\eta_t = 0.90$ and $\eta_c = 0.85$. Reduction in output due to friction flow losses in heat-exchanger flow passages.

esting effects of the use of a heat regenerator. The best cycle pressure ratio for 1500°F turbine inlet temperature with $\eta_t = 0.90$ and $\eta_c = 0.85$ would be about 14:1 without a heat regenerator. Cycle efficiency is approximately 31 or 32 percent, depending upon combustion losses, etc. By using a 50 percent effective heat exchanger between the exhaust and the compressor outlet flows, the cycle efficiency is maximum at about 6:1 compression ratio, and the same cycle efficiency. The use of a larger heat regenerator with 0.75 or 0.90 effectiveness would still further shift the best compression ratio to 4.5:1 and 3:1, respectively; cycle efficiencies would increase appreciably (to 34 percent and 38 percent, respectively). Unfortunately, leaving cycle compression ratios in the range of 6:1 or 8:1 results in minor increases of efficiency with the high-effectiveness heat exchangers, and operation at the lower compression ratios seriously reduces the work output of the engine per pound of air. This may not be serious for stationary engines, but it is serious for aircraft engines where low heat-to-work factors may mean excessively large and heavy engines.

However, regenerators of approximately 0.50 effectiveness do aid low-compression gas-turbine designs for aircraft use from the fundamental stand-point of cycle efficiency. Therefore, the single benefit of a possible reduction in fuel requirements of the order of one-third or one-fourth must be balanced against the added weight and complication of the heat exchanger. New developments in heat exchangers may possibly make them practical in the future.

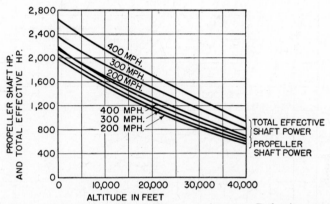

Fig. 194. Power availability of Bristol Theseus turboprop. Reduction-gear efficiency assumed 0.975. Total effective power includes jet thrust horsepower divided by assumed propeller efficiency of 0.80.

In applying a heat exchanger to a turbojet engine, the hot exhaust must not be taken through the regenerator immediately after the turbine, but after the gas leaves the jet nozzle. Otherwise, heat would be removed before expansion was completed, and the entire purpose of the regenerator would be defeated. Therefore, the entire jet flow at a flow velocity close to Mach 1.0 must be taken through a heat exchanger of large surface with but small friction loss and negligible reduction in velocity. The requirements of a large wet area of heat exchanger and small flow friction loss at high flow Mach numbers are not consistent. The successful application of heat exchangers as regenerators in turbojet engines is most doubtful.

In a turboprop engine in which the jet velocity is low, with flow Mach numbers of the order of 0.2 to 0.3, a heat exchanger may be applied without serious flow losses. Such an engine is the Bristol Theseus shown in a cutaway view in Fig. 229. The compression ratio is 4.35:1, and rated air flow is 30 lb/sec through a compressor consisting of 9 axial-flow stages followed by 1 centrifugal stage. The compressor is driven by a direct-connected 2-stage turbine on a quill shaft, followed by a single-stage turbine on a separate central shaft to power the propeller. The two turbines are not connected mechanically, but are operated at a relatively constant speed ratio through propeller pitch control of the load; this is done in order to ensure operation of the output turbine at a speed near the most favorable velocity ratio. The heat exchanger is of annular cross-section behind the turbine section. Its effectiveness is not known to the authors, but is estimated to be of the order of 0.50. Calculated total

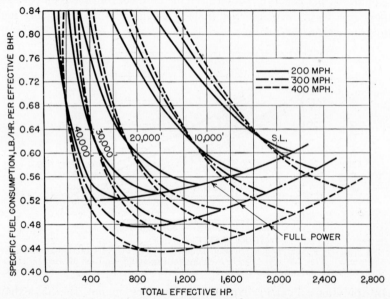

Fig. 195. Specific fuel consumption of Bristol Theseus calculated on basis of total effective shaft power (efficiency of gearing, 0.975; fuel, 18,600 Btu/lb). Total effective power equals propeller shaft power plus jet thrust power divided by 0.80.

effective shaft power and propeller shaft power are shown in Fig. 194 for this engine; effective shaft power is the sum of propeller shaft horsepower plus jet thrust horsepower divided by an assumed propeller efficiency of 0.80. Specific-fuel-consumption data are shown in Fig. 195, and should be compared with Fig. 191 for a straight turboprop engine without heat exchanger. It should be remembered that the cost in increased aerodynamic drag due to the large-diameter heat exchanger does not appear in this comparison.

45. The Ramjet or Athodyd. There have been numerous references to ramjet engines in preceding pages. The ramjet is just what its name implies, an engine that receives all its cycle compression from the forward motion of the engine through the air. Another descriptive name for this engine is athodyd, abbreviated from aero-thermodynamic-duct.

The ramjet operates on the Joule or Brayton cycle. Air flows into the ram inlet and is compressed to a degree determined by the flight speed, the efficiency of the diffusion process, and the velocity of the air flow in the actual compression space. Supersonic ramjet engines will obtain partial compression across shock waves at the inlet, and engines designed for flight at high Mach numbers may find it advantageous to use one or more inclined shocks for maximum efficiency (see Fig. 196).

Stage numbers shown on Fig. 196 correspond generally to the same numbers for equivalent flow states used previously for turbojet engines. Diffusion and compression are completed between 0 and 3; fuel is burned

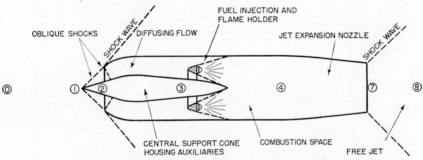

FIG. 196. Schematic example of ramjet in flight at $M_0 = 2$.

downstream from 3, and combustion is essentially completed at 4. Jet expansion occurs between 4 and 7.

Ramjet engines suffer from several serious difficulties. One of these is that the maximum outside diameter should be as close to the diameter of the mouth of the ram intake as possible. Otherwise, the frontal area of the engine will be large for the mass air flow through the engine; the parasitic or form drag of the engine body may then be excessively large at supersonic flight speeds. However, if the flow velocity at stage 3 is not low compared to the free-flight velocity M_0, the static pressure rise will be low, and M_3 will be high.

Combustion in ramjets is similar to combustion in other continuous-flow engines, except that the ratio T_4/T_3 is usually much higher than in turbojet or turboprop engines, and the inlet flow Mach number in the actual combustion zone is very much higher than in the other engines. High fuel/air ratios make burning easier, but high flow velocities are costly from the standpoint of momentum pressure loss, and it is difficult to anchor the flame front and prevent its being blown out of the engine. When M_3 and T_4/T_3 are both large, the combustion process may not be completed until M_4 is close to unity. The process is inefficient then because heat is being added at successively lower static pressures, and the limitations of Eq. (77) apply. Choking flow conditions may then occur if T_4/T_3 is large enough to result in $M_4 = 1$.

Instead of using a convergent jet nozzle as in Fig. 196, a straight pipe may constitute burner and nozzle together. Such an engine is shown schematically in Fig. 197 with pressure, temperature, and flow-velocity

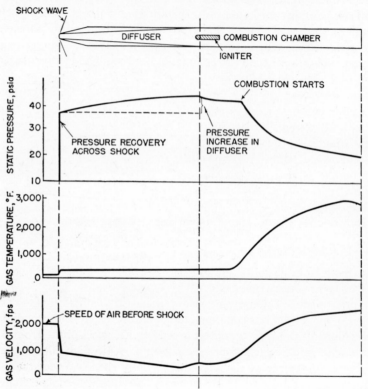

Fig. 197. Pressure, temperature, and velocity variations in a ramjet. (*By permission,* *Applied Physics Laboratory, United States Navy, Bureau of Ordnance.*)

variations progressively throughout the engine; flight Mach number is $M_0 = 1.86$ at 10,000-ft altitude. Compression is through a plane shock across the ram inlet, followed by subsonic diffusion. Combustion starts at $M_3 = 0.3$, approximately, and is completed near the end of the straight jet pipe with M_7 close to 1.0. The cycle efficiency of this engine is low, because both compression and expansion process efficiencies are low; however, it is a very lightweight engine well suited for its purpose of propelling a short-range missile. Specific thrust is approximately 23 lb/lb of air per second, and the specific fuel consumption is approximately 10 lb of fuel per hour per pound of net thrust.

Much more carefully worked out designs are necessary for long-range ramjet engines. If multiple oblique shocks are employed at high supersonic speeds, ram compression efficiency may be high, between 70 and 85 percent. Then if flow velocity at the burner entrance is low (below $M_3 = 0.2$) followed by efficient fuel burning and expansion through a jet nozzle, reasonably good cycle efficiency may be expected. Curves of specific thrust fuel consumption for two ramjets are shown in Fig. 198. The upper curve is for a ramjet with high pressure losses, approximating practical results that are now obtainable; the lower curve is for highly refined designs and probably represents a limit toward which designers may work.

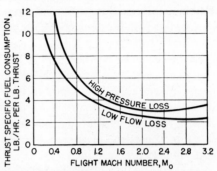

FIG. 198. Ramjet specific fuel consumption with normal shock entry and high-velocity combustion, and for an idealized ramjet with multiple oblique shock entry and low-velocity burner, combustion temperature 3000°F.

More details of the highly developed low-loss ramjet are shown in Fig. 199. The performance calculated is optimum at each flight speed for a 30-in.-diameter engine suitable for powering a large missile. The

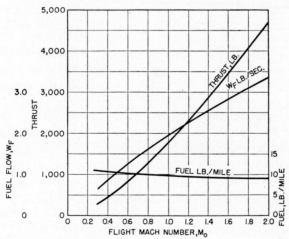

FIG. 199. Thrust and fuel characteristics of high-efficiency, 30-in.-diameter ramjet at 30,000 ft altitude (17-in.-diameter ram inlet).

ram inlet diameter is 17 in. Combustion at 3000°F takes place in the 30-in.-diameter section at an entry flow Mach number of about 0.2 at all flight speeds above $M_0 = 1.0$. There is some loss in thrust at flight speeds above $M_0 = 1.2$, because jet flows tend to be supersonic thereafter but are limited in velocity by the simple convergent nozzle. However, the loss is not great; the gain of a supersonic jet is not enough to pay for the added weight and complication of a DeLaval-type exit nozzle. Further, increased internal and external friction drags, due to the greater surface area of the longer engine, would reduce the net gain in thrust.

The optimum area of the jet exhaust nozzle is different for each flight speed if the peak temperature is held constant. Increasing the combustion temperature requires a larger exhaust area, and choking flows may occur in ramjets at low flight speeds. This condition results in a general increase in static pressure from the exhaust cone to the ram inlet; inlet flow is reduced with air spill-over at the inlet rim and a detached shock wave in the event of supersonic flow. Increased flight speed results in total nozzle pressure increases at a higher rate than mass flow increases, so that the ratio of outlet area to inlet area, A_7/A_2, can decrease with increases in flight Mach number. An inefficient ramjet with high pressure losses would not require as great a reduction in area ratio with increasing flight speed as would an efficient athodyd.

In general, a ramjet engine would be designed for flight at one speed only; it would probably encounter choking flow conditions at lower speeds, and too open a jet nozzle at higher speeds, with consequent loss of jet thrust efficiency. An adjustable tail cone might solve the nozzle-area problem, at the expense of added weight and complication. Temperature control in the combustion chamber would also provide a means of control, but since the maximum thrust is usually required of this type of engine, peak permissible temperatures are used at all flight conditions. The ramjet is not a very flexible propulsion device, although it is an extremely lightweight one and quite efficient at the supersonic flight speeds.

Ramjet characteristics discussed so far have been largely limited to internal flow characteristics. External flow characteristics are of equal importance in the useful flight speed range of this type of engine. Parasitic drag of the outer engine shell and parts exposed to the air stream is large and reduces the momentum thrust values of the internal flows plotted in Figs. 198 and 199.

Offsetting this drag loss to some extent at subsonic flight speeds is the ejector effect of the jet exhaust flow on the surrounding atmosphere. A sheath of air surrounding the issuing exhaust jet is entrained by the jet and mixes with it, thus inducing an increased flow velocity over the outside of the ram jet engine. Since the shell is straight or substantially straight after the rounded inlet-end ogive or cone surface is blended with the body diameter, this increased flow velocity serves to do two things.

It increases the friction drag over the shell, and it reduces the static pressure over the curved frontal surfaces. The reduction in static pressures over the curved frontal areas is equivalent to aerodynamic "lift," and an increase in thrust is experienced. This increase is not large, but the net thrust of an athodyd is not known until all the flow forces, both internal and external, have been integrated over all surfaces. At supersonic flight speeds, the ejector action is not felt, since its influence does not extend forward of the tail shock wave.

46. Corrected Variables and Engine Performance Plots. The useful power output of propjet and turbojet power plants varies in a complicated manner with atmospheric conditions, flight variables, and power-plant operating conditions. Thus it becomes a tedious procedure to calculate complete flight performance, since it depends on so many significant variables. We are interested in the variation of the performance, as measured by such quantities as thrust, fuel specifics, air flow, etc., with ambient temperature, pressure, and flight speed, and in the variation of engine performance with operating variables under all ambient conditions. In particular, the factors limiting engine performance must be known at all ambient conditions and flight speeds. As an example, the performance of gas-turbine compressors is critical with respect to high internal flow Mach numbers. It can be shown that this limits the performance of aircraft gas turbines in high-altitude low-speed operation. Further, turbine inlet temperatures and engine rotational speeds are subject to a limitation in maximum value. This results in performance limitations that depend on altitude and flight speed.

Without theoretical guidance as to the expected variation of performance with flight conditions, it would, for example, be impossible to extrapolate sea-level bench tests or low-altitude flight-test results to predict expected high-altitude flight performance.[1] The necessary guiding principles are provided by dimensional theory and the laws of similarity. It can be shown that a given gas-turbine power plant will have similar operating conditions (which means that all velocity triangles, Mach numbers, pressure ratios, and temperature ratios throughout the engine are fixed) at sea level and at altitude if

1. The compression ratio of the compressor is the same.

2. The ratio of turbine inlet temperature to static ambient temperature is the same.

3. The flight Mach number based on air speed is the same.

This represents an oversimplification but is an extremely useful approach

---

[1] An excellent treatment of this problem is given in a paper by C. A. Meyer, Characteristics of Turbojet Engines at High Flight Speeds, *Trans. ASME,* Vol. 69, p. 237, 1947.

to the problem.   It implies that certain variables and factors have only a secondary effect on performance.   Examples of such secondary factors are Reynolds number, heat-transfer coefficients, etc.

The similarity conditions 1, 2, and 3 can be used in many ways to assist in the analysis of engine performance.   As an illustration, the high-flight velocity high-altitude compressor-Mach-number problem can be treated quite simply.   It can be shown [e.g., see Eq. (125)] that the compression ratio of a given compressor is a function of the square of the rotational speed divided by the compressor inlet total temperature.

$$\frac{P_3}{P_2} = f\left(\frac{N^2}{T_2}\right) \tag{220}$$

The compressor inlet Mach number (which is the critical one) is proportional to $N/\sqrt{T_2}$.   Thus, to maintain the same Mach number at rated speed (and the same compressor compression ratio), the flight Mach number must be increased with altitude at such a rate that

$$T_2 = T_0 = t_0\left(1 + \frac{k-1}{2} M_0^2\right) = \text{constant} \tag{221}$$

We have seen (e.g., see Fig. 2) that temperatures of the order of $-70°F$ may be encountered at altitudes of the order of 40,000 ft.   This implies, for low flight speeds (say, $M_0 = 0.5$) and rated N, an increase of approximately 12 percent in compressor inlet Mach number.   Thus, gas-turbine compressors to operate under these conditions must be so designed that losses associated with high flow Mach numbers are not excessive at overspeeds of the order of 12 percent.

With the aid of a dimensional analysis of the problem, it is possible to show what test measurements should be made and under what conditions sea-level bench tests should be run in order to obtain maximum data for predicting flight performance at altitude.   One of the first results of such an analysis is that the bench tests must include measurements at various ram pressure ratios, P_2/p_0, that will be encountered in actual flight.   Theoretically, this requires the use of a ram blower or precompression ahead of the engine under test or, alternatively, suction at the exhaust.   Practically, such tests are run with the equivalent of exhaust suction produced by an exhaust diffuser immediately following the engine nozzle.   The effect of such a diffuser is to convert most of the velocity component of total nozzle pressure P_7 into static pressure.   This leads to a reduced pressure at station 7, which is equivalent to a certain ram pressure drop across the engine.

To supplement such bench data, tests of aircraft gas turbines in open wind tunnels at various tunnel velocities are now becoming common.

To date, however, the top velocities used in the tunnel tests are considerably less than top flight velocities. In order to get wind-tunnel results that will duplicate the performance of a given engine in a particular airplane, the test engine should be installed in a reasonable facsimile of the proper section of the airplane in question. Then, when tests are run for various tunnel velocities, the flow over the parts of the mock-up near the nacelle should approximate the flow in flight.

By the use of dimensional analysis, it has been shown that the performance of a given turbojet engine can be expressed in terms of relations of the following form

$$\left.\begin{aligned} \frac{F}{\delta} &= f\left(\frac{N}{\sqrt{\theta}}, \frac{V_0}{\sqrt{\theta}}, A_7\right) \\ \frac{T_4}{\theta} &= g\left(\frac{N}{\sqrt{\theta}}, \frac{V_0}{\sqrt{\theta}}, A_7\right) \\ \frac{W_a\sqrt{\theta}}{\delta} &= h\left(\frac{N}{\sqrt{\theta}}, \frac{V_0}{\sqrt{\theta}}, A_7\right) \end{aligned}\right\} \qquad (222)$$

where f, g, and h represent functions of the variables indicated within the parentheses.

$$\left.\begin{aligned} \theta &= \frac{t_0}{520} \\ \delta &= \frac{p_0}{14.7} \end{aligned}\right\} \qquad (223)$$

The quantities F/δ, $N/\sqrt{\theta}$, $V_0/\sqrt{\theta}$ are called corrected thrust, corrected rotational speed, corrected flight speed, etc., or, in general, corrected variables. It can be seen that equal values of $V_0/\sqrt{\theta}$ imply equal values of flight Mach number; simultaneous equal values of $V_0/\sqrt{\theta}$ and $N/\sqrt{\theta}$, equal values of compression ratio.

The fact that relations of the type of Eq. (222) exist means that the quantities $N/\sqrt{\theta}$, $V_0/\sqrt{\theta}$, and A_7 are ideal variables or parameters in terms of which general turbojet performance can be plotted. It is customary in such performance plots to substitute the corrected fuel-flow variable $W_f/\delta\sqrt{\theta}$ for the corrected top cycle temperature T_4/θ. Performance plots for given engines may be given without any reference to the nozzle exit area A_7. This may imply that this area is fixed for all operating conditions or that it is varied simultaneously with other quantities in such a way as to make the jet pressure at the nozzle exit equal to the atmospheric pressure.

The following table lists the important corrected variables encountered in gas-turbine engines:

	Uncorrected	Corrected
Flight speed	V_0	$V_0/\sqrt{\theta}$
Rotational speed	N	$N/\sqrt{\theta}$
Air flow	W_a	$W_a\sqrt{\theta}/\delta$
Fuel flow	W_f	$W_f/\delta\sqrt{\theta}$
Temperature	T	T/θ
Thrust	F	F/δ
Power	Power	Power$/\delta\sqrt{\theta}$
Specific fuel consumption (thrust)	W_f/F	$W_f/F\sqrt{\theta}$
Specific fuel consumption (power)	W_f/FV_0	W_f/FV_0

Operating limits for gas turbines and gas-turbine components are generally expressed in terms of such quantities as maximum allowable rpm or maximum permissible turbine inlet temperatures. These limits

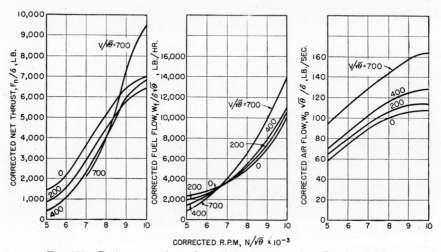

Fig. 200. Performance charts for turbojet in terms of corrected variables.

therefore are not expressed directly in terms of corrected performance variables. In terms of a performance chart, this means that it is not possible to draw in *fixed* lines to represent operating limits. Such charts in terms of corrected variables are extremely useful and widely used in spite of this deficiency.

Various types of performance charts are in common use. For the turbojet engine, for example, we may plot corrected thrust, fuel flow, and air flow against corrected rpm. Each plot consists of a series of curves for different corrected flight speeds. Typical performance plots of this type are shown in Fig. 200.

In another common type of performance chart for turbojet engines, corrected thrust is plotted against corrected flight speed for various corrected rpm. If on this same chart contours of equal corrected fuel rates and equal corrected airflows are drawn, this single chart will provide the same information as is given in Fig. 200. Figure 201 is a performance chart of this type for a hypothetical turbojet engine. One disadvantage of this type of chart lies in the fact that it tends to become cluttered and difficult to read if the contours are closely spaced.

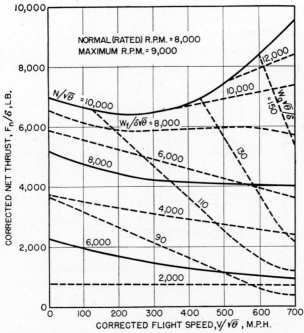

Fig. 201. Combined performance plot for turbojet engine in terms of corrected variables.

The turbojet engine of Fig. 201 has a variable nozzle area A_7, which is adjusted with flight speed and rpm to give optimum performance. In particular, for maximum rotational speed at standard sea-level flight conditions, A_7 is varied with flight speed in such a way as to maintain T_4 at its maximum permissible value of approximately 2000°R. It can be shown that the corrected turbine inlet temperature T_4/θ is the sum of T_2/θ plus the compressor corrected temperature rise [proportional to $(N/\sqrt{\theta})^2$] plus the corrected temperature rise in the combustion chamber (which is proportional to $W_f/W_a\theta$). Thus, one could draw on Fig. 201 contours of T_4/θ so that this single chart would contain all the desired performance information plus all needed information on operating limits.

The data of Figs. 200 and 201 are used in the following way to obtain expected engine performance under nonstandard conditions. Suppose, for example, that we want to know the performance at an ambient temperature $t_0 = -40°F$ or $420°R$ and an ambient pressure of 3.68 psi (these conditions are roughly the average ambient values for 35,000-ft altitude) and at a flight velocity of 600 mph. The correction factors θ and δ are, then,

$$\theta = \tfrac{420}{520} = 0.81$$

$$\delta = \frac{3.68}{14.7} = 0.25$$

The corrected flight speed corresponding to these conditions is then $600/\sqrt{0.81} = 667$ mph. Corrected rotational speeds corresponding to rated and maximum rpm, respectively, are $8,000/\sqrt{0.81} = 8,900$, and

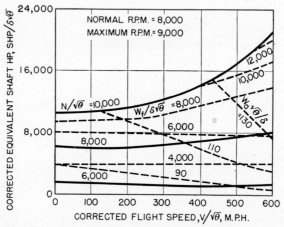

FIG. 202.   Corrected-variable performance chart for turboprop engine.

$9,000/\sqrt{0.81} = 10,000$ rpm. From Fig. 200 or 201, the net thrust F_n/δ corresponding to these values is

$$\frac{F_n}{\delta} = 6,400 \text{ lb at } 8,000 \text{ corrected rpm}$$

$$\frac{F_n}{\delta} = 9,200 \text{ lb at } 10,000 \text{ corrected rpm}$$

Thus, at 8,000 actual rpm under these ambient conditions, the net thrust $F_n = 0.25 \times 6,400 = 1,600$ lb, while at 9,000 actual rpm, the thrust output is $F_n = 0.25 \times 9,200 = 2,300$ lb. The corrected fuel rate $W_f/\delta\sqrt{\theta}$ for actual maximum and rated rpm, respectively, is, from Fig. 201, 14,000 and 8,700 lb/hr. This leads to actual fuel rates of

$$W_f = 14,000 \times 0.25 \times \sqrt{0.81} = 3,150 \text{ lb/hr}$$

and

$$W_f = 8,700 \times 0.25 \times \sqrt{0.81} = 1,960 \text{ lb/hr}$$

Air flows and fuel specifics can be calculated in a similar manner. For example, the thrust power specific at rated speed would be

$$\tfrac{1960}{1800} \tfrac{375}{600} = 0.77 \frac{\text{lb fuel/hr}}{\text{thrust hp}}$$

Essentially the reverse process is used in going from flight-test data to the corrected-variable performance plots of Figs. 200 and 201.

A corrected-variable performance plot for a hypothetical turboprop engine is given in Fig. 202. Here the corrected equivalent shaft horsepower is plotted against corrected flight speed for various corrected rotational speeds. The equivalent shaft horsepower is equal to the actual shaft horsepower plus the thrust horsepower of the jet exhaust divided by an assumed propeller efficiency of 0.80.

47. Matching of Gas-turbine Components. The performance of a gas-turbine engine can be calculated for any assumed set of operating conditions provided that the complete characteristics of all the gas flow devices employed in the construction of the engine are known. Until quite recently, testing laboratories with adequate air-handling capacity and power available for the testing of large gas-turbine engine components did not exist. Nearly all the aircraft turbine engines now in use have been designed and built without benefit of extensive testing of components before final designs were determined. Characteristics were estimated from actual engine test results of previous engines and a limited number of laboratory tests of components.

A cut-and-try method of computation must be used because of the large number of variables, even for a simple jet engine with fixed jet nozzle area. There are a number of approaches that may be used in solving the problem (all of them tedious). A common method is described here.

For a given flight Mach number M_0 and a specified shaft speed, select a compression ratio ψ_c for the compressor, and from the compressor flow chart, similar to Fig. 102, find the standard mass air flow. The volumetric flow Q of the compressor in cubic feet per second is therefore known, and using the methods outlined in Sec. 12, Chap. 3, for ram flow into ducts, calculate the actual mass flow W_a and the total ram pressure recovery in the inlet system. The inlet diffuser pressure ratio $\psi_d = P_2/p_0$ is the ram-pressure-recovery ratio, and multiplied by ψ_c yields the total cycle pressure ratio P_3/p_0. Conditions at the burner inlet are now known, since the total temperature at the compressor inlet is known, and from the known efficiency of the compressor, the exit total temperature is also known. With compressor inlet and exit total temperatures known, the compressor shaft power input requirement is also known, using the enthalpy calculation methods of Sec. 40.

Dimensionless or corrected variables may be used for flow, rpm, etc., but their use can lead to small inaccuracies in the combustion zone, so that we prefer the use of uncorrected variables throughout trial calculations. After trial calculations have been completed and component flows matched, corrected variables may be used without serious loss of accuracy.

The next step in the trial calculation is the selection of the fuel/air ratio in the burner. A ratio is selected that will yield a burner exit or turbine inlet total temperature in the operating range of interest to the designer. With the actual combustion-chamber pressure and flows known, combustion efficiency and total pressure loss are estimated from the measured characteristics of the burner, and exact turbine inlet state variables P_4, T_4, and $W_g = W_a + W_f$ are known, where W_a is corrected for any compressor air that may have been bled off for cooling or auxiliary purposes.

In the case of a jet engine, the shaft power requirement of the turbine element is known from the compressor input requirement plus the auxiliary power load. Then from data similar to that plotted in Fig. 145, the pressure ratio is found across the turbine necessary to produce the required output for the gas flow, inlet pressure, and temperature conditions at a turbine shaft speed that matches the compressor. With turbine efficiency known, the turbine exit conditions are then known.

The pressure ratio across the tail pipe and jet nozzle downstream from the turbine is then P_5/p_0, and with known flow characteristics for the exit system, the effective exit area of the jet nozzle may be calculated for the flow to match the turbine exit flow expanded to atmospheric pressure at the known efficiency of the exhaust system.

If the turbojet engine is equipped with an adjustable-area jet nozzle, the last calculation indicates the effective-nozzle-area adjustment that must be made at the nozzle in order for the gas turbine to operate under steady conditions at the flight Mach number, shaft speed, and turbine inlet temperature conditions selected for the trial calculation.

If the turbojet engine has a fixed-area exhaust nozzle whose effective area (as much as 15 or 20 percent less than actual area) does not match the calculated nozzle-area requirement, then the engine will change speed if the fuel/air ratio is not changed. With an effective nozzle exit area larger than required by calculation, the pressure drop across the nozzle will be smaller than the calculated value; the turbine pressure fall will therefore be greater, and turbine shaft output will be in excess of that required to drive the compressor. The engine will accelerate, at a rate that can be calculated from the excess turbine shaft power and the inertia of the rotating parts. If the exit area is smaller than required, the nozzle pressure drop will be large, with a corresponding excessive back pressure on the turbine. The engine will decelerate.

When exit conditions for the fixed-nozzle jet engine do not match in the trial calculation, different values of turbine inlet temperature may be tried until exit-flow-area calculations match the actual effective flow. The expanding-flow calculations may be considerably simplified if the flow characteristic of the combined turbine plus fixed-area jet nozzle is plotted in a manner similar to Fig. 145 but for pressure ratios P_4/p_0 instead of P_5/P_4. With an initial estimate of the required fuel/air ratio to fix the probable total flow volume and with the turbine power requirement known, the turbine-plus-nozzle flow characteristic curves may be entered to find the required turbine inlet temperature for the calculated inlet pressure P_4. If the fuel/air ratio corresponding to this temperature is reasonably close to the estimated value, the trial calculation need not be corrected.

A turboprop engine presents a somewhat different problem, although the simplest aid to calculation is to plot turbine-plus-nozzle flow characteristics as described in the preceding paragraph. The flow charts are then entered with total gas flow, turbine inlet temperature, and turbine inlet pressure above atmospheric pressure at the specified engine rpm; turbine power output is then found. The excess of turbine shaft power available over the requirements of compressor and auxiliaries is the power available to drive the propeller through its reduction gear. The propeller-blade pitch must be adjusted exactly to absorb this power. If the turbine power is not sufficient to drive the compressor, the turbine inlet temperature is too low.

A turboprop engine with adjustable-pitch propeller and adjustable-area exhaust nozzle adds still another variable, and performance may be calculated by adjusting both propeller pitch and nozzle area simultaneously to meet initial assumptions about the division of energy between propeller and jet. With assumed values of turbine and nozzle efficiencies, this division is readily made on the basis of expansion pressure ratios.

A few further comments about the nozzle flow calculations are appropriate here. Since a simple, convergent nozzle is universally used on all contemporary gas-turbine engines, the appearance of pressures at the nozzle inlet in excess of those required for critical nozzle flows should be watched for in performance calculations. If this occurs (see Fig. 31), the critical flow condition should be calculated with static pressure p_7 at the nozzle exit above p_0 by whatever ratio remains after the sonic flow condition is reached in the jet. The critical flow area required for the known mass flow of gas at static pressure p_7 and calculated temperature t_7 (or T_7) is then compared with the actual effective area of the jet nozzle exit.   Jet thrusts are calculated in the conventional manner from the exit flow velocities, making the usual static pressure difference thrust addition for the case of critical flows.

The foregoing procedure is repeated a sufficient number of times to establish all the points required to plot gas-turbine performance curves over the required flight and engine speed ranges.   Many of these repetitive computations may be avoided by using a method of graphical solution for the compressor-turbine matching problem.[1]

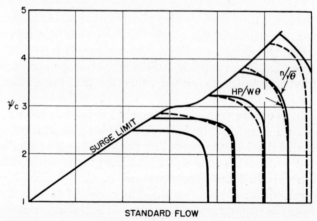

Fig. 203.   Compressor flow chart in terms of corrected variables.

In order to use this graphical method, a compressor flow chart similar to Fig. 102 is required, along with a flow chart for the combined turbine plus fixed-exit-area nozzle.   The three fundamental relations of compressor rpm equal to turbine rpm, compressor flow plus fuel flow equal to turbine flow, and turbine power equal to compressor power (plus auxiliaries and propeller in the case of a turboprop engine) still rule.   The flow charts are plotted in terms of corrected variables.   It is necessary to add a parameter indicating power to the conventional compressor flow chart. This is most conveniently represented by specific power, or power per unit air flow, and is denoted by hp/$W\theta$ on the compressor map of Fig. 203.

The requirement that the compressor flow plus fuel flow equal the turbine flow is satisfied by the following process.   Pressure ratio across the combustor and turbine plus nozzle is plotted vs. flow (corrected for W_f) for constant values of turbine inlet total temperature divided by compressor inlet total temperature.   The total pressure ratio across the

[1] HALL, R. S., Aircraft Gas Turbines with Centrifugal Compressors, *SAE Preprint*, April, 1946.

turbine and nozzle is increased by the pressure-loss ratio of the burner, so that the ratios plotted for the expansion flows are in terms of compressor ratios.

In order that the compressor and turbine speeds may match, the speed parameter of the compressor map is used in plotting the above turbine map. For a given turbine inlet temperature and turbine flow (referred to compressor standard flow) and for a given shaft speed, both turbine power and turbine-plus-nozzle pressure ratio are known. After correcting the total expanding-flow pressure ratio to the compressor ratio by multiplying by P_4/P_3, the burner pressure ratio, and turbine and nozzle flow characteristics may be plotted over the compressor map of Fig. 203.

There are five variables in the corrected turbine data, three of which must be matched simultaneously to the data on Fig. 203 while a fourth variable is treated as a parameter. This parameter is the specific turbine power. For a given turbine flow [corrected to compressor flow by the multiplier $W_a/(W_a + W_f)$], the turbine data are searched for a point of correspondence between compressor and turbine speed simultaneously with compressor ratio and corrected turbine-plus-nozzle pressure ratio, without regard to turbine inlet temperature. This is most readily done by plotting a few experimental points on the pressure-ratio-vs.-flow chart for the expanding flow, for the selected shaft speed and specific turbine power. The place at which a line through these points crosses the corresponding compressor-speed line is the only point of coincidence of compressor and turbine flows at the selected turbine specific power and speed. The turbine inlet temperature, or the ratio of turbine inlet temperature to compressor inlet temperature, at this point of coincidence is noted from the turbine data. The other experimental points used to plot the line for the coincident point are of no further use since they do not represent the two conditions of equal shaft speed and matching compressor and turbine flow.

By repeating this process a number of times for different shaft speeds and different turbine specific power parameters, a plot of lines of constant turbine specific power may be drawn on the same pressure-ratio–speed–flow map as used for the compressor. From the turbine inlet temperature ratios noted on the points of coincidence, lines of equal turbine inlet temperature ratio may also be plotted (see Fig. 204).

Now, if the parameters of Fig. 204 are plotted over the compressor map of Fig. 203, the complete performance map of the jet engine at static condition is shown (see Fig. 205). The locus of the points where compressor specific power matches turbine specific power is the operating line, shown as a heavy line on the plot. At other points on the plot, either compressor power is greater than turbine power and the engine decelerates, or turbine power exceeds the compressor power, and unless turbine inlet temperature is decreased, the shaft speed will increase. The amount of power differential between compressor and turbine specific power parameters is available by inspection of the plot, so that rates of acceleration or deceleration may be calculated, if the inertia of

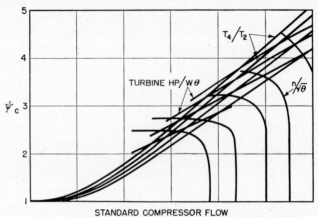

Fig. 204. Turbine flow chart in terms of corrected variables.

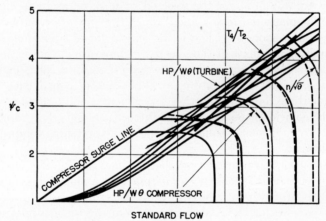

Fig. 205. Combined compressor-turbine performance map for jet engine under static conditions.

the rotating system is known. Therefore, not only the steady-state performance of the jet engine may be calculated, but also the transient characteristics. Data are presented in terms of corrected quantities, so that performance at any pressure-altitude and ambient temperature may be calculated readily, if combustion efficiency does not fall to such low values that the turbine mass flow requires further corrections. If the effective nozzle exit area is changed, a new map must be constructed for each new area.

The effects of inlet ram pressures and temperatures due to flight speed change the operating-line locus on Fig. 205, except for the condition where critical flow is already established in the jet nozzle at static conditions. With critical flow in the nozzle, the flow is independent of the static pressure of the atmosphere surrounding the exhaust. The nozzle static exhaust pressure is always higher than the atmospheric static pressure with critical flows, but the actual pressure difference has no influence upon the flow within the nozzle. Therefore, the portion of the jet-engine performance map for which sonic jet velocities exist at static conditions must be corrected for the new ram total pressure and ram total temperature conditions at the compressor inlet for any flight speed condition. This will occur only at the upper turbine inlet temperatures and shaft rpm (near the design point as a rule) for the conventional jet engine. At low turbine temperatures and speeds, the heat-to-work factor is too low to yield sonic jet velocity.

Critical or choking flow conditions may occur in the turbine nozzle inlet ring even though the jet nozzle effective pressure ratio is below critical. This is most apt to occur in high-impulse turbine designs rather than in nozzles for turbines with reaction blading. When this happens, the operating line on the performance map changes position with changes of flight speed. If the performance map of the compressor, Fig. 203, is replotted on log-log paper, and if the turbine performance map, Fig. 204, is similarly replotted on a transparent overlay with a log-log scale, the problem may still be solved graphically. The logarithmic scale of the pressure ordinate permits the linear addition of ram pressure at the compressor inlet to the compressor-pressure-ratio scale. The transparent turbine overlay plot is placed over the compressor plot with the turbine map shifted along the ordinate by an amount corresponding to the ram-pressure-ratio increase. The crossing points of matching compressor and turbine specific power parameters then establish the new operating line on the compressor map, at the new compressor inlet temperatures and pressures.

For the situation where flows in both turbine and nozzle are subsonic, the turbine-map transparency is shifted upward along the ordinate by an amount corresponding to the ram pressure ratio, and along the abscissa by an amount corresponding to the change in the corrected flow relationship. This solution is approximate to the extent that the effect of the change in turbine velocity ratio on the turbine efficiency is ignored.

Jet engines operated at high flight speeds are almost certain to encounter critical flow conditions in the jet nozzle, while at lower flight speeds and at low turbine inlet temperatures, all flows are subsonic. Therefore, the use of the turbine overlay shift may be necessary in mapping performance up to a different critical flight Mach number for each corrected engine rpm. When the flight Mach number that results in sonic jet flow for a given engine rpm is reached, the position of the turbine overlay on the compressor map is fixed for further flight-speed increases, and the position of the operating point does not shift on the map. Ram pressure and temperature corrections are applied to the standard flow calculations.

It should be noted that a turbine inlet nozzle with an early choking flow condition may move the operating line of the engine up into the pulsation or surge region of the compressor operating characteristic for very moderate flight speeds. The widening of the operating line into a band of considerable width during acceleration and deceleration conditions, particularly at the low ambient temperatures of high altitudes, may also intersect the pulsation region unless care is taken in determining the location of the design point in the compressor performance field.

The performance map of Fig. 205 with the turbine flow transparency on log-log scales will also serve effectively to describe the performance of the turboprop engine. The location of the operating point shifts continuously with changes in the power being absorbed by the propeller. The use of a variable-pitch propeller, of course, introduces an element of flexibility that will permit moving the engine operating line over a wide area of the performance map. The fixed-pitch propeller designed to absorb a major part of the engine output, to the practical exclusion of jet thrust power, imposes severe limitations upon the engine in flight.

Figure 206 shows the performance map for a propeller-drive engine on a somewhat larger scale than the preceding figures and includes only the region of interest in connection with normal operations. The engine design point for a fixed-pitch-propeller load is determined for a specified altitude and flight speed. If the aircraft's flight speed and altitude could always be maintained so that the propeller would operate at a constant value of advance ratio J, the operating line of the engine would follow the same line as that for a pure jet engine.

However, under static conditions, the advance ratio is zero. If $J = 1.0$ at the design flight speed, then at $J = 0$, the propeller's power coefficient has increased approximately by the ratio of 1.5:1. It is apparent then that the turboprop engine with fixed-pitch propeller absorbing engine output to the practical exclusion of jet thrust, will, in all probability, not be able to operate under static conditions at full engine speed without pushing the operating line up into the unstable compressor region on the performance map. A limit of approximately

60 percent of the engine's static design output would be the normal expectation at the reduced engine rpm necessitated by the fixed-pitch propeller. If, on the other hand, the design point corresponds to static conditions where J is equal to zero, the fixed-pitch propeller will not be able to absorb more than about 60 percent of the engine's design power at

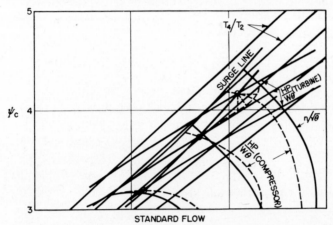

Fig. 206. Performance map for turboprop engine. Only the region of interest in connection with normal operations is included.

rated engine rpm at a flight speed corresponding to $J = 1$. Absorbing a smaller proportion of the engine's power output in the fixed-pitch propeller and more in the jet thrust would relieve this situation to some extent. The use of a fixed-pitch propjet engine with adjustable jet nozzle area would also introduce the required degree of control flexibility provided that the propeller did not absorb more than about 50 percent of engine energy output at the design flight speed. Most thrust-augmenter designs lack this refinement.

CHAPTER 9

VARIANTS OF SIMPLE GAS-TURBINE CYCLES

48. Turbine Thrust Augmenters. An attempt to achieve a compromise between the properties of the straight turbojet and the turboprop engine is found in a number of different forms of gas-turbine power plants having directly driven fixed-pitch propellers, either open or ducted. The general term thrust augmenter has been applied to these types. A schematic example of a ducted-propeller power plant is shown in Fig. 207, in which the propeller or fan forms part of the compressor and by-passes low-pressure air around the engine to mix downstream with the hot turbine exhaust at the turbine exhaust pressure. The mixed cold air and

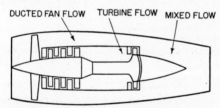

DUCTED FAN FLOW   TURBINE FLOW   MIXED FLOW

FIG. 207. Thrust augmenter with flow from ducted fan mixing with turbine efflux.

hot exhaust gases are then expanded through a jet nozzle. The over-all cycle efficiency benefits somewhat through mixing of the hot exhaust with the cold air pumped by the fan. The larger the ratio of cold by-pass air flow to hot turbine air flow, the better the propulsive efficiency at low speeds, as would be expected. At higher flight Mach numbers, the advantages of the thrust augmenter begin to disappear as jet-propulsive efficiencies become competitive with the propulsive efficiency of the ducted fan or propeller.

Other thrust augmenters may use lower speed propellers driven by exhaust turbines on separate shafts immediately downstream from the compressor-driving turbine. The propeller or fan efflux may mix with the turbine efflux either before or after hot jet expansion occurs.

These engines all have the advantages of higher take-off thrust and efficiency at intermediate and low flight speeds, coupled with the disadvantages of greater weight, complicated construction, fixed-pitch-propeller characteristics, and indifferent performance at the higher flight speeds.

The use of a fixed-pitch propeller driven by a turbine wheel on a shaft separate from the compressor and its turbine alleviates to some extent the disadvantages of a directly driven fixed-pitch propeller. An engine designed for a particular flight speed with a direct-driven fixed-pitch propeller will be overloaded at the same engine rpm under static or zero flight speed condition, as described in the preceding chapter.   A separate turbine for the propeller permits a small decrease in propeller turbine speed at static condition without dropping the compressor speed and pressure ratio; this is because the turbine velocity ratio may change through a moderate range with but small change in efficiency and power

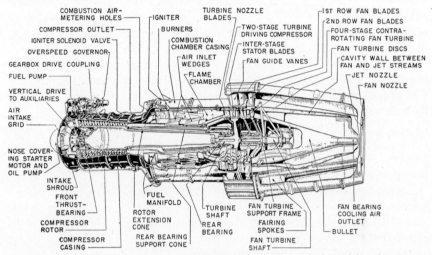

Fig. 208.   Section of Metropolitan Vickers F-3 gas turbine with ducted-fan thrust augmenter.   (*Flight magazine.*)

output.   The thrust augmenter with separate turbine drive for the fan or propeller is thus more flexible and efficient than the direct-drive type.

49. Afterburning in Turbojet Engines.   The simple turbojet engine may have its thrust output increased by rather substantial amounts if additional fuel is burned in the turbine exhaust ahead of the jet expansion nozzle.

Thermodynamically, the effect is that of a reheat stage in the expansion process.   The immediate result is an increase in jet energy roughly proportional to the ratio of total tail-pipe temperature following afterburning to the total temperature prior to afterburning.   The ratio of jet velocities, with and without afterburning, is then approximately proportional to the square-root of this temperature ratio.

In a turbojet engine with 1960°R turbine inlet temperature and total turbine exhaust temperature of the order of 1560°R, sufficient oxygen remains in the exhaust gas to burn additional gasoline or kerosene fuels to an afterburner top temperature of the order of 3500°R at 95 percent combustion efficiency.   Thus the afterburner temperature ratio is $\frac{3500}{1560} = 2.25$, and the jet velocity is increased in the ratio $\sqrt{2.25} = 1.5$.

Since the jet flow velocity is increased by 50 percent, the static thrust is increased by the same amount.

The above rough analysis of the static thrust increase of a contemporary turbojet engine with maximum-temperature afterburning has neglected momentum pressure losses in the afterburner combustion chamber. Such losses would be negligible for an unusually low turbine efflux velocity. Actually, flow velocity in the tail-pipe afterburner is a serious problem. From Fig. 126, a temperature ratio of 2.25 at inlet flow Mach number 0.3 results in a 10 percent loss in total pressure and an exit flow Mach number of 0.6 in a constant-cross-section combustion space.

Returning to the previous example, the fuel/air ratio without afterburning was about 0.015, with a static specific fuel consumption of about 1 lb of fuel per hour per pound of thrust. With afterburning, the total fuel/air ratio has increased slightly beyond the stoichiometric ratio, *i.e.*, to $W_f/W_a = 0.07$. At the same time, the thrust has increased by 50 percent, so that the static thrust specific fuel consumption with afterburning is approximately $0.07/0.015/1.5 = 3.1$ lb of fuel per hour per pound of gross thrust.

From the foregoing, it is evident that afterburning in turbojet engines is uneconomical and must be limited to periods of short duration at the lower flight speeds. Assuming that a turbojet engine will weigh $\frac{1}{3}$ lb/lb of rated static thrust and that the installed volume of the engine is 0.03 cu ft/lb of rated static thrust, the additional 50 percent thrust available through tailburning at low flight speeds will cost as much extra weight of fuel burned in only 3.2 min as the extra weight of engine for a 50 percent larger engine without afterburning. Similarly, the increased volume of fuel burned in 14 min would equal the increase in installed volume of the larger engine.

The unfavorable efficiency characteristics of the afterburner reheat cycle begin to disappear at high flight velocities. The pressure ratio across the jet nozzle is usually less than 2 : 1 in the conventional turbojet engine at zero flight speed. However, at high flight speed, the effect of ram pressure ratio is, in general, a proportionate increase in total pressure ratio across the jet nozzle. The heat added in the afterburner is therefore added at a more favorable state condition for the recovery of mechanical energy, and the effectiveness of the afterburner increases. At very high flight velocities between $M_0 = 1.0$ and $M_0 = 2.0$, over-all efficiency may be higher when the compressor pressure ratio is low.

The turbojet engine with tailburner then approaches the characteristics of the ramjet. Specific fuel consumption rates and specific thrusts in pounds per pound of air per second are plotted in Fig. 209 against flight Mach number for different compressor pressure ratios and afterburner

temperatures T_6. All compression flows are assumed to be 85 percent
efficient; turbine inlet temperature $T_4 = 1500°F$ in all cases; combustion
efficiency is 95 percent, and expanding flows are assumed to be 85 percent
efficient. These assumptions are somewhat optimistic at the higher
flight speeds, particularly since DeLaval jet nozzles for supersonic jets
are not yet practical for aircraft turbines.

Physical space requirements of afterburners depend upon the turbine
efflux velocity, the static pressure in the tailburner combustion zone, and

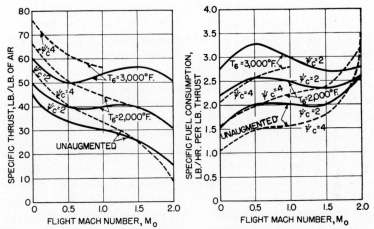

FIG. 209. Effect of tailburner reheating on specific thrust and specific fuel consumption
for turbojet engines with compressor compression ratios $\psi_c = 2$ and $\psi_c = 4$.

the amount of heat to be added. The actual jet nozzle can be short as
in the case of the conventional jet engine. Normally, a diffusing passage
will follow the turbine, the length of which may be as great as two turbine
diameters. The density of the gas in the tailburner will be about one-half
of the air density in the normal combustion space at low flight speeds, so
that a much greater volume is required for the same heat release. Also
a greater total heat release is called for in the afterburner than in the
normal combustor, so that the combustion-zone volume necessary will be
several times as much as that of the preturbine burner. The diameter
of an afterburner may then be of the same order as the turbine nozzle
ring, or somewhat greater; the length of the complete afterburner with
diffuser, combustion space, and variable-area jet nozzle will normally be
at least as great as four turbine diameters. Thus the afterburner for an
axial-flow jet engine is about the same size as the engine itself, and it
could hardly weigh less than 25 percent of the bare engine weight without
afterburner.

50. Intake Coolant Injection for Gas-turbine Engines.   The work of compression of a gas can be reduced by cooling the gas before or during compression.   In the case of the gas-turbine aircraft power plant, whether turbojet or turboprop, the use of intercoolers between compressor stages seems limited in applicability because of stringent weight requirements. It is possible, however, to secure some of the advantages of cooling by the evaporation of small quantities of liquid ahead of or within the compressor.   Because of their high latent heats of vaporization, water or water-alcohol mixtures are used.

Practically, water or the water-alcohol mixture is sprayed into the air intake ahead of the compressor.   Depending upon the fineness of the spray, the temperature and relative humidity of the air, temperature of the liquid injected, completeness of dispersion of liquid spray in the air, turbulence, and the length of time the spray is air borne before entering the compressor blading, a greater or lesser portion of the liquid evaporates ahead of the compressor blading.   With water injection at the air intake of an I-40 (J-33) engine as installed in the F-80A airplane, the compressor air inlet temperature is normally lowered by 20 or 30°F at a water flow rate of the order of 26 gpm.[1]   This is approximately 4.5 percent of the air flow rate to the engine by weight.   The air-temperature fall indicates that about one-ninth to one-sixth of the water injected was evaporated.

The decrease in temperature of air at the compressor inlet results in an increase in air density and mass flow through the engine.   A tail-pipe rake survey indicated approximately 10 percent increase in mass flow in the case referred to above.   About half of this increase was due to the mass of water injected, and the remainder to higher air density at the intake, which checks with the observed air-temperature changes.

The evaporated portion of the water spray enters the compressor as a gas; the unevaporated liquid spray droplets may carry on through the compressor or may be further evaporated in the compression process. Liquid evaporated in the passage through the compressor acts as an inter-stage cooling means, and the volume flow increases progressively through the compressor because of this evaporation.   Because of the uncertainty as to exactly when the liquid evaporates to a gas, at the same time providing flow cooling, it is difficult to estimate accurately the effects of spray injection upon compressor performance.

Experimental results with water sprays show as high as 30 percent increase in static thrust for a turbojet engine.   Data are not available on turboprop engines, but somewhat greater proportional increases would be expected there.   Experimental results with an I-40 engine are shown

[1] JOHNSON, C. L., *J. IAS*, vol. 14, p. 666, 1947.

in Fig. 210. The maximum injection rate of 26 gpm corresponds to approximately 4.5 percent of the rated air flow of the engine. Effects of water injection rates upon engine temperatures and pressures are interesting. The temperature rise through the compressor decreases progressively with increased water injection rates, indicating a decrease in compressor power input requirements. At the same time, the compression ratio increases, which would follow from the density increase in the gas flow through the compressor. There is also an observed increase

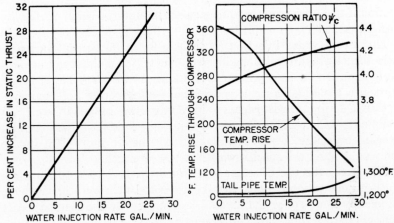

Fig. 210. Effects of water injection rates on jet-engine static thrust, engine temperatures, and engine pressure. Rated air flow 79 lb/sec. (*C. L. Johnson, J. IAS, vol.* 14, *p.* 659, 1947.)

in the tail-pipe temperature of the jet engine, which may be due in part to the lowered compressor power input requirement.

Injected liquid that carries through the compressor and into the combustion space unevaporated is evaporated in the burner. The action is that of a flash boiler; more fuel must be burned to evaporate the liquid and heat it to the burner exit temperature, if the liquid itself is noncombustible. The effects of introducing liquid into the combustion zone are bad for cycle and fuel efficiencies, but the increased mass flow through the turbine leads to much-increased energy availability in the gas flow leaving the burner. This will lead to either greater net shaft output for the turboprop engine or more thrust for the turbojet.

Water injection into jet-engine air intakes has some serious operational disadvantages. If compressor air is bled off for fuel-transfer purposes and for instrumentation uses, water finds its way into fuel tanks and into instruments. Further, water freezes in cold weather and at high altitudes. Alcohol can be added to the water to prevent freezing, but the other disadvantages still remain. The addition of 30 percent alcohol by volume to replace water in water-alcohol injection reduced the static thrust increase of a J-33 engine (with 28 gpm of fluid injection) from 28 to 23 percent. Sixty percent of alcohol by volume further reduced the static thrust increase to 16 percent.

Compressor air bleed for cabin-pressurization purposes leads to fogging of the cabin atmosphere and windshield surfaces when water injection occurs. This is not serious at low altitudes or at take-off when cabin pressurization is not required and can be shut off; it is serious at high altitudes. The use of alcohol-water mixtures is, of course, out of the question if compressor air is to be passed through the cabin during fluid-injection periods.

The use of water injection to achieve 25 or 30 percent increase in static thrust of a turbojet engine requires 4 to 5 percent flow of water referred to air flow as a parameter. Using a thrust specific of 55 lb of thrust per pound of air per second for contemporary jet engines, an increase of 15 lb in thrust is gained for a water flow of 0.05 lb/sec. With an engine specific weight of the order of 0.35 lb/lb of jet thrust, the above water-injection case would run about 2 min before the weight of water used would equal the specific weight of the jet engine.

Therefore, the use of water injection is limited to very short term thrust-augmentation periods, else the water to be carried will weigh more and occupy more space than would be required by the installation of a larger engine without water injection.

Liquid ammonia as a compressor intake coolant is more effective than water, under favorable conditions. Although ammonia has only one-half the latent heat of evaporation of water, it has a much lower boiling point than water at the pressures encountered in the compressor. A 10 percent ammonia injection leads to a theoretically expected augmentation of about 60 percent. Ammonia injection has the further advantage that much of the evaporation and cooling can occur in the compressor inlet duct rather than in the later stages of compression, so that the compressor has the benefit of a cold intake from the start.

Experimental injections of 5 percent ammonia have given actual thrust increases of 23 percent as compared with a theoretical value of 28 percent. These results were obtained in dry air. On a humid day, the thrust augmentation with 5 percent ammonia injection was negligible.[1] This is explained by the fact that ammonia reacts with water vapor in the atmosphere to form ammonium hydroxide, with a release of heat of formation that offsets the cooling effect of evaporation of the liquid ammonia.

Ammonia or ammonium-compound dissociation is practically com-

[1] Cox, H. ROXBEE, British Aircraft Gas Turbines, *J. Aeronaut. Sci.*, vol. 13, p. 53, 1946.

plete in the combustion chamber by the time gas temperatures have risen to 1000°F. Ammonia breaks down into nitrogen and hydrogen gases, and it is almost certain that the portion of hydrogen gas that flows through the primary combustion zone burns with the oxygen of the air. It is necessary to reduce the fuel/air ratio when cooling with ammonia if the turbine inlet temperature is not to be permitted to increase.

51. The Pulse Jet Engine. Pulse jet, resojet, or aeropulse engines are not continuous-flow engines, although at very high flight speeds they may revert to ramjet operation if favorably proportioned. A pulse jet engine designed for subsonic flight is shown schematically in Fig. 211.

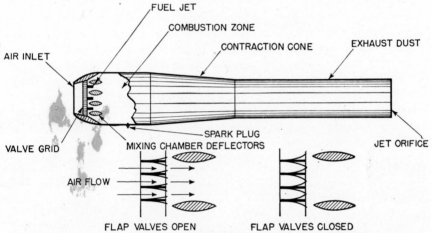

Fig. 211. Cutaway schematic view of pulse jet engine for subsonic flight speeds.

To start the engine, fuel is sprayed into the cold combustion chamber, perhaps aided by a compressed-air jet in the Venturi space between the mixing-chamber deflectors. The resulting combustible mixture ignites from the spark plug and burns very rapidly in an explosion (normally without detonation); the hot gas expands out through the nozzle and jet pipe; back pressure of the explosion closes the flap valves in the valve grid, preventing flow at the inlet; inertia of the leaving column of hot gas through the exhaust pipe pulls down the static pressure in the combustion chamber; the flap valves open, admitting a fresh charge of air, and the cycle is repeated. The frequency of the operation is controlled by the resonance frequency of the hot gases in the long tail pipe and combustion space, and the air flow is pulsating in a regular series of explosions. This engine will therefore operate under static conditions. The effect of forward flight is to increase the flow of air.

The thermodynamic cycle is not rigidly defined, but is represented approximately by air induction at ram (or static) pressure less (considerable) flow pressure losses, constant-volume combustion, and adiabatic expansion to the atmospheric pressure. Pressure-volume diagrams are shown in Fig. 212, with enthalpy-entropy diagrams for both static and in-flight conditions.

Fuel injection is usually continuous, with combustion occurring when an explosive fuel/air ratio is reached at an ignition point. Starting ignition is by spark plug, but it is sustained by residual pockets of hot gas after the first few cycles. Combustion is very rapid, and the assumption that it takes place under constant-volume conditions introduces only small errors in calculations. Expansion starts at the beginning of the

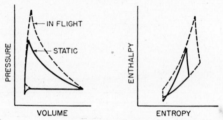

FIG. 212. Approximate pressure-volume and enthalpy-entropy diagrams for pulse jet engine.

combustion process, but most of it occurs after the fuel charge is burned. Because of the intermittent operation and the simple construction, peak combustion temperature is not a limit, and fuel/air ratios are run very close to the stoichiometric ratio to achieve maximum thrust.

The recurrence frequency of the explosions is slightly lower than the resonance frequency of the engine when considered as a quarter-wave-length oscillator with the valve grid closed. The approximate equivalent length of the oscillator is the distance from the valve grid to the end of the exhaust pipe or nozzle. The increased volume of the combustion chamber and of the contraction cone makes the actual length somewhat lower than the length of an equivalent straight-pipe resonator closed at one end. The opening of the inlet valves to admit a fresh air charge and the time required for combustion to be completed also contribute to make the actual frequency of pulsations lower than the estimated frequency, in cps, $f = a_m/(4l)$ where l is the length of the engine behind the valve grid and a_m is the arithmetic mean velocity of sound in the gas in the engine. An approximate value of a_m may be arrived at through the relation

$$a_m = \frac{a_4}{2}\left[1 + \left(\frac{p_0}{P_4}\right)^{\frac{k-1}{2k}} \right] \tag{224}$$

where a_4 is the velocity of sound and P_4 is the maximum pressure of the gas at the end of combustion. The value of a_4 is connected to the final combustion temperature T_4 through the usual relation.

The pressure in the combustion chamber immediately preceding combustion, indicated as P_3, is dependent upon the configurations of the inlet, valve system, and combustion chamber, as well as upon the ram pressure of the air at the inlet and the magnitude of the negative pressure wave reflection behind the valve grid somewhat less than a half cycle after the combustion explosion. For simplified calculation purposes, it is assumed that all the ram pressure rise is free-stream pressure recovery ahead of the inlet, and the corresponding mass air flows and internal pressure relations are corrected accordingly from pressure and flow data obtained for the engine under static or other flight-speed tests. Ordinarily, flow pressure losses are quite large through the flapper valve grid and fuel-mixing zones, so that only about one-half of the total stagnation pressure P_0 ahead of the inlet is normally recovered in the combustion chamber preceding ignition of the fuel.

Combustion is carried out at an assumed constant volume, and the approximate relation for the heat added in the combustion chamber is

$$h_b = c_v(T_4 - T_3) \tag{225}$$

The addition of heat in the combustion chamber at constant volume results in a considerably greater temperature increase than when the same amount of heat is added at constant pressure. The data of Fig. 111 may be multiplied by $c_p/c_v = k$ (approximately, $k = 1.33$ in the ramjet temperature range) to obtain constant-volume temperature increases. Maximum temperatures are of the order of 5300 to 5400°R for kerosene or gasoline combustion in dry air at constant volume, while maximum temperatures for the same fuels at constant pressure are in the range of 4200 to 4300°R. Dissociation of products of combustion takes place to a sufficiently large extent that corrections must be made in calculating gas flows. The same gas data that have been used for the calculation of reciprocating-engine behavior will be found useful and in the correct temperature range.

To simplify the problem, the instantaneous flow into the tail pipe or exhaust duct is assumed to be the same as the flow that would be obtained under steady-state flow conditions for steady-state temperature and pressure conditions corresponding to the instantaneous temperature and pressure conditions. Inertia effects in the combustion chamber and expansion nozzle are thus neglected.

The long exhaust duct or tail pipe usually has a constant cross section with straight walls. Its length is chosen to fix the pulsation frequency by resonance tuning of the entire system. Therefore, apart from frictional losses, which may be considerable at high flow Mach numbers, the tail pipe does not influence the thrust. If the instantaneous values of gross momentum thrust or impulse at the contraction-cone exit are integrated over the complete expansion of the charge of gas in the combustion chamber, the total impulse of the charge is obtained. Impulse is the product of velocity change and mass, while thrust is velocity change multiplied by mass rate of flow in slugs per second. Total impulse divided by total time yields average thrust.

The ideal discharge flow velocity through the contraction-cone exit is

$$V = \sqrt{2gJc_pt\left[1 - \left(\frac{p_0}{p}\right)^{\frac{k-1}{k}}\right]} = \sqrt{\frac{2k}{k-1}\frac{p}{\rho}\left[1 - \left(\frac{p_0}{p}\right)^{\frac{k-1}{k}}\right]} \quad (226)$$

where V, p, and ρ are instantaneous values of velocity, pressure, and density (slugs per cu ft) in the combustion chamber and p_0 is the static atmospheric or final discharge pressure.

The impulse that results from the discharge of an incremental mass of gas Δq at velocity V is

$$\Delta I = V \Delta q \quad (227)$$

Expansion out of the combustion-chamber reservoir and the nozzle is assumed to be isentropic so that

$$\Delta q = -\frac{q}{kp}\Delta p \quad (228)$$

$$\Delta I = -\frac{q}{kp}\sqrt{\frac{2k}{k-1}\frac{p}{\rho}\left[1 - \left(\frac{p_0}{p}\right)^{\frac{k-1}{k}}\right]}\Delta p \quad (229)$$

The total impulse due to the expansion of the entire initial charge of gas in the combustion chamber is $I = V_e q_4$, where V_e is the effective exit velocity and q_4 is the initial mass in slugs. Therefore

$$V_e = \frac{I}{q_4} = \frac{1}{k}\sqrt{\frac{2}{k-1}}\int_{p_0}^{p_4}\sqrt{\frac{q^2}{q_4^2}k\frac{1}{p\rho}\left[1 - \left(\frac{p_0}{p}\right)^{\frac{k-1}{k}}\right]}\,dp$$

Since q/q_4 is equal to ρ/ρ_4 in a constant-volume reservoir,

$$V_e = \frac{1}{k}\sqrt{\frac{2}{k-1}}\int_{p_0}^{p_4}\sqrt{\frac{kp_4}{\rho_4}\frac{\rho}{\rho_4}\frac{1}{pp_4}\left[1 - \left(\frac{p_0}{p}\right)^{\frac{k-1}{k}}\right]}\,dp$$

$$= \frac{a_4}{k}\sqrt{\frac{2}{k-1}}\int_{p_0}^{p_4}\sqrt{\frac{1}{p_4^{\frac{k-1}{k}}p^{\frac{k-1}{k}}}\left[1 - \left(\frac{p_0}{p}\right)^{\frac{k-1}{k}}\right]}\,dp \quad (230)$$

Equation (230) may be solved as a rational integral for certain specific values of k, such as $k = \frac{4}{3}$, and by graphical methods for all practical values of k.   The estimated specific thrust of the pulse jet engine is then

$$F = \frac{W_a + W_f}{W_a} \frac{V_e - V_0}{g} \tag{231}$$

Using stoichiometric fuel/air ratios for gasoline and assuming that p_3 is equal to one-half of the ideal total ram pressure at all flight speeds, the momentum thrust per pound of air per second flowing through the pulse jet engine is plotted in Fig. 213 for sea-level standard conditions.

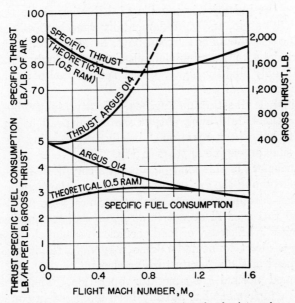

Fig. 213.   Performance characteristics of pulse jet engine.

The theoretical thrust specific fuel consumption is also shown as well as actual thrust specific fuel consumption for the Argus 014 pulsejet engine. Gross thrust is also plotted for the same engine (also known as the V-1 engine) of 23-in. diameter.

Theoretical studies usually estimate that the pulse frequency should not change significantly with changes in flight speed and that the average air flow is proportional to the equivalent density of the air at ram stagnation pressure before the inlet.   Actual engine performance with inlet valves of the type used in the German-built Argus 014 indicates that flow is seriously restricted at static and low-flight-speed conditions.   At higher flight speeds, ram pressures are proportionately much higher than the fixed flapper-valve-spring restoring forces, and greatly increased air flows result.   The effects of low air-flow rates and the attendant low precombustion-chamber pressures appear in high parasitic or form drag, low thrust, and high specific fuel consumption at low flight speeds.

Pulse jet engines induct air, inefficiently, during less than half of each explosion cycle; they therefore have much lower air-flow rates per unit of frontal area than do turbojet engines at low flight speeds or ramjets at high speeds. The static thrust obtainable from an axial-flow turbojet engine of approximately the same diameter as the Argus 014 pulsejet engine is about 3,000 lb for 1500°F turbine inlet temperature against 400 to 600 lb for the pulse jet static thrust.

However, the pulse jet is capable of delivering static thrust, which the ramjet will not do, and is fundamentally a mechanically simple light-weight engine that should be inexpensive to build. It is not size sensitive, as is the turbojet engine, and model pulse jet engines only 2 in. in diameter operate with only slightly higher thrust specific fuel consumption rates than do the larger engines.

52. Multishaft Gas-turbine Engines. Gas-turbine engines with separate turbine elements driving output shafts independently of the compressor shaft have been mentioned briefly in preceding chapters. An example of such an engine appears in Fig. 229.

An arrangement of this kind permits of a certain degree of flexibility between the load and the gas-generator portion of the engine, as the compressor-burner-turbine elements are sometimes known. Because the conventional turbine will accept flows at off-design conditions without serious changes in efficiency or load coefficient, a load characteristic that would stall a direct-connected engine may only result in a sufficient change in speed of the separate turbine element to drop the excess load with continued normal gas-generator operation. The desirability of this kind of arrangement has already been discussed in connection with fixed-pitch-propeller loads.

Treatment of performance characteristics of gas generators coupled by means of gas flow to separate turbines is no more difficult than the matching of flows in simpler types of gas turbines, provided that the complete characteristics of all elements are known or may be estimated accurately. A method developed by Driggs[1] employs the use of the gas generator as a separate element, ahead of power output turbine or jet nozzle.

Large turbojet and turboprop engines have rather substantial power requirements for starting, particularly turboprop engines. The gas turbine with output turbine on a separate shaft reduces the gas-generator shaft torque loads at starting.

[1] Preliminary Performance Analysis of Gas Turbine Power Plants, *SAE Preprint*, 1947.

53. The Comprex Compressor. An entirely different type of flow device from any of the preceding engines is the Comprex.[1] With the exception of the pulse jet engine, all the gas-flow engines considered hitherto have been continuous-flow devices. The Comprex operates on the transient characteristics of intermittent gas flow. Briefly, air is admitted suddenly at one end of a cell, closed at the other end. A pressure wave moves into the cell, and the air-admission valve is closed at the peak of the reflection pressure wave, trapping the charge of air at an average pressure considerably above that corresponding to air inlet pressure. A transient condition still exists in the cell, and the pressure wave reflects from the opposite end and then from the closed entrance end. After the reflection pressure wave leaves the closed inlet end of the cell, another valve admits a charge of hot gas at a relatively high pressure; this charge of hot gas moves down the cell, pushing and compressing the cold-air charge ahead of it. There is very little mixing of the hot gas and cold air, the hot gas acting as an expanding piston.

A strong pressure wave moves down the cell, developing reflection pressures at the far or exit end, and the charge of compressed cold air is valved out of the cell at that point. The total average pressure of this charge of air is slightly above the average pressure of the hot-gas inlet, owing to the reflection pressure wave in the cell at the time the exit valve opens. This charge of cold air then flows through a combustion chamber where fuel is burned; part of the resulting hot-gas flow is returned to the hot-gas inlet duct of the Comprex, and the remainder is taken to the inlet of a multistage turbine.

The hot gas remaining in the cell after expulsion of the cold-air charge is allowed to escape and expand through lower pressure stages of the turbine, effectively voiding the cell of high-pressure hot gas and returning it to the initial condition. The cycle then begins again.

The physical arrangement is shown in Fig. 214, and a development of the Comprex rotor composed of a number of cells arranged axially about the axis of rotation is shown in Fig. 215. The cylinder rotates at high speed in order that the valve timing shall coincide properly with the movements of pressure waves in the multiplicity of cells. Cells move past individual valve ports at the rate of 3,000 per second in one experimental unit. The only power involved in rotating the rotor is that necessary to overcome friction. In addition, there is a small scavenging blower in the compressed-air duct from the Comprex to aid in overcoming duct flow friction and burner losses, particularly at starting. Power to drive this blower is obtained from the turbine.

The Comprex acts as a combined compressor and turbine, and the two

[1] MEYER, *Elec. World*, Jan. 4, 1947, pp. 38–40.

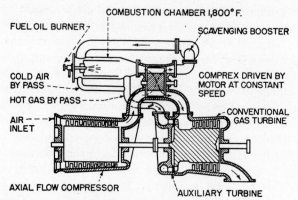

FIG. 214. Diagram of Comprex unit installed as second-stage compressor for 4,000-hp locomotive gas turbine. (*Aviation magazine.*)

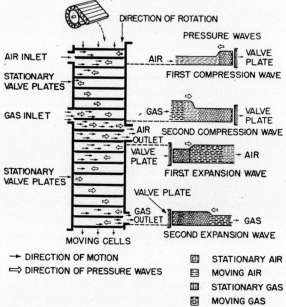

FIG. 215. Schematic sketch of Comprex unit with cells unrolled, showing simplified cycle of air and gas pressure waves. (*Aviation magazine.*)

functions may not be separated, with compression and expansion flow efficiencies assigned respectively. An over-all figure of merit may be assigned, similar to the product $\eta_c\eta_t$, and on that basis experimental units are competitive with turbines and compressors of 0.80 to 0.85 efficiency.

The Comprex is a gas generator capable of increasing the effective cycle pressure ratio by a factor of 2 or more. Since alternate flows of hot gas and cold air pass through each cell, the average temperature of the cell walls is far below the peak combustion temperature. With combustion gas at 1800°F, the cell wall temperature averages slightly over 1000°F with cyclic variations of cell wall temperature less than 4°F.

Peak cycle temperature limits may thus be increased significantly along with cycle pressure ratios, resulting in as much as a 60 percent increase in heat to work per pound of air flow through the complete engine. Basic cycle efficiency of 18 percent for an experimental locomotive gas turbine is increased to about 22 percent for the same engine with the Comprex booster. This flow device has not yet been applied to aircraft gas turbines. It is of considerable theoretical interest as a means of raising the cycle efficiency of turboprop engines.

54. The Compound Engine. Conventional reciprocating engines have pressure-volume diagrams like the simplified one in Fig. 216. Because the volume expansion ratio of a constant-displacement engine is the reciprocal of the compression ratio, in other words, the piston sweeps out the same volume for every stroke, the gas pressure remaining at the end of the power stroke is high. The energy of this compressed hot gas is normally lost through the exhaust system without effective utilization.

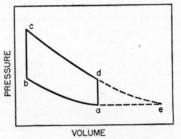

FIG. 216. Simplified pressure-volume diagram of reciprocating engine *abcd* with addition of exhaust turbine *dea*.

If an exhaust turbine is connected to the engine, additional energy is extracted from the gas after it leaves the cylinder, and the area under the dotted line in Fig. 216 is recovered as useful power. A part of the exhaust energy has been used to drive turbosuperchargers on aircraft engines, and an experimental power plant has recently been constructed, consisting of a conventional reciprocating engine with its shaft geared to an exhaust turbine for increased shaft power and better fuel economy.

Effective compounding is not practical at low engine-exhaust back pressures. High supercharging pressure at the reciprocating-engine intake is therefore required. Modern reciprocating aircraft engines operate at engine-exhaust back pressures in the range of 25 to 30 psi absolute at maximum output; the exhaust back pressure is relatively independent of altitude if the engine is supercharged to constant output at all altitudes. The available energy in the exhaust gas for typical reciprocating-engine exhaust conditions at various effective engine back pressures is plotted in Fig. 217. The increases in available energy with increasing altitude are due to the greater expansion ratios possible across the ideal turbine.   Actual turbine shaft outputs are connected to the ideal available-energy curves through turbine efficiency, but here turbine efficiency includes leaving losses (which differs from the definition of turbine efficiency used heretofore in this book).

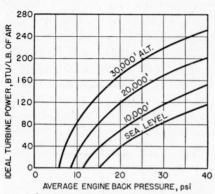

Fig. 217.   Available energy in the exhaust of typical aircraft reciprocating engines at various effective exhaust back pressures and flight altitudes.

Connecting a turbine to the engine exhaust results in a small decrease in reciprocating-engine output, owing to the pumping loss in the engine scavenging stroke. Because critical flow conditions exist through the exhaust valves for a considerable portion of the exhaust scavenging stroke, only the latter part of the stroke feels the presence of the turbine, and additional pumping losses are small.   The engine normally pumps about one-quarter of the total flow to the turbine in the high-exhaust-back-pressure operating range where turbine compounding is effective.

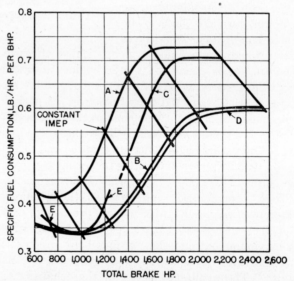

Fig. 218.   Typical specific fuel rates of various reciprocating engines: *A.* Uncompounded engine with turbosupercharger at sea level.   *B.* Compound engine with infinitely variable nozzle area at sea level.   *C.* Compound engine with fixed nozzle area at sea level.   *D.* Compound engine with infinitely variable nozzle area at 20,000 ft.   *E.* Compound engine with fixed nozzle area at 20,000 ft.

By matching the turbine to the engine, the engine back pressure may be increased to higher than normal values. Less energy is then delivered on the crankshaft and more from the turbine. Ordinarily, the optimum operating point from the standpoints of both total power availability and fuel economy is found when the exhaust back pressure is just slightly below the supercharger pressure at the engine inlet manifold.

A turbine geared directly to the crankshaft will operate efficiently only over a limited engine output range. The flow characteristic of the engine in its best cruising range does not match the turbine very well if the turbine matches the engine at take-off rating. Various schemes have been proposed for matching control, one of which is the use of controllable partial-admission turbine inlet nozzles to maintain engine back pressures at optimum levels for all flight conditions. There are obvious mechanical difficulties connected with these schemes. However, for the sake of presenting compound engine performance under good circumstances as well as bad, Fig. 218 shows estimated specific consumption figures for an engine rated at 800 hp cruise (1,400 to 1,600 hp military rating) uncompounded, and compounded with different nozzle-control schemes.[1]

[1] BACHLE, *Trans. SAE*, vol. 53, p. 345, 1945.

CHAPTER 10

AIRCRAFT-GAS-TURBINE ACCESSORIES AND CONTROLS

55. The Starting Problem. Starting the small turbojet engine presents a relatively minor problem. A source of power must be found to bring the shaft up to a speed where the engine becomes self-sustaining. This speed is usually of the order of 25 percent of normal operating rpm. Turbojet engines producing 3,000- to 4,000-lb thrust under static sea-level conditions will require approximately 10-hp d-c electric starters weighing about 30 lb.

This power may be supplied by a high-discharge-rate storage battery of such a capacity that it can provide several starts without recharging. Because of the heavy current loads and the fact that the battery must provide satisfactory starting under partially discharged conditions, we must expect a high voltage drop in the connecting cables and a high internal voltage drop in the battery itself. A 28-volt battery may deliver as little as 12 volts to the starter motor terminals during the starting cycle. Such a battery with a normal rating of 28 volts, 50 amp-hr, may weigh from 100 to 150 lb.

Such a battery is substantially heavier than would be required for the normal electrical system requirements of a small aircraft of about 10,000 lb gross weight (such as might be powered by a 3,000- to 4,000-lb-thrust turbojet). However it is not too large for heavier aircraft with multiple power plants and larger electric power requirements. Unfortunately, the heavier aircraft will require larger (or more) turbojet engines, and this in turn will impose heavier starting loads. The 150- to 200-lb airborne electric starting system that we have discussed seems very close to the practical upper limit as far as weight and size are concerned.

The turboprop presents a still greater starting problem in that minimum self-sustaining speeds may be as high as 40 to 60 percent of normal operating rpm. At these speeds the propeller load may contribute a very substantial part to the total starting power required. Propeller blades must be set in the flattest pitch possible, and even then the power loss may, at half speed, amount to as much as 0.5 to 1.0 percent of the engine's normal rated output.

Thus propeller idling losses must be added to the cranking requirements of the compressor and turbine. This is shown in Fig. 219 for a turboprop engine with a rating of 2,200 hp and 600 lb static jet thrust at 13,000 rpm. This particular engine is started with an electric starting motor.

Engines with higher efficiency components will have lower starting power requirements, as will engines whose turbines can tolerate higher inlet temperatures during the brief period of the starting cycle. It is true also that the sooner combustion can be initiated in the starting cycle, the smaller the maximum power required from the starter. As an example, the maximum power required from the starter for a 4,000-hp turboprop, with somewhat higher efficiency than the engine of Fig. 219, has been estimated to lie between 40 and 60 hp, which is to be compared with roughly 34 hp maximum for the 2,200-hp turboprop of Fig. 219.

The excess torque delivered by the starter, above that required to maintain engine speed constant, is available for acceleration of the engine to higher speeds in the starting cycle. This acceleration is therefore equal to

$$\alpha = \frac{gT_\alpha}{2\pi I} \quad \text{rev/sec}^2$$

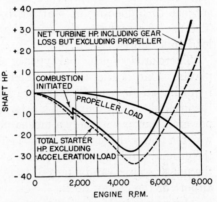

FIG. 219. Typical turboprop starting power requirement (engine rating, 2,200 hp at 13,000 rpm). (*A. G. Bardwell, Jr., Trans. ASME, vol.* 69, *p.* 577, 1947.)

where T_α is the excess starter torque at the engine shaft and I is the moment of inertia of the engine rotor in lb-ft^2. The engine of Fig. 219 has a turbine-compressor rotor moment of inertia of 130 lb-ft^2; and since the reduction-gear ratio is approximately 11:1, the inertia at the propeller shaft is about 16,000 lb-ft^2. This is nearly ten times the inertia of the propeller itself. The inertia of a centrifugal-compressor-type jet engine of 4,000-lb thrust rating, of the types described in this book, is approximately 150 lb-ft^2 at the engine shaft, and that for a high-flow-rate axial-flow-compressor jet engine of 3,000-lb thrust rating is about 75 lb-ft^2.

Tactical requirements for military aircraft make 60-sec-duration engine starts mandatory and 30-sec starts desirable. Since the Rolls Royce Nene jet engine will accelerate from the self-sustaining speed of 2,500 rpm to rated speed of 12,300 rpm in as little as 4.5 sec, the principal delay in starting is accelerating the engine by means of the starter in the initial starting period. A 60-sec start may require twice the starter horsepower that would be needed for a very long starting time (in which starter torque barely exceeds engine torque requirements), and a 30-sec start over three times as much. Initial starting torques of engines with antifriction bearings consist almost entirely of inertial loads, since friction is very low and aerodynamic loads are small at low speeds. However, bearing friction can be a problem at low temperatures.

Turbojet engines with adjustable-area jet nozzles are started in the maximum-area nozzle position. The pressure ratio across the turbine is then a maximum, and the turbine is contributing its maximum torque toward overcoming the compressor load. Turboprop engines are designed with relatively large pressure drops through the turbine and are little subject to unloading at starting by means of nozzle-area adjustment. The use of a separate shaft for the output turbine relieves the starting load to a limited extent.

There are two principal types of starters for aircraft-gas-turbine power plants. One is the self-contained starter mounted on the engine and requiring an air-borne battery or fuel supply for actuation. The other is the ground- or ship-powered starter. The simplest system is the ground-powered starter with only a mechanical connection point on the engine to which a power-driven shaft from a suitable source of mechanical power on the ground can be brought. After starting, the shaft is disconnected, and the power source can be moved to other engines at other locations on the airport or the carrier deck.

Other gas-turbine starters may consist of the d-c electric motor starters discussed above, a-c electric motors, hydraulic motors, pneumatic motors or turbines, or starting turbines powered by self-contained cartridge gas supplies of the monopropellant or bipropellant types.

Still another type is the completely self-contained reciprocating-engine starter mounted directly on the gas turbine and burning the same fuel as the gas turbine, or its own special fuel supply. German-built turbojet engines were found to be equipped with such starters; Riedel reciprocating-type engines weighing about 50 lb were capable of starting turbojets in the range of 1,500- to 2,000-lb static thrust rating. It is probable that these engines are adequate for starting much larger gas turbines, provided that the turbine engines are more efficient than the early German designs.

Gas turbines equipped with electric, hydraulic, or pneumatic motors may be started from power supplies located in remote positions in the aircraft or on the ground. Electric motors are by far the heaviest of these starters, and d-c motors may weigh twice as much as a-c motors for the same average output rating because of commutator speed limitations. Alternating-current motors may not be run from a battery, however, and are adapted for use only where there is a suitable source of a-c power, as on the ground or in very large aircraft equipped with an a-c electrical system.

Hydraulic motors require that high-pressure hydraulic fluid be piped to and from the engine. This is undesirable under all circumstances but particularly so at subzero temperatures. However, it is estimated that a hydraulic motor with a short-time rating of 500 to 1,000 hp may weigh no more than 50 lb. Starting power requirements of this order are not inconceivable for future gas-turbine-powered aircraft of 250,000 to 500,000 lb gross weight. A high-speed a-c electric motor for the same service would have a weight in the range of 175 to 250 lb. However, this same a-c starter motor, at the cost of a small increase in weight, might be used as an alternator for auxiliary electric power in flight. Combination d-c starter-generators are in use on the TG-180 turbojet at a small over-all weight saving. It is not anticipated that the d-c electric motor starter will be practical for much larger engines, however, even at higher battery voltages.

Primary power sources to drive hydraulic pumps, air compressors, or electric generators are a small problem on the ground or on board the aircraft carrier and will be given no further consideration here. The airborne source of prime power for starter systems is a different matter. Batteries are heavy and bulky, and coupled with the limitations of low-voltage d-c motors, are suitable only for engines of lower power ratings. In a similar classification are small reciprocating engines, limited by several minutes warm-up requirement on starting and lack of power at high altitudes, as well as weight, bulk, and special fuel requirements.

Possibly the lightest weight engine starter for a self-contained or remote-powered type would be a small starter turbine with a cartridge-type gas producer. Either a solid fuel reacting at a controlled rate to produce hot gas, or a liquid fuel system, may be used. Of the liquid fuel systems, 85 to 90 percent purity hydrogen peroxide holds the most promise. High-concentration hydrogen peroxide can be stored and shipped safely if held in clean containers free of easily oxidized materials. The liquid may then be permitted to flow into a catalyst reaction chamber, where it gives up 1 oxygen atom per molecule with the release of a great deal of heat. Superheated steam and oxygen at several hundred pounds pressure and at temperatures in the range of 1000 to 1300°F comprise the working fluid for the starter turbine. This system is similar to the fuel-pump drive turbine successfully used in the V-2 rocket. The weight of propellant required depends upon many factors, but should be of the order of 0.2 lb/min per horsepower of starter requirement. The principal disadvantage of this kind of engine starter is the supply problem for the propellant.

The other possibility for a large air-borne starting system is a small gas-turbine prime mover, small enough in itself to use a battery-powered starter.   Such a gas-turbine engine of 50- to 400-hp rating will not have an economical specific-fuel-consumption rate, particularly under part-load conditions, but fuel economy of the starter is not particularly important provided that it can take fuel from the main engine fuel tanks.   Such auxiliary gas turbines are very light in weight and occupy a minimum of space.   A gas-turbine engine capable of supplying 100 shp at 40,000 ft altitude, adequate for cabin-supercharging power requirements for large aircraft, as well as for auxiliary electric and hydraulic power require-

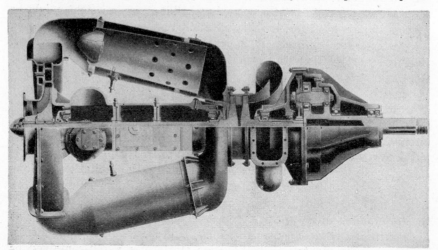

FIG. 220.   Section of small experimental Boeing gas turbine, shaft power unit; maximum diameter, 22 in.; over-all length, 40 in.; static sea-level normal rating, 160 bhp; 50-lb jet thrust; weight, 140 lb.

ments when used in multiple units, will supply approximately 400 hp on the ground.   Such an engine may be used to drive an electric generator, a hydraulic pump, or an air compressor for starting purposes.

After an aircraft is in flight, ram at the engine inlet causes a sufficient flow of air through the engine to windmill the rotor, and after a sufficiently high speed has been reached, the fuel may be ignited, and the engine will start.   Typical windmilling characteristics of turbojet engines are shown in Fig. 221.   The centrifugal compressor is a low-efficiency flow device under windmilling conditions, so that the axial-flow engine demands a lower flight speed to produce the same percent of rated rpm.   Windmilling speeds should not be confused with minimum engine-starting speeds. The data of Fig. 221 are without combustion.   When the burners are ignited, engine speeds increase considerably above the data of Fig. 221, and engines will start at very much lower flight speeds than would be required for cold windmilling to engine-starting speed. Because of limitations of combustion chambers, it is not always possible to ignite the burners at all flight speeds at high altitudes. Limitations on flight starting for a particular turbojet are shown in Fig. 222.

The turboprop engine will start under windmilling conditions at very low air speeds compared with turbojet engines. It is necessary only to have sufficient forward speed to derive the relatively small starting torque requirement from the propeller as a windmill. Since the air mass flowing through the propeller disc is so very much greater than that flowing through an engine, starting may be accomplished at flight speeds under 100 mph.

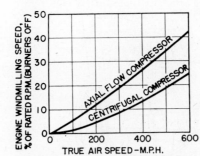

Fig. 221. Windmilling characteristics of typical turbojet engines at all altitudes.

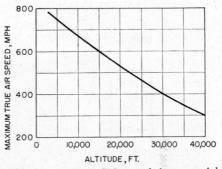

Fig. 222. Maximum flight speeds for successful starts with engine windmilling, as a function of altitude.

56. The Lubrication System. There are relatively few bearings to lubricate on the turbojet engine, and except for the auxiliary drive gears, no gear lubrication. The turboprop engine has a propeller reduction gear, which must be lubricated and cooled with lubricating oil. Otherwise, it is about the same as the turbojet engine. Figure 223 shows a schematic layout of an I-40 turbojet lubricating system that is representative. The I-40 has a row of air pumping vanes on the front of the turbine disc, and these vanes pump cooling air over the bearings and then over the disc surface. Therefore an oil cooler is not used except for air flow over the auxiliary gear case. Other engines that depend almost entirely upon lubricating oil for bearing cooling need small oil coolers, as on the Westinghouse 19XB and 24C engines (see Fig. 114).

In Fig. 223, the oil pump has two elements, a lubricating pressure element and a scavenging element. The lubricating element takes oil from a reservoir in the bottom of the accessory drive casing, and passes it through a filter before delivering it to the four main bearings, the accessory drive coupling, and the shaft coupling sleeve. Oil from these points either drains back directly to the gear case or is picked up by the scavenging pump and returned to the oil reservoir. Accessory-drive gear lubrication is by splash. At rated engine rpm, the scavenging pump has a displacement of about 10 gpm, while the lubricating oil pump circulates about 3 gpm.

Other lubrication systems have used air-atomized oil sprays on ball and roller bearings for mist lubrication, but the most satisfactory method appears to be delivery of high-pressure oil to vents or jets where needed. Loss of oil from the system is small, usually less than 1 pt/hr, so that the reservoir capacity need not be large.

Lubrication of reduction gearing for turboprop engines is a separate problem. However, except for proper lubrication and cooling of the planet gear bearings, it is not particularly difficult.

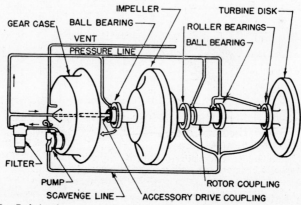

Fig. 223. Lubrication system diagram of General Electric I-40 turbojet engine.

57. The Fuel System. The primary control for all aircraft gas turbines is the fuel-throttle lever. Secondary controls are jet nozzle area or propeller pitch. Various functions such as engine rpm, turbine inlet or exit temperatures, air density, shaft power output, etc., may become a part of the general control scheme, but eventually we return to the necessity for a change in fuel-flow rate if we wish to make a major change in engine operation.

Fuel supply systems fall into two basic groups. The simplest system mechanically is a constant-displacement fuel pump geared to the gas-turbine shaft or driven by a separate electric motor. Full manifold pressure is regulated by a by-pass or relief valve, and fuel flow to the spray nozzles is controlled by a simple throttling valve or by adjustment of the manifold pressure at the by-pass valve. The other basic system is a variable-displacement pump driven directly from the engine shaft or by a separate electric motor. Pump displacement is changed to meet varying fuel-flow requirements.

Under starting conditions, directly driven main fuel pumps usually do not have sufficient capacity at low starting speeds to ensure equal manifold pressure behind the spray nozzles.   Therefore, either a separate, electrically driven starter pump is operated in parallel with the main fuel pump during the starting cycle, or an accumulator is employed to obtain a steady flow of fuel.   The separate starter pump is the more positive measure, and can serve as an emergency fuel pump in the event of main-fuel-pump failure.   The fuel line from the starter pump is provided with a check valve to prevent backflow of fuel when the starter pump is not in operation.   A separate main fuel pump with an electric motor drive would avoid the necessity for a starter pump or accumulator; but for reasons of reliability and mechanical simplicity, directly driven pumps have been used instead.

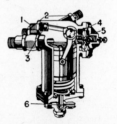

1. PUMP INLET CONNECTION
2. MAINFOLD CONNECTIONS
3. RELIEF VALVES
4. HIGH-PRESSURE COCK
5. TRIP VALVE
6. SPILL TO ATMOSPHERE

Fig. 224. Lucas accumulator for Rolls Royce Derwent turbojet engine. (*Flight magazine.*)

When an accumulator is used in starting, the fuel manifold is shut off by a valve between the spray nozzles and the accumulator.   The accumulator is a cylinder connected to the fuel manifold so that it is subject to fuel-pump pressure and flow. The cylinder contains a piston backed up by a heavy spring so that when manifold pressure is low, the piston is at the upper end of the cylinder and the accumulator has only a small volume. When the starter motor begins to turn the engine rotor, the positive-displacement fuel pump finds the fuel-manifold valve closed and therefore forces fuel into the accumulator instead, at a very low flow rate but at whatever pressure is required to move the piston against the force of the spring.   Fuel flows into the accumulator until the piston reaches the end of its stroke, and the accumulator contains perhaps a pint of fuel, backed up by the piston and its spring.   By then, the engine has been brought up to ignition speed by the starter motor, and either by means of a cycle control in the starter panel or by an over-pressure trip on the accumulator, the manifold shutoff valve is opened and high-pressure fuel flows from the accumulator to the spray nozzles. Fuel continues to flow until the accumulator is empty, and by then the engine should have accelerated to the point where the regular fuel pump is able to handle the flow requirement.

A diagrammatic layout of the main fuel system for the Rolls Royce Nene jet engine is shown in Fig. 225.   A booster fuel pump located at the fuel tanks is not shown.   The two main fuel pumps are of the variable-displacement type.   Operating in parallel into duplex nozzles, they have adequate capacity to handle starting requirements at low starting speeds without an auxiliary starting pump. Throttle control is by means of a variable-area, manually operated valve. An idling by-pass is provided so that the high-pressure shutoff cock is used to stop the engine.

Fuel-pump delivery pressure is regulated at a constant value by means of pump displacement control (see Fig. 226). The pump is of the wobble-plate type; the pump body carrying the pistons rotates with the shaft geared to the engine. Control of the angle of tilt of the cam or

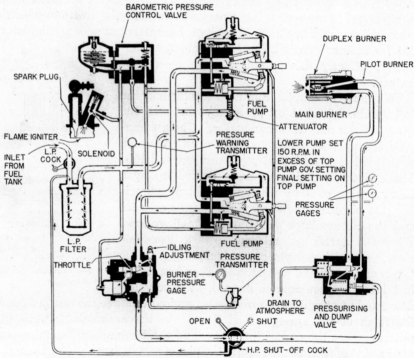

Fig. 225. Diagrammatic layout of engine fuel system for Rolls Royce Nene turbojet. (*Flight magazine.*)

wobble plate determines the piston stroke and therefore the delivery at any given shaft speed. The cam plate angle is fixed by means of the spring-backed pressure-control piston servo. Fuel at pump delivery pressure is admitted to both sides of the servo control piston, but admission on the spring side is through a restricted opening. If a relatively large leak is then opened behind the piston, the fluid pressures are unbalanced, and the piston moves against the spring to reduce the tilt angle of the cam plate and thus the pump displacement.

Connected to the fuel pump and its displacement-control servo is a pressure regulator with an altitude-density control modulator. This is the barometric control unit also shown in Fig. 226. Pump delivery pressure is balanced by a spring. Any unbalance of pressure may result in closing the leak from the servopiston, which will reduce the fuel flow and therefore pressure; or too low a delivery pressure will close the leak and result in servopiston movement under the spring force to increase displacement and pressure. Connected to operate in opposition to the pressure-regulating spring in the barometric control is the barometric capsule, which is an evacuated Sylphon-type bellows. Variations in atmospheric pressure, and therefore air density, reset the fuel pressure regulator so that fuel flow through the throttle valve is approximately

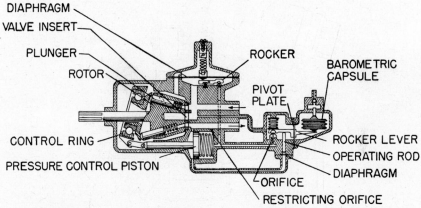

Fig. 226. Diagram of pump and barometric-pressure control unit showing interconnections. (*Flight magazine.*)

proportional to air density at varying altitudes. The fuel/air ratio therefore changes but little when the aircraft changes altitude, and the pilot does not have to shift the throttle lever continually to maintain constant engine rpm. The barometric control is not corrected for ambient temperature changes, although it is mounted on the front of the engine where it is subject to ram pressure in the air inlet plenum chamber.

Also incorporated in the Nene fuel pump is a governor to prevent engine overspeeding. There are a number of drilled holes in the rotating pump body, indicated by dotted lines in Fig. 226. These holes communicate on the inlet end with the inlet to the pump and act like flow passages in the rotor of a centrifugal pump when the pump body rotates. A diaphragm in the upper part of the pump body is subject to fuel inlet pressure on one side and to the pressure developed by the centrifugal pump action on the other. An unbalanced fluid pressure force on the diaphragm appears, proportional to the square of the pump and engine speed.   This force is normally opposed by a spring, so that a second leak from the servopiston remains closed.   However, if the engine speed exceeds a preselected value, centrifugal pump pressure will overbalance the governor spring and open the servopiston leak, leading to an immediate response to reduce fuel flow and therefore engine speed.   This type of overspeed governor is quite simple, but is sensitive to changes in density of the fuel.

Another device common to all aircraft gas turbines is the fuel dump valve.   If the engine shutoff valve is closed and the engine stops, the

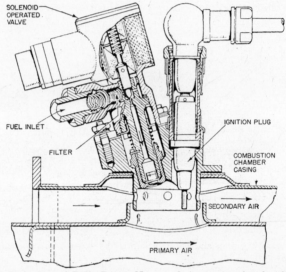

Fig. 227.   Flame igniter of Rolls Royce Nene turbojet engine (used only for starting). (*Flight magazine.*)

fuel standing in the fuel lines and in the burner manifold ring will drain out through the lower spray nozzles and burn in pools in the lower combustion chambers.   This may cause local overheating of the engine and warping of burner parts, in addition to constituting a fire hazard in the aircraft.   The dump valve is normally held closed by fuel-line pressure. When pressure drops, it opens to immediately drain the engine manifold and fuel lines overboard to the ground before the engine has coasted to a stop.   A dump valve is shown in Fig. 225, combined with a pressure-control valve to restrict fuel flow to the pilot burner section of the duplex nozzle until the pumps can supply fuel at sufficient pressure for the main nozzle flow.

Spark plugs must be located so that they are not overheated by the primary burner flame under normal operating conditions.   As a consequence, ignition may be difficult with the small fuel sprays under starting conditions. The Rolls Royce Nene is fitted with flame igniters on two of the nine can-type burners (see Fig. 227). The flame igniter is a low-pressure fuel spray nozzle with its own spark plug, in a recess away from the main burner space. It is used only for starting and projects a jet of flame into the primary burner zone to ensure positive ignition of the main fuel spray.

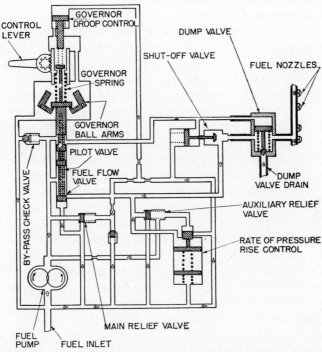

FIG. 228. Schematic layout of fuel system with constant-displacement pump and all-speed governor control.

A different fuel supply system utilizing an all-speed governor is shown in Fig. 228. There are a great many individual variations possible with this system, but basically it operates by governor control of the fuel supply to the engine, so that engine rpm is kept constant at all altitudes and flight conditions after the governor control lever is once set.

The fuel pump shown is a gear pump of a type capable of delivering up to 600 psi continuously if necessary. It could just as well be of the variable-displacement type shown in Fig. 226.

The governor is a simple flyball type, operating directly on the main fuel-flow throttling valve with droop characteristic control by means of hydraulic feedback to an auxiliary governing spring. Actually, control characteristics are not as accurate as could be desired with the governor operating directly on the fuel-flow control valve, and later models utilize a governor that controls the main fuel-flow valve through a hydraulic servo. Manual override of the throttle control is also desirable. The fuel pump builds up pressure until the main relief valve begins to by-pass fuel to the pump inlet again, and the fuel system then operates at that basic pressure level. Other valves for safety relief, etc., are shown, as well as a pump by-pass check valve to permit the use of an auxiliary pump for starting or emergency purposes. The rate-of-pressure-rise control unit cooperates with the auxiliary relief valve to limit the rate of response of fuel flow to sudden position changes in the governor speed-control lever. This prevents excessively high fuel/air ratios in starting and acceleration with too-high turbine inlet temperatures. It also eliminates too-lean mixtures under deceleration that might result in flame extinction.

Fuel-flow rates are sufficiently high in gas-turbine engines for the fuel itself to be used as the cooling medium in heat exchangers for a variety of purposes. Sufficient thermal capacity exists in normal fuel flows that lubricating-oil cooling, etc., may be accomplished readily by this means. However, if fuel is to be used as the heat absorber in aircraft air-conditioning heat exchangers, the temperature increase of the fuel may prove troublesome. Such heated fuels may cause vapor-lock difficulties unless maintained at high pressure until utilized in the combustion chamber.

58. Gas-turbine Controls. The simplest gas-turbine engine for aircraft is the turbojet with fixed-area exhaust nozzle. There is one control, the pilot's throttle lever, regulating the amount of fuel flowing to the burner spray nozzles. Auxiliary devices to prevent overspeeding of the engine or excessive turbine inlet temperatures may override the pilot's manual control, but in the end, the only adjustment possible is rate of fuel flow.

The next engine variation is the addition to the turbojet of an adjustable-area jet nozzle. This complicates the control problem in that changes in either fuel flow or jet nozzle area, or both, may result in changes in engine rpm, efficiency, and thrust. These changes are apparent under steady operating conditions and during the transient conditions of acceleration or deceleration. The simplest type of flight control for this engine from the standpoint of the pilot would be a single control. This single control lever would adjust engine output for approximately constant thrust in a given flight speed range and altitude, with changes in thrust proportional to altitude-density changes. It would require a computing-type mechanism receiving data from a barometer, flight-speed indicator, engine-speed indicator, jet nozzle-area data, and turbine-temperature indicator along with the control-lever adjustment in order to solve completely the problem from the standpoint of most efficient operating speed, turbine inlet temperature, and jet-nozzle adjustment for a given set of flight conditions. From the known operating characteristics of the engine, it is possible to predict best rpm and jet nozzle area to meet the operating requirement with minimum fuel consumption. A computer type of control can then be constructed to yield engine-adjustment data along the lines of maximum fuel economy. The computer output would then dictate the position of the tail-cone adjustment for jet nozzle area and the speed-governor setting. The governor would regulate fuel flow to meet the speed requirement.

Necessary modifications of the above plan would include engine over-speed protection and devices for limiting turbine inlet temperature. The conditions would also be changed during acceleration or deceleration in going from one control-lever adjustment to another, so that a transient lag linkage between the control lever and the computer is desirable to ensure that the engine response will follow the control lever as rapidly as is consistent with combustion-chamber and turbine limitations.

By eliminating the automatic features of the computer-type engine control, engine adjustments may be left to the discretion of the pilot in selecting best engine speed and best jet nozzle area.

The problem of the turboprop engine has all the elements of the turbo-jet with adjustable-jet nozzle plus a few others; particularly in the case of a turboprop with an adjustable-area exit nozzle. It is almost impera-tive that the turboprop engine be operated at or near its rated maximum rpm if maximum economy and engine life are to be obtained. The least penalty in increased fuel consumption at reduced power ratings is usually incurred when the engine is operated at rated rpm and reduced tempera-ture. This serves to simplify the control problem, although positive governor control is necessary to prevent overspeeding during transient load changes.

Maximum turbine power is available almost instantaneously with maximum fuel admission to the burners. With the propeller adjusted for low reduced load at rated engine speed, the above change in fuel flow could result in a 5 percent overspeed condition in a matter of $\frac{1}{4}$ sec or less for a representative turboprop engine, and a 30 percent overspeed condi-tion in approximately 2 sec.

The maximum rate of propeller-pitch control may result in instability if the speed governor is not stabilized with acceleration-responsive con-trols for antihunt measures. Inertia of the rotating system contributes to instability.

One system of control for turboprop engines would provide for power-output control at a regulated speed, the speed governor acting as a topping or overspeed control. An overtemperature control would also be necessary. Propeller-pitch control would then be made by means of a torque-measuring device on the propeller shaft, to be overridden by the overtemperature control. The governor would admit sufficient fuel to maintain the required propeller rpm, within the permissible limits of turbine inlet temperatures. Altitude adjustments, either manual or automatic, would be necessary to recalibrate the power control with changes in altitude. This system should be stable.

Figure 206 showed a performance map for a turboprop engine. Changes in propeller-pitch control may be made according to several different schedules. Constant advance angle ratio J for the propeller

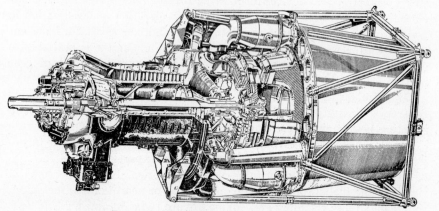

Fɪɢ. 229.   Bristol Theseus turboprop engine.

would follow the dashed line to the left of the operating point, corresponding to a fixed-area-turbojet operating line.   Constant air flow through the engine would follow the vertical operating line, and constant pressure ratio across the compressor would follow the horizontal line. The generally preferred operating line lies between the constant-speed line and the line of constant J, when the jet energy is a considerable part of the engine power output.   Therefore, for maximum combined propeller-plus-jet economy, the actual operating line might lie close to the constant-air-flow line, and the speed-governor setting would require some small adjustments with changes in power requirement. An adjustable-area jet nozzle on the turboprop engine would shift the direction of the most desirable operating line toward the constant-speed line. The problem then would be division of power between jet and propeller for most efficient over-all operation.

59. Heat Exchangers.   There was a brief discussion of heat exchangers in Chap. 8.   There is not a great deal more that can be added here without going into specific design details. Figure 229 shows the Bristol Theseus turboprop engine with exhaust heat exchanger. A calculation of an experimental tubular heat exchanger with about 0.50 effectiveness yields the following characteristics:

Turbine Exhaust

Flow, lb/sec.. 50
Inlet pressure, psi.. 15
Pressure drop, psi... 0.75
Inlet temperature, °F...................................... 900
Outlet temperature, °F..................................... 650

Compressor Flow

Flow, lb/sec... 50
Inlet pressure, psi.. 45
Pressure drop, psi... 1.3
Inlet temperature, °F...................................... 400
Outlet temperature, °F..................................... 650

This heat exchanger would occupy 31 cu ft of space and weigh 1,100 lb, using stainless-steel tubing 0.010 in. thick. By going to thinner tubing and increasing the flow pressure losses, the weight and space requirements could be reduced by a factor of $\frac{1}{2}$ approximately.

Other types of heat exchangers have been suggested using porous bodies or perforated rotors through which the hot gases would flow for a part of the time and the cold air would then flow, picking up heat from the metal or ceramic body. No satisfactory mechanical arrangement has yet been suggested for an aircraft application of such a heat exchanger.

CHAPTER 11

PRESENT DEVELOPMENT STATUS OF GAS TURBINES FOR AIRCRAFT

60. Tabulation of Current Aircraft Gas Turbines. It is not intended to give here a history of the development of gas turbines for aircraft use nor is it our purpose to tabulate the characteristics of all the gas turbines that have been developed within the last 10 years. Rather we have selected for tabulation current operational engines or development engines for which fairly complete performance information is available. Earlier models are, in general, omitted. The tabulation is restricted to British and United States gas turbines.

Any attempt to present performance characteristics of turbojet or turboprop engines in tabular form must necessarily be somewhat arbitrary, for it is not possible to represent a complete performance picture in terms of a few columns of numbers. For each engine listed in Table 9, information is given on type of compressor and combustion section, maximum power ratings, normal or recommended cruising ratings with corresponding rates of fuel consumption, maximum diameter, over-all length of engine, dry weight including the weight of propeller reduction gearing for turboprop units, and remarks dealing with special features. In addition, specific fuel consumption and engine specific weight, as well as thrust (or power) per unit engine frontal area, are listed.

It will be noted, on a first study of this table, that turbojet engines outnumber shaft-horsepower units in the approximate ratio of 2:1. This reflects two facts: (a) that the dominant interest in developing aircraft gas turbines is still on the maximum-speed military applications for which turbojets are especially adaptable, and (b) that the turboprop engine involves a development task of greater magnitude than the turbojet. As has been pointed out previously, several of the turboprop engines listed have been developed by modification of a previous turbojet design.

Designs with axial compressors outnumber those with centrifugal compressors. A few engines have mixed centrifugal-axial compressors. The greater popularity of the axial design is due to the fact that it makes possible a unit with a smaller frontal area for a given power output. The axial units have from 6 to 14 stages and yield compression ratios at maximum speed ranging from about 3 to 6. A corresponding range of

TABLE 9. TABULATION OF CURRENT GAS TURBINES FOR AIRCRAFT Turbojets

Manufacturer and type	Compressor	Combustor	Maximum thrust rating (ssl)		Normal thrust rating (ssl)									Remarks
			Thrust, lb	Rpm	Thrust, lb	Rpm	Fuel, lb/hr	Fuel specific, lb/(hr)(lb)	Maximum diameter, in.	Overall length, in.	Weight, lb	Specific weight, lb/lb max. thrust	Thrust (max.) per unit frontal area, psf	
Boeing Model 500....	Centrifugal	2 burners	.....	......	140	36,000	180	1.28	22	29	85	0.60*	55*	Experimental turbojet
De Havilland:														
Goblin III..........	Centrifugal, $\psi_c = 3.15$	16 cans	3,300	10,750	2,240	9,500	2,640	1.18	50	100	1,575	0.48	240	Single-entry impeller
Ghost.............	Centrifugal, $\psi_c = 4.3$	10 cans	5,000	10,000	2,825	8,500	3,170	1.12	53	115	2,010	0.40	330	Axial intake, single-entry impeller
General Electric:														
I-40 (J-33).......	Centrifugal, $\psi_c = 4.1$	14 cans	4,000	11,500	3,400	11,000	4,000	1.18	48	101	1,850	0.46	320	
TG-180 (J-35).....	Axial, 11-stage, $\psi_c = 4.0$	8 cans	4,000	7,600	......	......	......	......	38	166	2,400	0.6	520	
Metropolitan Vickers:														
F-2/4A...........	Axial, 10-stage, $\psi_c = 4.0$	Annular	3,850	7,750	3,400	7,400	3,670	1.08	37	129	1,550	0.40	520	
F-3..............	Axial, 9-stage, $\psi_c = 4.0$	Annular	4,600	7,390	3,900	......	2,660	......	46	140	2,300	0.50	400	Ducted-fan thrust augmenter
F-5..............	Axial, 10-stage, $\psi_c = 4.0$	Annular	4,710	7,700	2,300†	......	2,050†	0.90†	37	146	2,200	0.47	630	Open-fan thrust augmenter
Rolls Royce:														
Derwent V........	Centrifugal, $\psi_c = 4.0$	9 cans	3,600	14,700	2,675	13,600	2,880	1.08	43	83	1,280	0.36	360	
Nene II..........	Centrifugal, $\psi_c = 4.0$	9 cans	5,000	12,300	4,000	11,600	4,270	1.07	50	97	1,640	0.33	365	
Westinghouse:														
19XB (J-30)......	Axial, 10-stage, $\psi_c = 3.8$	Annular	1,700	17,000	1,360	15,700	1,470	1.08	26	94	660	0.39	450	
24C (J-34)........	Axial, 11-stage	Annular	3,000	......	......	......	......	......	31 equiv.	121	999	0.33	580	Two-stage turbine, fixed area nozzle

TABLE 9. TABULATION OF CURRENT GAS TURBINES FOR AIRCRAFT.—(*Continued*)

Turboprops

Manufacturer and type	Compressor	Combustor	Maximum thrust rating		Normal thrust rating									Remarks
			Shp	Rpm	Shp	Rpm	Fuel, lb/hr	Fuel specific, lb/hr per equiv. shp	Maximum diameter, in.	Overall length, in.	Weight, lb	Specific weight, lb/shp	Shp (max.) per unit frontal area, hp/sq ft	
Boeing Model 502...	Centrifugal	2 burners	....	....	160 + 50 lb jet thrust	36,000 (2,500)‡	180	1.00	22	40	140	0.79*	70*	Experimental shaft power unit
Armstrong Siddeley: Python...........	Axial, 14-stage, ψ_c = 5.0	11 cans	3,670 + 1,150 lb jet thrust	8,000	2,720 + 950 lb jet thrust	7,600	2,420	0.79	48	96	3,150	0.77	330	
Mamba...........	Axial	6 cans	1,010 + 320 lb jet thrust	14,500	750 + 265 lb jet thrust	13,750	660	0.78	27	56	750	0.67	285	
Bristol Theseus 21....	Axial, 9-stage, + centrifugal, ψ_c = 3.1 × 1.4 = 4.4	9 cans	1,930 + 500 lb jet thrust	9,000	1,180 + 330§ lb jet thrust	8,200§	825§	0.55§	48	106	2,310	1.08	170	This unit is fitted with heat exchanger giving 15 percent improvement in specific fuel consumption at cost of 450 lb weight and reduction of power output of 180 equivalent shp
General Electric TG-100.	Axial, 14-stage, ψ_c = 5.5	9 cans	2,200 + 600 lb jet thrust	13,000	....	....	.....	.....	37	113	2,000	0.84	325	
Napier Naiad........	Axial, 12-stage, ψ_c = 5.5	5 cans	1,500 + 240 lb jet thrust	18,250	900 + 270 lb jet thrust	17,000	805	0.81	28	102	1,095	0.69	370	
Rolls Royce Clyde....	Axial, + centrifugal, ψ_c = 6.3	9 cans	3,020 + 1,225 lb jet thrust	6,000	....	....	.....	0.9	47	121	2,800	0.81	290	

* Specifies in terms of normal rating.
† 400 mph at 20,000 ft altitude.
‡ Shaft driven by second-stage turbine, at this rpm through 10:1 reduction gearing.
§ 300 mph at 20,000 ft.

compression ratios is attained in the single radial stage of the centrifugal compressor designs.

Can-type combustors are used in most designs with the number of individual combustors ranging from 6 to 16. The trend, however, seems to be toward annular combustion sections, especially for the high-gas-flow axial designs.

Maximum static sea-level thrust ratings for the turbojet engines listed range from 1,500 to 5,000 lb. Larger units in the thrust range from 5,000 to 10,000 lb are undoubtedly under development. The maximum thrust power output of the largest current turbojets at top flight speed is over 8,000 hp.

The maximum shaft power of the turboprop engines under static sea-level conditions ranges from 1,000 to 4,000 hp with appreciable residual jet thrust. Of the units listed, the maximum thrust power under flight conditions is not over 5,000 hp.

Actual fuel consumption rates are given in Table 9 for the various engines under the specified operating conditions. Specific-fuel-consumption figures for the turbojets average slightly over 1.0 lb/hr per pound of thrust, while for the turboprop units the power specifics range from 0.5 to 0.8 lb/hr per equivalent shaft horsepower.

Actual engine weights are tabulated as well as the specific weights (*i.e.*, weight per unit thrust or per unit power output). Turbojet specific weights, in terms of maximum thrust outputs, range from approximately 0.3 to 0.5 lb/lb of thrust, while the specific weights for the turboprops in terms of maximum equivalent shaft power at flight speed range from 0.6 to 1.0 lb/hp.

It should be emphasized that specific fuel consumptions or engine specific weights derived from Table 9 are not figures of merit to be used loosely in comparing individual engines. For example, one particular engine may have a higher specific weight than others of the same type, yet if it has even a slightly lower specific fuel consumption it may yield better over-all performance when used to power a particular aircraft.

Another figure of merit of considerable interest for comparative purposes is given in this table. This is the thrust or power output per square foot of engine frontal area. For turbojet units with centrifugal compressors, the current average value is 300 lb of thrust per square foot of frontal area (the engine's frontal area is taken as the area of a circle whose diameter is equal to the engine's maximum diameter). For jet engines with axial compressors, the corresponding average figure is roughly 525 lb of thrust per square foot. A rough figure for the listed turboprop units with axial compressors is 300 shp/sq ft. For reciprocating aircraft engines the corresponding figure will vary considerably from engine to engine but is approximately 150 to 200 shp/sq ft for current operational engines.

Assuming that engines of all these different types are installed in nacelles with a frontal area, let us say, 50 percent greater than the engine frontal area but of equal aerodynamic cleanliness, the above ratios of thrust per unit frontal area permit a comparison of the fraction of the engine's output that is used up in dragging the engine itself through the air. We find that a reciprocating engine with shaft horsepower/area ratio equal to 200 shp/sq ft can just about propel itself at flight Mach numbers in the neighborhood of $M_0 = 1$, assuming that the shaft power can be converted to thrust power with reasonable efficiency and that cooling drag is not excessive. In contrast, an axial-flow turbojet with a thrust per unit frontal area of 500 lb/sq ft will use up only about 20 percent of its power in pulling itself through the air at the same flight speed.

The small experimental Boeing gas turbines are included in Table 9 for a particular purpose. They were not developed primarily for aircraft propulsion but for auxiliary power purposes. It is interesting to note, however, that these very small units compare quite favorably with the much larger propulsion units in specific weight and even in efficiency as measured by specific fuel consumption.

61. Examples of Current Installations of Gas Turbines in Aircraft. The Lockheed F-80 Shooting Star provides an excellent example of the installation of a single turbojet engine in the fuselage of a fighter-type military plane. The engine used in the F-80A is the General Electric I-40 (J-33), and in the F-80B the Allison-built J-33. This engine has a double-entry centrifugal compressor requiring a plenum-chamber type of installation. Twin side inlets slightly forward of the wing leading edge are used. These are shown in Figs. 230 and 231, which show the F-80A and F-80B in flight. The use of such side inlets rather than a nose inlet is justified on the grounds that it provides as good ram recovery as the nose inlet and that removal of air at these points improves the flow in the neighborhood of the wing-fuselage juncture, and thereby raises the critical Mach number at this intersection. The ram pressure recovery is about 70 percent of what would be attained in a 100 percent efficient diffusion process. The jet exhaust is at the tail of the plane. The fuselage-tail assembly is detachable to permit ready access to the engine, which is mounted in such a manner that the entire engine can be removed and changed in a minimum of time.

The F-80 will occupy a special place in the history of United States military aviation because it was our first operational jet plane and because of outstanding performance. The F-80 in June, 1947, established an official world's record, for a 3-km course, of 623.8 mph. Figures 230 and

FIG. 230.   Lockheed F-80A, powered by General Electric I-40 (J-33) turbojet.

FIG. 231.   Lockheed F-80B in flight.   This jet plane uses the Allison version of the J-33 turbojet.

231 show the use of droppable wing-tip fuel tanks. It is advantageous that installation of these tanks does not increase the plane's total drag. This is because their presence improves flow conditions near the wing tips sufficiently to offset the drag forces on the tank. The F-80B has a wing span of 38 ft 10 in., over-all length of 34 ft 6 in., weight empty of about 8,000 lb, and maximum weight loaded of about 14,000 lb. Thus the thrust loading is approximately 3 lb of plane per pound of thrust.

The Douglas D-558 Skystreak, developed for the United States Navy as a research aircraft for very high speeds, is an outstanding example of a

FIG. 232. The Douglas D-558 Skystreak, developed as a research aircraft for the United States Navy. The General Electric TG-180 (J-35) engine is used.

plane powered by a single turbojet unit. The General Electric axial-flow TG-180 is used. Figure 232 is a cutaway view of this aircraft. Air is taken in at the divided nose inlet and discharged through a nozzle in the tail of the fuselage. This plane has a wing of thin section and a sharp leading edge. Great care has been taken in all aerodynamic details. In August, 1947, this plane established a new official world speed record of 650.6 mph. The wing span of the Skystreak is 25 ft, length 35 ft, gross weight less than 10,000 lb. The thrust loading for the record flight was probably less than 2.5 lb/lb of thrust.

In Fig. 233 two twin-engine jet fighters are illustrated. These are the XFD-1 Phantom and XF2D-1 Banshee, developed for the United States Navy by McDonnell. The Phantom is powered by two Westinghouse 19XB (J-30) axial-flow engines and the Banshee by two 24-C (J-34) turbojets. The similarity of these two planes, except as to size, is obvious. Note the location of the inlets. It was found that the engines could be buried in expanded wing roots next to the fuselage with less drag than if they were located farther outboard in conventional nacelles. Very little performance data have been released on the Banshee. Rate of climb is over 9,000 fpm; the wing span is 41 ft and the length 39 ft; weight at take-off is more than 14,000 lb; total thrust 6,000 lb.

FIG. 233. The McDonnell twin-jet-engine Navy fighters Phantom and Banshee. The Phantom is powered by two Westinghouse 19XB (J-30) axial engines and the Banshee by two Westinghouse 24C (J-34) axial-flow turbojets.

The North American B-45 Air Forces heavy bomber is a good example of adaptation of conventional aircraft design to turbojet power. This plane, shown in flight in Fig. 234, is powered by four J-35 turbojets manufactured by Allison. These are installed in pairs in wing nacelles of rather unconventional form in which the engines are supported well forward of the wing's leading edge. Wing-tip fuel tanks are also evident. This bomber has a wing span of 89 ft 6 in. and a length of 74 ft. Detailed performance figures cannot be given.

Figures 235 and 236 show two widely divergent solutions to the problem of installing six turbojets in a large high-speed bomber. Figure 235 shows the Martin XB-48 Air Forces bomber powered by six General Electric J-35 turbojets. Here the problem of integrating the triple nacelle with the wing has been carefully handled. Otherwise this plane is fairly conventional in design.   Figure 236 shows the Boeing XB-47 Air Forces bomber.   This is also powered by six J-35 engines, but the installation problem has been handled in a radical manner.   The thin wing is swept back 45 deg to delay the incidence of critical compressibility phe-

Fig. 234.   The four-engine North American B-45 Air Forces bomber.   Powered by four Allison J-35 axial turbojets installed in twin wing nacelles.

Fig. 235.   The Martin XB-48 bomber powered by six General Electric J-35 turbojets.

nomena.   Two engines are suspended, in a twin nacelle well below and forward of the wing, by a streamlined strut.   This inboard nacelle is roughly one-third of the way out from the root of the wing.   The outboard engines are suspended below the wing in a single-engine nacelle of more conventional form.   This nacelle is located roughly 80 percent of

the way out from the fuselage.   The unconventional manner in which the
four inboard engines are suspended below the wing was undoubtedly
arrived at because of the desire to keep the thin swept-back wings as
clean, aerodynamically, as possible.

Fig. 236.   The Boeing XB-47 jet bomber using six J-35 engines.   Note the thin swept-
back wing and the unusual disposition of the engines.

Fig. 237.   The Northrop YB-49 flying-wing bomber powered by eight J-35 axial-flow
engines.

The Northrop jet-powered flying-wing bomber YB-49 is shown in
Fig. 237.   This aircraft of unusual design is powered by eight TG-180
(J-35) engines.   The clean installation of the high-output axial-flow
engines in this type of plane is apparent.   Performance information is
not available at the time of writing.

Illustrations of turboprop engines, installed, have not been included in this chapter for two reasons. First, as we have noted, most of these engines to date have been experimental adaptations of turbojet units. Second, they have generally been installed in a conventional manner in conventional-type planes. Much remains to be done on the development and application of this type of aircraft power plant.

One of the claims for superiority of turbojet engines in high-speed applications has been that the small frontal area for a given power would permit buried engine installations. That this claim has been only partially realized is evident from Figs. 230 to 237. For wing installations we must, however, point out that, although turbojets (particularly, axial-flow) have excellent thrust-per-unit-frontal-area characteristics, the simultaneous trend toward thinner wing sections on high-speed planes has operated against the realization of the completely buried engine installation.

62. Influence of Engine Characteristics on Aircraft Performance and Design. At the time of the appearance of the first practical gas-turbine turbojet units, development of the reciprocating-engine–propeller power plants had, in certain directions, reached the point of diminishing returns. For high-speed applications, we had to face the situation of propeller efficiencies falling off with increasing speed because of blade-tip compressibility losses. At the same time the larger powers required for higher speed flight called for larger power units. The lower limit of engine specific weights had practically been reached in available power ratings, and there was reason to believe that it would increase again for engines of larger output. Then, too, as we have pointed out in Sec. 60, the power per unit frontal area of aircraft reciprocating engines (150 to 200 shp/sq ft) is so low that such an engine installed in its nacelle might have difficulty in propelling itself at flight Mach numbers in the neighborhood of unity. Thus the possibility of extending our flight experience into the range of sonic and supersonic speeds with the reciprocating-engine–propeller type of power plant seemed unpromising.

Accordingly the appearance of the turbojet engine with markedly smaller specific weights and higher thrusts per unit frontal area greatly stimulated interest in high-speed flight. This has been directly responsible for the recent great advances in high-flight-speed research, the results of which are now beginning to appear in the designs of the aircraft themselves.

Present types of turbojet power plants may be used up to flight Mach numbers in the neighborhood of $M_0 = 1.5$, and it is possible that variants, such as the use of afterburning, may extend the useful speed range up to

$M_0 = 2.5$. Experimental aircraft for these flight speeds are now under development.

One of the popular methods of contrasting the reciprocating-engine–propeller combination with turbojet units has been to point out that the former is essentially a constant-thrust-power device (vs. flight speed), while the latter is essentially a constant-thrust device (vs. flight speed). In consequence, two such power plants producing equal thrust horse-power at a given flight speed, say, 400 mph, will produce widely different effective thrusts at take-off. For these conditions, the reciprocating-engine–propeller combination may produce two to three times the effective take-off thrust of the turbojet unit. This has led to the idea that the take-off characteristics of turbojet-powered aircraft tend to be poor. Owing to the fact, however, that present-day jet planes are being adequately powered for top flight speeds of 600 mph or greater, the take-off characteristics are found to be quite satisfactory judged by customary standards.

There is, of course, always the desire to get greater useful loads into the air with any given power plant. For this reason, thrust augmentation of turbojets and assisted take-off of jet-powered planes is receiving considerable attention. Augmentation by coolant injection of a water-methanol mixture is producing 20 percent or larger increases in maximum thrust. Experiments with afterburning promise greater thrust increases, with the percentage increase going up rapidly with flight speed. For this reason, reheat augmentation by afterburning is being considered as a means of extending the practical top flight speed of turbojet craft. As pointed out in Secs. 49 and 50, the weight and drag penalty of such schemes must be carefully balanced against the weight involved in the use of a larger power plant.

Because of its high rate of fuel consumption, the turbojet power plant has been used largely to power high-speed short-range aircraft. The low specific weight of these engines and their high thrust per unit frontal area tend, however, to offset the poor fuel economy. Whereas the range of reciprocating-engine-powered aircraft is practically independent of altitude, the jet plane's maximum range increases markedly with increasing altitude (approximately 25 percent for each 10,000-ft increase in flight altitude). As a consequence, jet planes operating under maximum range conditions must fly at or near their service ceiling.

With jet engines of current efficiencies, specific weights, and thrust/ area ratios installed in clean planes of current conventional design, the maximum range for a craft of 60,000 lb gross weight, with a full fuel load, is approximately 3,500 miles. Optimum conditions for range are realized for wing loadings of the order of 50 lb/sq ft and thrust loadings in the range of 3 to 4 lb of gross weight per pound of thrust.   The maximum-range air speed is about 400 mph and the flight altitude about 45,000 ft.[1] The fuel necessary for such a maximum-range flight would be of the order of 25,000 lb or 0.4 times gross weight.   The loaded weight of the plane during the flight would vary from 60,000 lb at take-off to 35,000 lb at the end of the flight.   For maximum-range flight, the air speed, altitude, power required, etc., must change continuously from take-off to end of flight.   With fuel load so large a fraction of the total take-off gross weight, the weight of the fuel must be centered near the center of gravity of the empty plane.   Otherwise, the center of gravity will shift too much during the flight.

The output of turboengines, whether turboprop or turbojet, at a given flight speed falls with increasing altitude at a rate between that of a supercharged and an unsupercharged reciprocating engine.   Quantitatively, the output varies roughly as the two-thirds power of the relative density at altitude.   At the same time the specific fuel consumption decreases with increasing altitude, owing to the improvement in cycle efficiency with the lower ambient temperatures encountered at high altitude.

The specific fuel consumption of turbojet engines at a given altitude and rated rpm falls off with increasing flight speed roughly as the inverse of V.   In contrast, the thrust specific fuel consumption for a reciprocating-engine–propeller combination increases practically linearly with V. Turboprop fuel-specific variation lies between these two.

The change of rated *thrust power* output with flight speed also differs for the different power units.   For the turbojet, rated thrust power output increases roughly proportionally to V.   For the reciprocating-engine propeller, output is roughly independent of V.   Again the turboprop power-output variation is intermediate.

The combination of all these factors into a quantitative analysis has led to the generally accepted conclusions that the natural field of application of turbojet engines is in the region of high-speed and high-altitude flight, while the reciprocating-engine propeller will satisfy the low-speed and low-altitude requirements.   Turboprops will again occupy an intermediate place.   Quantitative discussion will be omitted here because results depend on engine efficiencies, propeller efficiencies, assumptions regarding aircraft design, etc.

There is a marked difference between turbine power plants and reciprocating engines in regard to partial power characteristics.   Maxi-

[1] TIFFORD, A. N., The Application of Gas Turbines to Aircraft, *Aeronaut. Eng. Rev.*, vol. 7, pp. 33–41, 1948.

mum fuel economy for reciprocating engines is obtained at roughly 50 percent maximum power output. For turbines engines, maximum economy may coincide with maximum output. There is considerable interest in the partial power characteristics of turbine engines, and work is being done on the advantages of partial power operation with reduced turbine inlet temperatures, use of variable-area jet nozzles, etc. On multiengine jet planes, the advantages of partial power operation must be weighed against operation with some of the engines shut down.

63. Design Trends in Aircraft Gas Turbines. In Fig. 238 average curves of engine specific weights, specific fuel consumption, and thrust per unit frontal area are drawn for American, British, and German turbojet engines against a time scale in years. The empirical points upon which these curves are based scatter rather widely, so that there is some freedom of choice in drawing average curves for the period 1942 through 1947. This uncertainty will reflect itself in the 4-year projection included in these graphs.

It will be noted that the average specific weight of turbojet units has decreased approximately by a factor 2 in the 6-year period 1942 to 1948. Current high-performance turbojet units have specific weights in the range of 0.35 lb of weight per pound of maximum thrust. The indicated decrease in specific weights includes not only weight-saving improvements in design and use of materials but also the effect of the trend with time toward larger engines. We may soon reach the period of diminishing returns on weight-saving improvements per se, so the future specific-weight curve may reflect largely the weight improvement possible in the larger turbojets of the future. The first installations of turbojets were in high-speed, relatively short range aircraft, and this type of application emphasized the importance of low engine specific weights. As developments go forward in the direction of longer range applications, emphasis will shift more and more toward higher efficiency, and the significant weight parameter will become specific engine-plus-fuel weight. Additional engine weight, leading to improved efficiency, will then be justified if it leads to a lower value of this parameter.

Specific fuel consumption expressed as pounds of fuel consumed per hour per pound of (maximum) thrust is the commonly used parameter for expressing turbojet efficiency. This is also plotted against time in Fig. 238. The average curve indicates a 35 percent improvement from 1942 to 1948. The extrapolated portion is drawn with a decreasing slope and indicates an expected further improvement of 10 percent from 1948 to 1952. These improvements have resulted and will continue to result from improvements in component efficiencies, higher compression ratios, and higher turbine inlet temperatures. Higher compression ratios and higher turbine inlet temperatures will eventually react adversely on engine specific weights.

Figure 238 also gives a trend curve for thrust per unit frontal area. In drawing this average curve, points for engines having centrifugal as

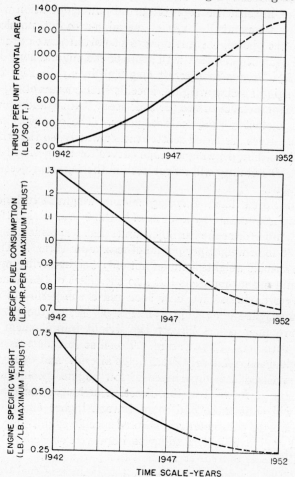

FIG. 238.   Average curves of turbojet specific weights, specific fuel consumptions, and thrust per unit frontal area plotted against a time scale in years.   The dotted portions represent an estimate of the future trend of these quantities.

well as axial compressors were used.   The fact that the "mix" has tended toward a larger percentage of axial turbojets, with their inherently smaller diameter for a given output, explains a part of the very large increase in this quantity (fourfold increase from 1942 to 1948).   The projected portion of the curve indicates the possibility of axial-flow engines giving maximum static sea-level thrusts of over 1,000 lb/sq ft within 5 years.

Average maximum turbine inlet temperatures have increased approximately 20°F per year during the period 1942 to 1948, with current values ranging from 1500 to 1600°F. New alloys designed specifically for gas-turbine application will permit this limit to be raised by significant amounts in the near future. Higher permissible turbine inlet temperatures will call for compressors of higher compression ratios in order to realize the full benefit of the increased temperature on engine efficiency.

The design compression ratios of contemporary turbojets range from 4 to 6. It is believed that a compression ratio of about 6 is the practical upper limit for single-stage centrifugal compressors. Approximately the same limit holds for multistage axial compressors. It is possible, however, to achieve higher over-all pressure ratios (perhaps as high as 10 to 15) by the use of two separate compressors in series.

For a turbine inlet temperature of 1500°F and reasonable component efficiencies, optimum cycle efficiency is realized for a compression ratio of about 9:1. This does not necessarily mean that we should strive for this compression ratio in a 1500°F turbojet. Engine specific weight increases with compression ratio, and it is found that minimum engine-plus-fuel weight for a medium-duration flight is obtained for a compression ratio of approximately 5. For longer range applications, minimum engine-plus-fuel weights will be found for compression ratios nearer to the compression ratio for optimum cycle efficiency. This fact and the fact that optimum pressure ratio for cycle efficiency increases with increasing turbine inlet temperature will tend to focus future development interest on compressors of higher compression ratio.

One should not expect rapid improvement in component efficiencies, combustion efficiency, ram entry efficiency, etc. Rather we should expect a steady slow improvement in these factors, which contribute so importantly to the over-all performance of aircraft gas turbines (particularly for off-design operation). Increases of 1 to 3 percent in these factors in the next 5 to 10 years should be considered a satisfactory rate of progress.

APPENDIX

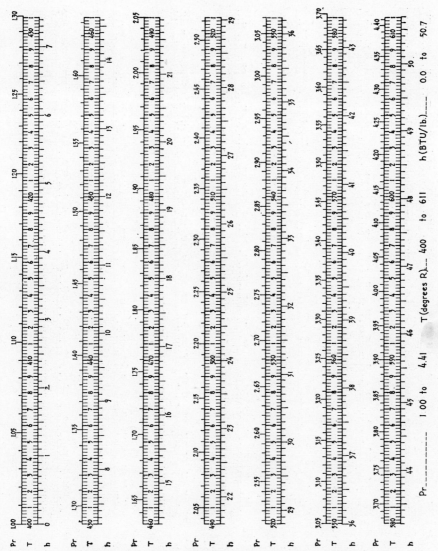

CHART 1. Thermodynamic properties of air. (*By permission of United States Navy Department, Bureau of Ships, Research and Standards Branch, Research Memo. No. 6-44.*)

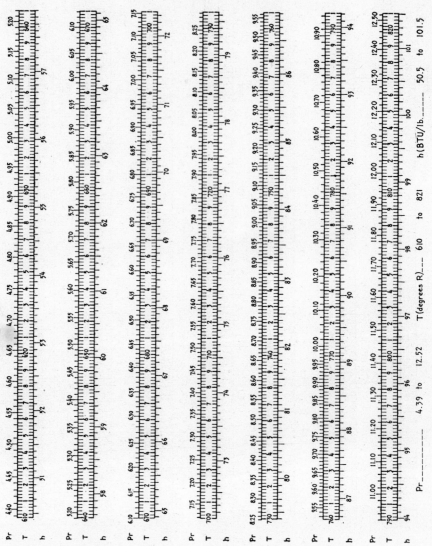

CHART 1.   Thermodynamic properties of air.   (*Continued.*)

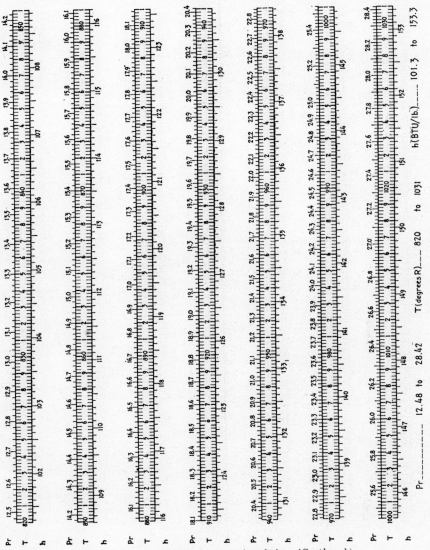

CHART 1.   Thermodynamic properties of air.   (*Continued.*)

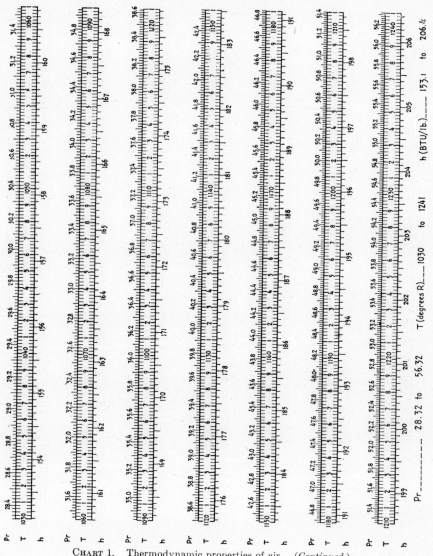

CHART 1. Thermodynamic properties of air. (*Continued.*)

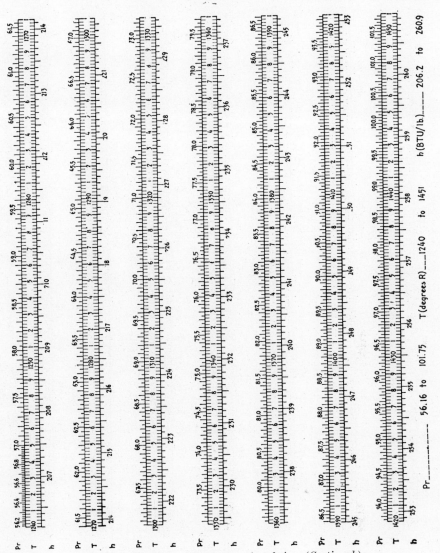

CHART 1. Thermodynamic properties of air. (*Continued.*)

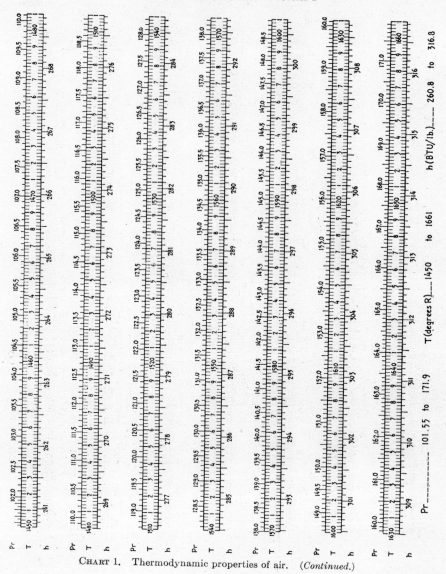

CHART 1. Thermodynamic properties of air. (*Continued.*)

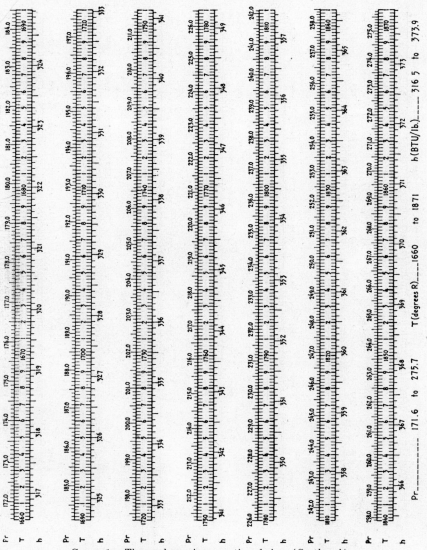

CHART 1. Thermodynamic properties of air. (*Continued.*)

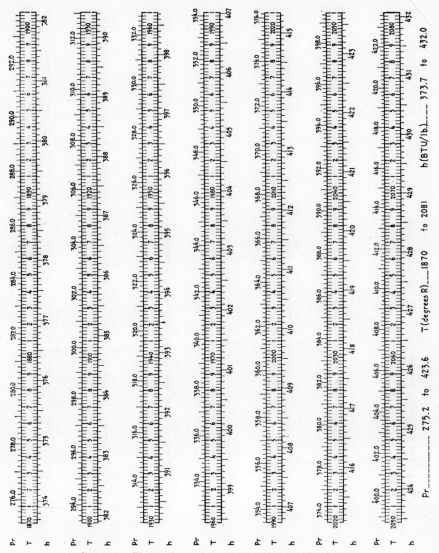

CHART 1.   Thermodynamic properties of air.   (*Continued.*)

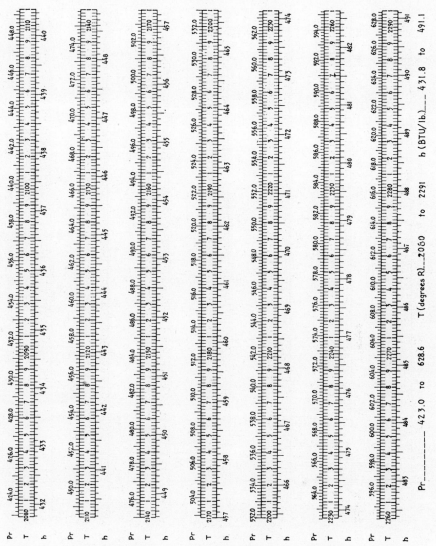

CHART 1.   Thermodynamic properties of air.   (*Continued.*)

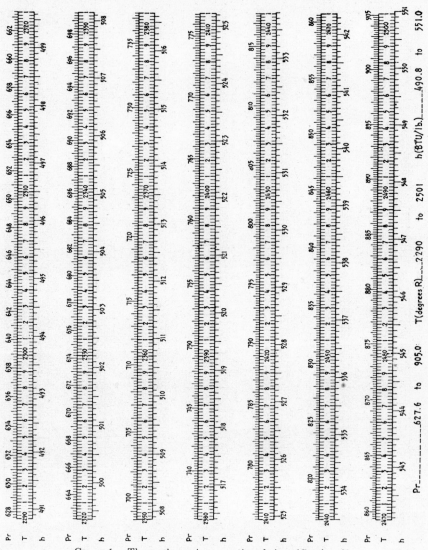

CHART 1.   Thermodynamic properties of air.   (*Continued.*)

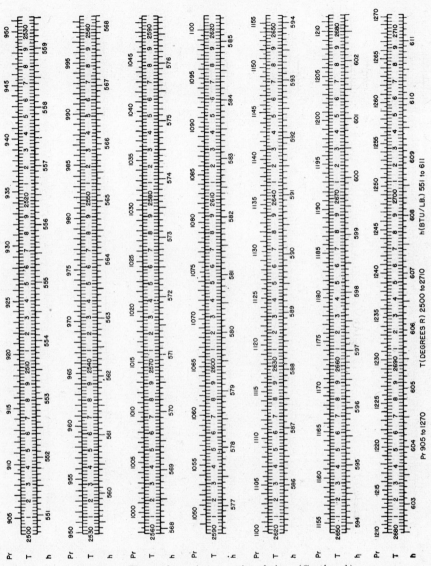

CHART 1. Thermodynamic properties of air. *(Continued.)*

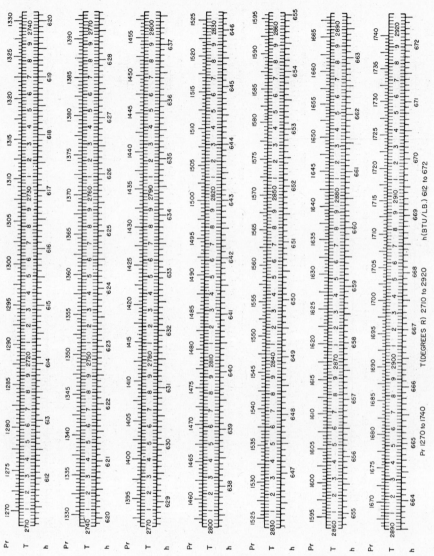

CHART 1. Thermodynamic properties of air. (*Continued.*)

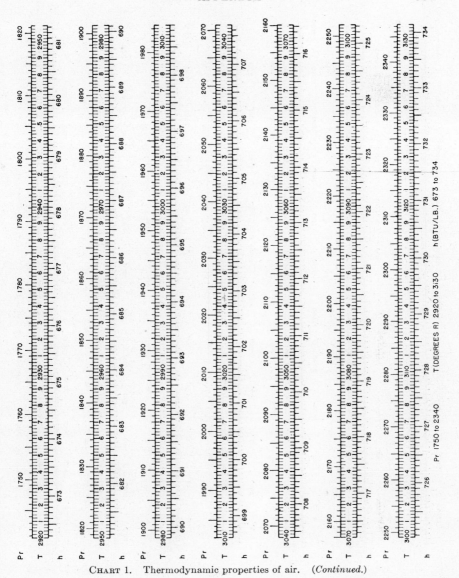

CHART 1. Thermodynamic properties of air. (*Continued.*)

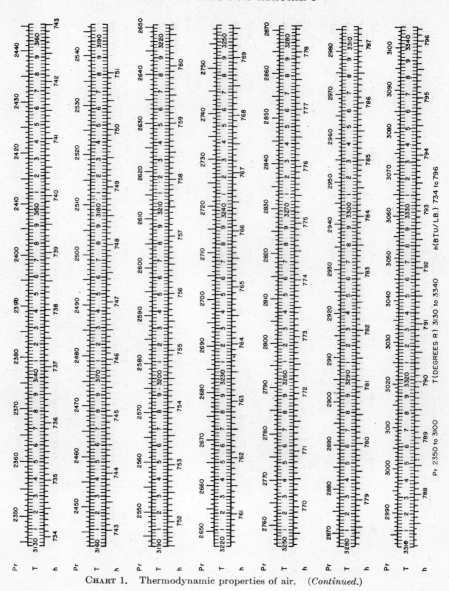

CHART 1. Thermodynamic properties of air. (*Continued.*)

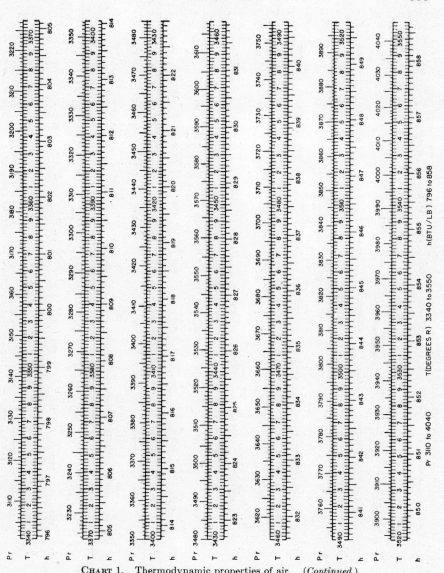

CHART 1. Thermodynamic properties of air. (*Continued.*)

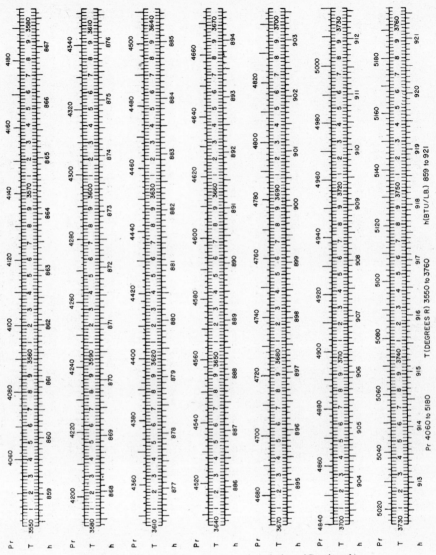

CHART 1.   Thermodynamic properties of air.   (*Continued.*)

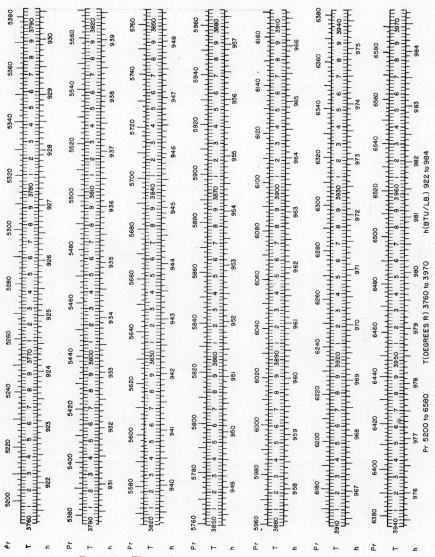

CHART 1. Thermodynamic properties of air. (*Continued.*)

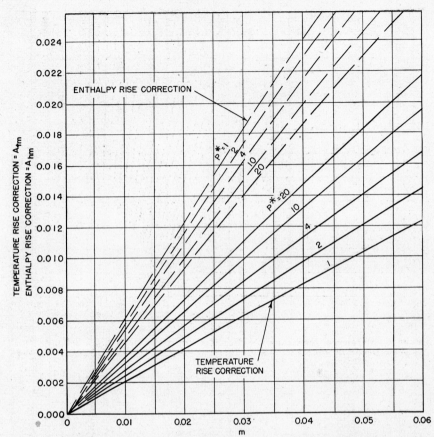

CHART 2. Compression, water-vapor correction for temperature and enthalpy rises where $\Delta T_g = \Delta T_a(1 - A_{tm})$ and $\Delta h_g = \Delta h_a(1 + A_{hm})$. (*By permission of United States Navy Department, Bureau of Ships, Research and Standards Branch, Research Memo. No. 6-44.*)

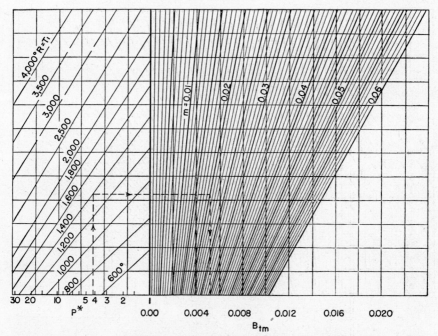

CHART 3. Expansion, temperature water-vapor correction where $\Delta T_g = \Delta T_a(1 - B_{tm})$. (*By permission of United States Navy Department, Bureau of Ships, Research and Standards Branch, Research Memo. No. 6-44.*)

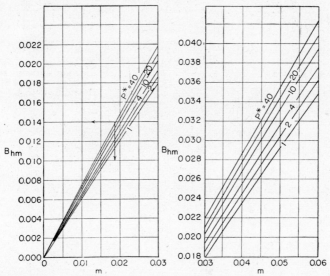

CHART 4. Expansion, enthalpy water-vapor correction where $\Delta h_g = \Delta h_a(1 + B_{hm})$. (*By permission of United States Navy Department, Bureau of Ships, Research and Standards Branch, Research Memo. No. 6-44.*)

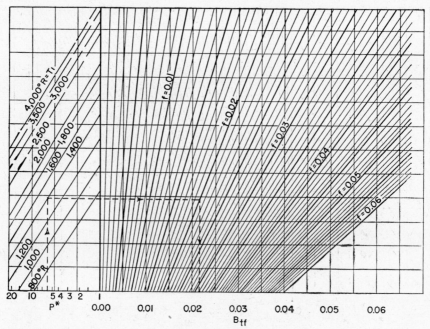

CHART 5.   Expansion, temperature fuel correction for fuel $H/C = 0.15$ to 0.18 where $\Delta T_g = \Delta T_a(1 - B_{tf})$.   (By permission of United States Navy Department, Bureau of Ships, Research and Standards Branch, Research Memo. No. 6-44.)

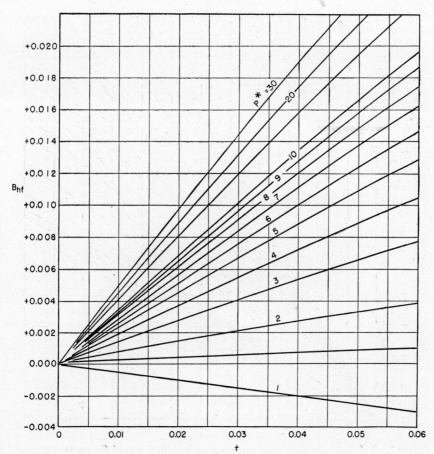

CHART 6. Expansion, enthalpy fuel correction for fuel $H/C = 0.15$ (diesel and fuel oil) where $\Delta h_g = \Delta h_a(1 + B_{hf})$. (*By permission of United States Navy Department, Bureau of Ships, Research and Standards Branch, Research Memo. No. 6-44.*)

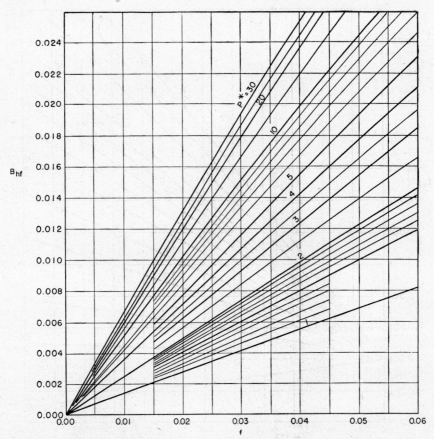

CHART 7. Expansion, enthalpy fuel correction for fuel $H/C = 0.18$ (kerosene and gasoline) where $\Delta h_g = \Delta h_a(1 + B_{hf})$. (*By permission of United States Navy Department, Bureau of Ships, Research and Standards Branch, Research Memo. No. 6-44.*)

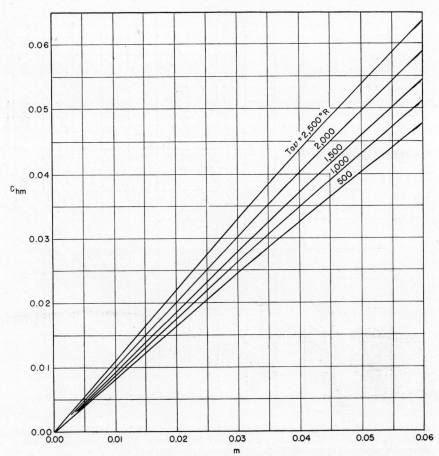

CHART 8. Heat exchange, enthalpy water-vapor correction where $\Delta h_g = \Delta h_a(1 + C_{hm})$.
(*By permission of United States Navy Department, Bureau of Ships, Research and Standards Branch, Research Memo. No. 6-44.*)

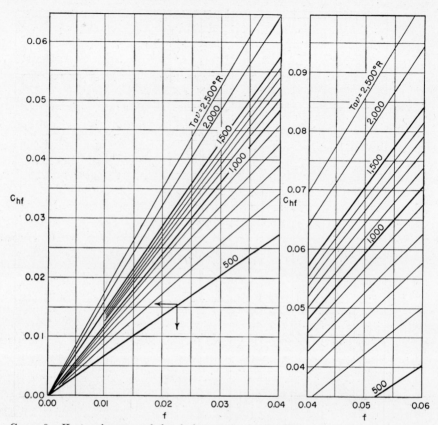

CHART 9.   Heat exchange, enthalpy fuel correction for fuel $H/C = 0.15$ (diesel and fuel oil) where $\Delta h_g = \Delta h_a(1 + C_{hf})$.   (*By permission of United States Navy Department, Bureau of Ships, Research and Standards Branch, Research Memo. No. 6-44.*)

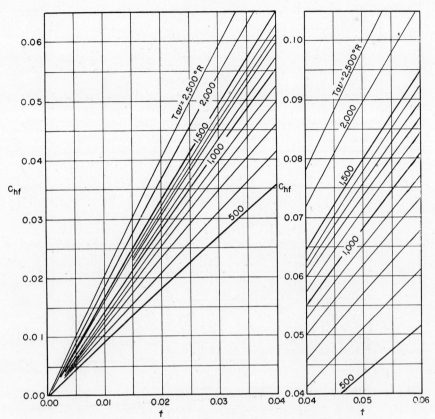

CHART 10. Heat exchange, enthalpy fuel correction for fuel $H/C = 0.18$ (kerosene and gasoline) where $\Delta h_g = \Delta h_a(1 + C_{hf})$. (*By permission of United States Navy Department, Bureau of Ships, Research and Standards Branch, Research Memo. No. 6-44.*)

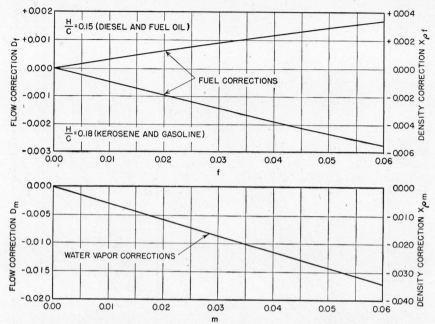

CHART 11.   Flow and density, water-vapor and fuel corrections where $W_g = W_a(1 + D)$ and $\rho_g = \rho_a(1 + X)$.   (*By permission of United States Navy Department, Bureau of Ships, Research and Standards Branch, Research Memo. No. 6-44.*)

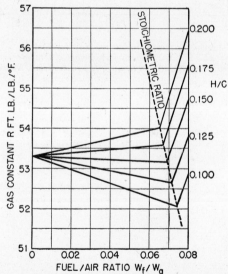

CHART 12.   The effect on the gas constant R for air with the addition of varying quantities of products of combustion for fuels of different H/C ratios.

INDEX

345